Tina

ANGELS AND C

The Author Anne Summers was born in North London in 1944.
She is an editor of *History Workshop Journal*, and a former
Community Education Organiser for Oxfordshire County Council.
Currently she is Wellcome Research Fellow at the Wellcome Unit
for the History of Medicine at the University of Oxford. She is a
tutor in university and adult education, and has published several
articles on the history of militarism, nationalism, philanthropy and
nursing in Victorian and Edwardian Britain.

ANGELS AND CITIZENS

British Women as
Military Nurses
1854–1914

ANNE SUMMERS

ROUTLEDGE & KEGAN PAUL

London & New York

FOR MY PARENTS

First published in 1988 by
Routledge & Kegan Paul Ltd
11 New Fetter Lane, London EC4P 4EE

Published in the USA by
Routledge & Kegan Paul Inc.
29 West 35th Street, New York, NY 10001

Set in 11/12pt Garamond
by Columns of Reading
and printed in the British Isles
by The Guernsey Press Co Ltd
Guernsey, Channel Islands

Library of Congress Cataloging in Publication Data
Summers, Anne, 1944–
    Angels and citizens.
    Bibliography: p.
    Includes index.
    1. Military nursing – Great Britain – History –
19th century.   2. Military nursing – Great Britain –
History – 20th century.   3. Women and war – Great Britain –
History – 19th century.   4. Women and war – Great Britain
– History – 20th century.   I. Title. {DNLM:
1. Military Nursing – history – Great Britain.
2. Women – history – Great Britain.   WY 11 FA1 S9a}
UH495.G7S86   1988   355.3'45'0941   87-20522

British Library CIP Data also available
ISBN 0-7102-1479-0 (c)
        0-7102-1338-7 (p)

CONTENTS

v

CONTENTS

ACKNOWLEDGMENTS

As there is no large central archive on the British military nursing service, I have to thank the staff of a very large number of archives and libraries for the courtesy and efficiency with which they have assisted my research. It would be invidious to list the institutions concerned in any but alphabetical order: the Bodleian Library, Oxford; the British Red Cross Society Archive, Barnett Hill, Surrey; the British Red Cross Society, Oxfordshire; the British Library; Churchill College, Cambridge; the Fawcett Library; the Greater London Record Office; the Imperial War Museum; the India Office Library; the National Library of Scotland; the National Registry of Archives; the library of the Order of St John of Jerusalem; the Public Record Office; QARANC Museum; the Royal Army Medical Corps Library and Muniment Room; the Royal Commission on Historical Manuscripts; the library of the Royal College of Nursing; the Wellcome Institute, London; the Wellcome Unit, University of Oxford.

Quotation from papers in the Royal Archives is by the gracious permission of Her Majesty the Queen. I am grateful to Lord Esher for permission to quote from the Esher MSS. Christopher Loyd MC of Lockinge, Wantage, most kindly gave me access to the Wantage Papers before their transfer to the British Red Cross Archive.

I am grateful to QARANC Museum for supplying the portrait of Sidney Browne; to the British Red Cross Archive for the print of the Princess of Wales's Committee, 1885; to the Red Cross,

Lancashire, and the Royal Sussex Regiment Museum Trust for the photographs of VAD field days; to the staff of St Helen's Town Hall and Central Library, and *St Helen's Newspaper* for the photograph of the Anglo-Boer War Memorial, St Helen's, Lancashire; to the Reverend Nicholas Wynne Jones for the photograph of the stained glass window of the Parish Church of St John, Great Clacton, Essex. The maps of the Crimea, from the late Sir Neil Cantlie's *History of the Army Medical Department*, vol. II, are reproduced with permission from the publishers, Churchill Livingstone. All other illustrations are reproduced by permission of the Bodleian Library.

Passages from Chapters 4 and 5 which first appeared in *Nursing Times*, March 1985 and March 1987, are here reproduced with the kind permission of the publishers.

A grant from the Wellcome Trust which covered the costs of travel for research in 1984 and 1985 is most gratefully acknowledged.

This book was originally written as a doctoral thesis of the Open University. My two supervisors, Dr David Englander and Dr Charles Webster, were pillars of support throughout the long period of its gestation; and all the staff and officers of the Wellcome Unit for the History of Medicine, University of Oxford, were endlessly helpful in a multitude of matters large and small. But the research was originally conceived outside the framework of an academic institution, and I am fortunate in the many friends and colleagues whom I have to thank, not only for comments on early drafts and suggestions for further reading, but also for sustaining me in an enterprise which was at one and the same time an endurance test, an exercise in faith, and a labour of love. I thank all my fellow-editors of *History Workshop Journal* for constituting the school in which I re-learned how to read and write; and I thank Sally Alexander, Monica Baly, Hugh Cunningham, Leonore Davidoff, Anna Davin, N.S. Gooding, the late Patricia Hanrahan, Brian Harrison, Jane Hawksley, the late Thomas Hodgkin, Jill Liddington, Christopher Maggs, Tim Mason, Sian Miles, A.J. Nicholls, Gabrielle Porter, Lyndal Roper, F.B. Smith, Myna Trustram, Raphael Samuel, Martha Vicinus, Jehane Hamilton-Williams, and Julia Piggot Wood for answering all my calls for help or information.

Without the support of R.W. Johnson and the example he sets of dauntless literary productivity, this book would almost certainly never have seen the light of day. Richard Gareth Johnson helped to compile tables, and propelled my writing into the computer age. Rebecca Johnson said she did not care what I wrote so long as her name was in print, and I have therefore succumbed to the temptation to say, with Shakespeare, 'sweet are the uses of adversity'.

I can cheerfully obey the convention which exempts everyone cited in these Acknowledgments from any responsibility for the contents of the book; but not that which names the author's 'greatest debt'. This presupposes a simplistic theory of historical causation which is alien to the spirit of what follows!

Anne Summers

Oxford, January 1987

ABBREVIATIONS

AHC Army Hospital Corps
AMD Army Medical Department
AMS Army Medical Services
ANS Army Nursing Service
BL Add.MSS British Library Additional Manuscripts
BP *Burke's Peerage*
BRCS British Red Cross Society
CAB Cabinet Papers
DNB *Dictionary of National Biography*
FANY First Aid Nursing Yeomanry
GOC General Officer Commanding
IANS Indian Army Nursing Service
IOR India Office Records
IWM Imperial War Museum
MO Medical Officer
MR Muniment Room, Royal Army Medical Corps
Library
NLOWS National League for Opposing Women's Suffrage
PMO Principal Medical Officer
PP Parliamentary Papers
QAIMNS Queen Alexandra's Imperial Military Nursing
Service
QARANC Queen Alexandra's Royal Army Nursing Corps
RA Royal Archive

ABBREVIATIONS

RAMC Royal Army Medical Corps
RBNA Royal British Nurses' Association
SJAA St John's Ambulance Association
SJAB St John's Ambulance Brigade
TFNS Territorial Force Nursing Service
VAD Voluntary Aid Detachment
WO War Office
WSPU Women's Social and Political Union
WSWCC Women's Sick and Wounded Convoy Corps
WVMSC Women's Volunteer Medical Staff Corps
WWW Who Was Who

INTRODUCTION

This book began, not as an account of the emancipation of women, nor as a piece of army history, but as an inquiry into the origins of the First World War. Why it broke out came to seem less important than why it went on for so long, and how the belligerent populations could consent to the sacrifice of their young men on so massive a scale. To find the answers to these questions, it seemed more important to study the attitudes of civilians than of soldiers; and women were, and are, the quintessential civilians, the furthest removed from the machinery and theatres of warfare. But in Britain, long before 1914, large numbers of women were accustomed to the prospect of war, and longed to play a vital role in it. They knew, too, what costume they would wear if the day came. It would be a nurse's uniform. How women pictured the figure of the military nurse is the key to what war meant to British women in the second half of the nineteenth century – how it penetrated their consciousness and shaped their ambitions. And the study of women on the eve of war takes us a long way towards understanding the capacity of that whole European generation to tolerate the intolerable.

The British military nurse was both a real and an imaginary woman in the Victorian period. Very few female nurses were in fact employed by the army. Military nursing was a predominantly male occupation. Before Florence Nightingale's expedition to the Crimea, British soldiers were nursed, not by wives or camp followers, but by male orderlies. Contrary to legend, Nightingale did not subsequently fill the army hospitals with professional nurses trained in her own image. Twenty-five years after the Crimean War, the British army employed barely a dozen female nurses. In 1898, a year before the Anglo-Boer War, there were still only seventy-two. It was only after that war that they began to be enrolled in their hundreds; and on the eve of the First World War thousands were in readiness for service.

For most of the nineteenth century, therefore, opportunities to nurse sick and wounded soldiers were few and far between, and the regular Army Nursing Service was almost hidden from public view. But the idea of military nursing had enormous appeal for British women. It inspired some of them to train as civilian nurses, in hopes of one day receiving a call to the battlefield; and others to organise female nursing corps when the War Office and Army Medical Department dragged their feet. It led many women to support the international Red Cross movement from its earliest days, and to join nursing expeditions to the armies of other nations engaged in war. Military nursing provided an outlet for religious compassion and political sympathies; it also gave respectable expression to less admissible female emotions. To be a nurse in war was to be abroad, free of domestic ties and comforts, ready to surmount hardship and encounter danger. It could bring a woman to the heart of the action on a world stage. It also meant being where the men were. The prosaic realities of most Army Nursing Sisters' working lives could not diminish the power of these images of freedom and agency.

Sixty years separate the 'lady volunteers' and paid nurses of the Crimean War from the VADs of 1914, and it would be a mistake to think that their outlook and motivations were identical. The women of 1854 perceived themselves, and were perceived by others, very differently from the women of the Edwardian generation. Women's acceptance as army nurses was a painful, long drawn-out process; it reflected changes in their position in the wider society; and it helped in turn to accelerate those changes. Women were ceasing to be regarded as purely private, domestic persons in the mid-nineteenth century. Tracing the history of this one occupation over time allows us a sharp insight into women's growing engagement with the public sphere — and their transition from a female world to a male one. No area of public service was, after all, as public as the army, or as masculine. If the chief dramatic interest of this period is the militarisation of civilians, there is an important sub-plot: the invisible actors are no longer confined to the wings; women are beginning to encroach on male territory. The connection between these two stories, complex and often paradoxical, is one of the chief themes of this book.

In the early Victorian period, 'woman's mission' was a much-used phrase. It was believed that women were endowed with qualities of gentleness and sympathy which were unique to their sex. These derived from the biological capacity for motherhood; and they qualified women for caring functions in society at large. But the concept of 'woman's mission' did not apply indiscriminately to the entire female sex. Those who were encouraged to take up what we should now call voluntary social work were leisured women, who did not have to earn their own living or do their own housework. The 'Lady Bountiful' was a class-specific, as well as a gender-specific phenomenon. The domestic experience which supposedly entitled her to dispense advice and comfort to the poor was not just the bringing up of children, but the management of servants. At once employer, tutor and surrogate mother, the ideal mistress of a household occupied a complex position in relation to her domestic staff. Today it is too easily forgotten that the 'angel of the hearth', subordinate and submissive as she was to her husband and her male relatives, nevertheless exercised managerial skills, and the power to hire and fire, within her own female domain.

Many of the women associated with the reform of hospital nursing in Britain brought this domestic experience to their work. Florence Nightingale and her contemporaries, Mary Stanley, Jane Shaw Stewart, and the founders of the nursing sisterhoods, may have differed in their approaches to their work, but they had this much in common: they were more accustomed to giving orders than taking them. They accepted that men exercised authority in their own sphere; women – or perhaps we should say, as they did, ladies – would brook no interference in theirs. When ladies took up the cause of hospital reform in the 1850s, they raised the question of 'separate spheres' in an acute form. Hospitals might appear to be a natural setting for female carers; but they were run by male boards of governors and male physicians and surgeons. Ladies wished to enter them on privileged terms. They showed every deference, in principle, to the superior knowledge of the medical men; but they refused to be seen as their servants; and they refused to allow the medical men to interfere in their own supervision of the nurses.

This replication of the structures of the middle- and upper-class household caused endless trouble in the wards. Hospitals were the site of a major power struggle between the sexes. The first regular army nursing service was nearly wrecked over this issue, and the spectre of female 'parallel power' haunted military medical officers throughout the nineteenth century. There were many objections to women's nursing in army hospitals, but the fundamental problem was that these particular women were ladies. As such they had the advantage, it was assumed, of being qualified to supervise ward work, and of being immune to sexual temptation from their lower-class patients; but they could not begin to be integrated in the army medical system until they ceased in some respects to be ladies, and turned into their opposites. They had to be seen to take orders, to be subordinate within a male hierarchy. They had, in short, to become servants – albeit public servants.

The creators of the Army Nursing Service were part of a larger 'woman's mission' to the army after the Crimean War. Ladies undertook Christian pastoral work, organised temperance canteens and healthy recreational facilities for privates, and helped in the running of hospitals for soldiers' families. These philanthropic activities did not make them part of the military machine. They were civilians; they kept their independence. Ladies who wanted to nurse soldiers had to accept an entirely different status. Yet what might have seemed a kind of defeat, or at least a swallowing of pride, for the first generation of lady nurses, had aspects of victory for the army sisters who were their successors. For years their service was 'in but not of' the army, and they came to hanker for absorption. They were proud of their uniforms; like the men they worked alongside, they wanted to decorate them with medals. They wished to be respected as officers. No longer satisfied with being part of the female sphere, they aspired to a recognised ranking within the male order.

The main impulse behind introducing female nurses into army hospitals was to bring standards of care in military hospitals into line with those of civilian ones. The post-Crimea programme of army reforms and missions represented middle-class Britain's attempt to 'civilianise' the army – to transform it in its own image, or at least to make it a less disreputable and alien body. The army sisters symbolised the process of civilianisation; but they also embodied the reverse process. They adjusted to military values, and adopted military ambitions. A similar metamorphosis could be observed in other sections of civilian society as the century wore on. Red Cross organisers, ambulance workers, royal princesses, nurses trying to raise the status of their profession – all of whom were anxious to improve army medical services – sought to take on auxiliary roles. They had to study military procedures and requirements, and to understand the army's priorities; and many of them, eager for official authorisation, were proud to become less civilian.

The nineteenth century has been characterised as an age of economic and scientific progress, and one in which political systems were democratised and social systems liberalised. But it can also justly be characterised as an age of war. Between 1859 and 1871, the struggles of the Italian states for national unification and independence from Austria, the French Emperor Louis Napoleon's intervention in that struggle, the aggrandisement of Prussia under Bismarck at the expense of Denmark, Austria and France, and the American Civil War, all affected the ways in which society was changing, even in remote and unlikely spheres. States which did not participate in these wars – and Britain, it must be remembered, was involved only in minor colonial skirmishes in this period – nevertheless altered under their impact. As Flaubert wrote from German-occupied France: 'everybody is going to emulate them, turn military. Russia now has four million troops. All Europe will be in uniform.'[1]

When the Napoleonic Wars ended in 1815, armed forces were essentially remote from the mainstream of society. Civilians paid for their services through taxation, and did not regard taking up arms for their country as an inescapable personal obligation. But the national wars of the mid-century involved civilian participation to a remarkable degree. Manpower needs could no longer be met by standing professional armies alone. Prussia's successes, in particular, were widely attributed to a system of massive military conscription. It was not just the conscripts and their families who were drawn into the war effort: all members of society who could, contributed to the provision of medical and welfare services for soldiers.

It was only when war became a more general civilian concern that it could become a more general female concern. The men who fought in the United States, or with Garibaldi's Thousand, were perceived as national heroes from respectable families, who were taking up arms for an ideal. If soldiers were no longer merely social undesirables or cannon fodder, then the women who organised hospitals for them and tended their wounds need not be dubious adventuresses or wretched camp followers. They could be worthy citizens and even heroines, claiming their right to participate in the great national struggles of their day.

Because wars now made greater demands upon ordinary citizens, they presented the modern industrial state in a new guise to both men and women. While they took place, the national community was no mere abstraction; they offered causes with which to identify and struggles in which to participate, at however many removes. In a sense, they made citizenship palpable. At a moment when many women were concerned to make the transition from private to public spheres, they made the public sphere accessible in a particularly exciting and glamorous way. The Italian struggle attracted the sympathies of women in Britain who were active in liberal causes in the 1850s, and beginning to raise the issue of the female suffrage; and the nurses of the American Civil War were seen as models of civic equality by some of the British feminists of the 1860s and 1870s. But long before the electoral process had offered women the vote, these wars offered them many of the social rewards the vote symbolised: vital occupations, honourable uniforms and distinctions, and a recognised position in the machinery of the state.

For British women and girls, it was the expanding Empire, rather than large-scale Continental warfare, which for several decades provided the greatest opportunity for 'national service'. In 1883, British nursing earned its ultimate accolade with the institution of the decoration of the Royal Red Cross. Caring for sick and wounded soldiers and sailors gained nurses the highest public recognition. It conferred on them a distinction denied to women who served the state in other capacities such as schoolteaching or social work. The archetypally feminine functions of caring, mothering, serving and housekeeping were given a setting of high drama, and elevated into the means by which women could achieve unequivocal public honour.

Both in the act and in contemplation, wars unified nations. They achieved this in part by making thousands of people the audience for a single epic spectacle. In Britain this spectacle was transmitted in a multitude of ways: the established church, official

6

commemorations, distributions of honours and medals, the press, the music-hall, and military exhibitions and tattoos, all played their part in creating a sense of shared experience, and an identification with the Empire's defenders. This process, which has been described as 'the invention of tradition',[2] became intensified as the century drew to a close. War – more particularly the glory of victory – undoubtedly dazzled civilians and muted or pre-empted criticism of aggressive foreign and colonial policies. It is, indeed, possible to see popular consent to war merely as the result of propaganda and manipulation. What is often underestimated, and not only by historians, is the extent to which this was a willing collusion.

Well before the outbreak of 'total war' in 1914, civilian volunteers experienced and relished the sense of being drawn together in the collective work of a military emergency. British society had been dislocated and transformed by the industrial revolution: the strong sense of class distinction which marked Victorian society was accompanied by fear, regret, and moral concern over the weakening of communal ties. At the beginning of the nineteenth century, religion had suggested one way of recreating community; war and Empire offered another way towards its end. During the Anglo-Boer War, J.A. Hobson wrote in disgust: 'Jingoism is the passion of the spectator, the inciter, the backer, not of the fighter.' But the combatant and nursing volunteers of that war showed how anxious the spectators were to lose their passive status. So did the 50,000 women who flocked to become VADs between 1909 and 1914; so did the million men who volunteered to fight for Britain in the First World War, before the advent of military conscription in 1916. This was a vast movement to join the actors on the national stage, even if only in supporting roles, and thus to become true members of a national community; and women were just as much a part of it as men.

Contemporary feminists, especially those active within the peace movement, may find this line of argument unwelcome. It has been suggested that there is a 'gender gap' in perceptions of war and peace. Because women themselves hardly ever take up arms, they might be thought to form a natural constituency for pacifism. But the history of British military nursing does not bear out these assumptions. Women's experience of nationalism before the First World War does not seem to have been markedly different from men's; and women were not noticeably more active than men in pacifist circles. What is perhaps most surprising is that there was no sharp divide between pre-war feminists and non-feminists over these issues.

If women were not preoccupied with the question of pacifism at the turn of the century, it may have been precisely because this was a minority, dissenting issue. By this time, women who were engaged in widening the social, economic and political horizons of their sex wanted to be mainstream, not marginal figures. Their ambitions could not be met by operating too far outside the social consensus. Many of the feminists who did formulate a critique of male-dominated society were none the less anxious to be incorporated within it. They accepted the legitimacy of its governing assumptions, particularly with regard to military matters. Ethel Bedford Fenwick, for example, was a suffragist nurse, leading the campaign for the state registration of her profession, who regretted the destruction of human life in other nations' wars; yet at the same time she worked strenuously for the creation of an army nursing reserve, and uncritically supported the policy of her own government during the Anglo-Boer War. The majority of suffragettes gave unthinking endorsement to the existence of the Empire; and this implied unquestioning assent to its maintenance by military means.

Women's earlier models of public activity had been in a fundamental sense sectarian: they derived from churches, from philanthropic societies and from political pressure groups. The emphasis had been on a privileged intervention in a particular cause: of membership of a minority, even if that minority were an elite one. These models were never completely superseded, but were gradually overshadowed by the desire to participate in the affairs of the whole nation, especially as represented by the army and the Empire. A decisive shift was made to the service of the secular national state as an end in itself.

Thus British women prepared for war, seeing it not so much as the organised destruction of mothers' sons, but as symbolising citizenship, social legitimation and personal challenge. If in this they were not very different from their male contemporaries, it was because the gap between the social opportunities and expectations of women and men had begun, very slowly, to narrow. The mid-Victorian 'woman's mission' was disappearing. But it was not replaced by a strong dissenting feminist voice, or one which had much power to bargain over the conditions of women's participation in the public sphere. After 1902, female nurses were brought into the army hospital system largely as numerical substitutes for men. Between 1914 and 1918, women were brought into the war effort and the economy on the same basis. At the war's end, far from being fully incorporated in society, women found themselves rejected as the 'surplus two million'. At the heart of these changes and disappointments, the figure of the war nurse can be seen: a symbol of motherhood and domesticity, required to play a part on the public stage of international war; a symbol of healing, required to consent to a policy of collective slaughter; a symbol of service and self-abnegation, encouraged to respond to challenge and responsibility. Her history embodies all the contradictions of the social position of women in the Victorian and Edwardian eras.

PART I

WOMEN IN A MAN'S WORLD

CHAPTER 1

BEFORE THE NIGHTINGALES

It is customary to speak of nursing history in terms of a great divide. The period before Florence Nightingale impressed her ideas and personality on the movement for hospital reform is often assumed to have been nursing's equivalent of the Dark Ages: modern times are reckoned to have begun in 1854, when she took a party of women to Scutari to help nurse the sick and wounded soldiers of the Crimean War. Certainly Florence Nightingale deserves to rank among the pioneers of her profession. But her achievements, like those of most distinguished men and women – especially women – rested on foundations laid by less celebrated predecessors. The early decades of the nineteenth century were marked by a wide variety of medical, religious and philanthropic movements in Britain relating to the care and cure of the sick. By the 1840s, women of the middle and upper classes were beginning to participate actively in these movements. Florence Nightingale's contribution can only be appreciated when it is realised that her voice was one among many. The history of nursing in general, and of military nursing in particular, is not one of straightforward progress towards modernity, but of rivalries and disagreements surrounding the project of reform.

There was not, in the middle of the nineteenth century, any simple consensus on the definition of the function of nursing, on the training appropriate to the work, or on the type of person who should undertake it. A great number of meanings attached to the word 'nurse'. Perhaps the most important difference between the early Victorian use of the word and our own is that it was much less closely associated with hospitals and public institutions. To nurse still meant to suckle a baby. The nurse or nursemaid was often a domestic servant whose sole or principal occupation was the care of small children – later entitled 'nanny'. Most households in time of sickness would rely on a female relative, or engage a private nurse, whose work was something of a specialism within domestic service. Only the very poor, and by no means all of them, encountered the nurse as a hospital or institutional employee. Even within the hospital, the line drawn between nursing as medical work and nursing as domestic service was often far from clear. A matron was appointed chiefly as a housekeeper; and the daily work of a ward could require a woman to cook, scrub floors, empty chamber pots and perform all the 'usual duties of a housemaid' as well as follow a doctor's instructions on medical care.[1]

SARAH GAMP AND COMPANY

Who nursed? Dickens's fictional characters, the drunken and dissolute Sarah Gamp and Betsy Prig, have stamped our imagination indelibly with a stereotype of the pre-Nightingale nurse. But Sarah and Betsy are caricatures, not historical portraits. They would have caused great offence to such a woman as Elizabeth Davis, who was sixty years old when engaged for the Crimea; respectable, literate, the daughter of a Welsh dissenting preacher, she had supported herself by turns as domestic servant, hospital nurse and private nurse.[2] But it is as impossible to generalise from her career as it is from Dickens's fiction: the nurses of the mid-century were a variegated body on whom, as yet, very little information exists.

We do know that most nurses were women. Men were sometimes employed in private nursing; they were in demand in lunatic asylums, where the overwhelming emphasis was on physical restraint; the military hospitals, as we shall see, were staffed by men; there were also civilian hospitals where certain skilled nursing functions were performed by male medical students, or the incumbents of junior medical posts known as dressers or clinical clerks. In most hospitals, however, both skilled and unskilled nursing was women's work; and there was a growing

14

tendency to divide the nursing staff into two grades. Domestic duties and simple attentions to the sick were carried out by the lower grade, usually referred to as nurse or ward-maid; the higher grade, known as head nurse or sister, supervised the nurses and attended in person the more serious cases in the ward.[3]

The two grades were recruited separately, and there were few opportunities for promotion from lower to higher. A Bristol surgeon, for example, selecting women for the Crimean expedition, categorised them as 'Upper' or 'Under' nurses, not according to age, or to institutional or private nursing experience, but according to personal qualities such as 'intelligence and respectability'. Sisters at St Thomas's Hospital, London, where Florence Nightingale was later to establish her training school, were taken on as supernumeraries in the matron's office. They were women of about thirty, and their turnover rate was not high; here there was a parallel with the domestic sector where, in London at least, the higher grade of household servant stayed longer in post than the lower, and was usually separately recruited. Head servants in gentlemen's families were indeed thought the most suitable candidates for sisters' posts, as were respectable widows in reduced circumstances. Ward-maids, on the other hand, were said to be 'like many household servants, fond of change'. They might stay as little as three months in a hospital post; and we can speculate that they may have had a special kind of market value, and consequent job mobility, arising from their willingness to perform objectionable tasks.[4]

THE CALL FOR REFORM

The movement to redefine the function of sick nursing, and to separate it more clearly from domestic work and management, almost certainly originated in the voluntary hospitals which were established by charitable subscription in London and the main provincial centres in the eighteenth and early nineteenth centuries. It has been suggested that with the development of more ambitious and specialised surgical and medical treatment in this period, and the expansion of the teaching function of hospitals, surgeons and physicians became more interested in the results of hospital treatment. Consequently they began to look for more reliable auxiliaries in the wards. A constant watch over patients, and the accurate distribution of medicines and application of external remedies, were necessary if the efficacy of new forms of treatment were to be tested. Writing in 1857, J.F. South, the senior surgeon at St Thomas's, maintained that 'only those who have operated much know how greatly the success of operations depends on good nursing', and particularly commended Mrs Roberts, an experienced St Thomas's nurse who went to the Crimea, for her skill in the treatment of accident victims, and of patients who had been operated on for the stone.[5]

Voluntary hospitals were institutions providing for only a minority of the sick poor. The medical needs of the majority were met by the public authorities, under the terms of the Poor Law. In many cases treatment was not institutional, but came under the heading of 'outdoor relief'; this meant that the sick received medical attention in their own homes. For those whose condition required 'indoor relief', both before and after the Poor Law Amendment Act of 1834, there was a variety of institutional provision. Patients might be sent into voluntary hospitals, where these were geographically accessible. If they lived in the remoter rural areas, or if their illness were one of many which the voluntary hospitals refused to treat – cases of cancer, scurvy, consumption and smallpox, for example, might all be barred – they had to receive treatment in their local workhouses.[6]

In some areas workhouse medical care was provided to a high standard. Isolation hospitals were constructed for smallpox sufferers, and other inmates were often inoculated or vaccinated against the disease. The elderly and the infirm were given separate accommodation from the able-bodied; midwifery provision was more than adequate.[7] But in many places overcrowding was rife, and there was very little classification or segregation of cases. Moreover, the men and women who staffed the Poor Law sick bays and infirmaries were rarely expected to have any special qualification in nursing. In the 1840s a number of workhouse and asylum scandals and tragedies brought these problems to the attention of medical observers and of middle-class and professional enthusiasts for sanitary reform. The hospital treatment of the poor became one of many public health issues causing concern in this period. Decades of urbanisation and industrialisation had produced a high incidence of typhus and consumption amongst the poorer classes, and periodic outbreaks of infectious disease such as smallpox and cholera had caused much alarm, especially between

1831 and 1854. Some writers considered that the overcrowding in workhouses ensured the spread of infection amongst the inmates, and the persistence of disease in the community at large.[8]

It is an interesting index of the new medical value being placed upon sick-nursing at this time that in 1849, as the physician Edward Sieveking reported: 'we actually find that it is already the custom in many workhouses to permit such of the inmates as have proved themselves to be trustworthy, to go as nurses to the neighbouring poor in cases of sickness'. An expedient whereby many an overworked Poor Law medical officer must have attempted to relieve some of the pressure on his time and resources was seized upon by Sieveking as the germ of a scheme for turning Poor Law infirmaries into training institutions for nurses. He appealed for public support on the grounds that it was not only the Christian duty of the rich to help the less advantaged; their very health and well-being depended upon their tackling sources of infection in the homes of the poor.[9]

Sieveking's scheme attracted criticism from those who thought pauper women ineducable; and it seems to have been doomed to failure by the lack of doctors and senior nurses in the workhouse system who had the time or the ability to train nurses.[10] It was in the voluntary hospitals – to which many Poor Law patients continued to be sent – that the nursing function was evolving, and standards being set against which all institutional nursing would eventually be measured. Not until the voluntary hospitals were themselves supporting major initiatives in nurse training could the reform of workhouse nursing become a serious possibility. From the mid-1840s onwards, an important group of reformers began to promote such initiatives. The main thrust of their efforts was to strengthen the two-grade system, and to increase the supply, and improve the calibre of the superior grade of nurse.

LADIES AND NURSES

The first practical steps to develop new and systematic methods in nurse training originated, paradoxically perhaps, outside the spheres of medicine and public health. But, as Sieveking's plan for workhouse nurses showed, medical questions were inextricably bound up with the larger social concerns of the mid-Victorian period. The industrial revolution in Britain had given rise, as is well documented, to much social distress and dislocation; but within the classes which profited from economic change, there were many groups and individuals who felt impelled to relieve the misery of those who had lost by the process. Their sympathy for the victims of destitution and disease was often mixed with fear that the growing social and physical distance between the 'two nations' might foster political disturbance, and even revolution. Charity of all kinds furnished a precious medium of conciliation and communication.[11]

It was also a medium for the teaching of Christianity. The migration of agricultural workers in search of employment in the newly expanding conurbations put them largely beyond the reach of Anglican parish organisation; and within all sections of the church in Britain there was a growing sense of the need for internal missionary work.[12] Many denominations chose to form institutions devoted to the relief of sickness among the poor. Not only was this a service which could not be criticised (as much charity was) for encouraging laziness and improvidence in the able-bodied pauper; but it was also one which appeared to go to the heart of the Christian purpose. The state of medical knowledge in this period was not such that the sufferer could be assured of recovery. The sickbed might be the last place where the soul could be brought to recognise the necessity and the source of salvation, and be rescued from the pains of hell. Care of the body was not ignored, but its prime importance lay in facilitating the cure of the soul.

The sick poor were for the most part visited in their homes by these missionaries; but those of them who were admitted to hospital suggested an even more fruitful field for labour. 'An excellent clergyman, who was for some years chaplain to one of the great London hospitals' extolled the advantages of a captive audience:[13]

In the visits paid by the parochial minister to the poor of his flock, . . . The necessary arrangements of the family, the noise of the children, the interruptions from other causes, frequently distract the attention, and interfere with the solemnity of the occasion. In the Hospital, all these inconveniences are obviated. *There* the sick are in quiet and comfortable wards; the heart is already in some measure softened by the kindness received, and the mind is prepared to attend to the great concerns of eternity.

18

What an opportunity for winning their souls to the Saviour! . . .

In the best-regulated parish there are many persons almost removed by circumstances from the happy influence of pastoral visitation. . . . These are brought by sickness, or by casualty, to the Hospital; and experience has proved that many of them have left it, no more to return to the broad run of sin and folly, but to walk in the narrow way that leadeth unto life. . . .

The minister of a parish . . . longs to conduct the thoughtless and the giddy, for one brief hour, to the house of mourning. He would gladly carry the youth, to whom sin is presenting its allurements, to the wretched chamber where its consequences are displayed in the most loathsome aspect. In the ward of the hospital this great practical benefit is not unfrequently attained. There the remorse and despair of the hardened offender speak far more powerfully to the consciences of those around them, than the most pointed address can do. There, scenes of an opposite character leave a sacred impression. and have often drawn from the once careless and unconcerned the heartfelt prayer, 'May I die the death of the righteous, and may my last end be like his!'

Let us now briefly survey the organisations inspired by such sentiments as these, each of whom was represented in the female nursing parties despatched to the Crimea. The first specifically religious mission to the sick poor in Britain was a Catholic initiative. Between 1827 and 1831 Catherine McAuley founded an institution dedicated to the 'service of the poor, sick and ignorant' in Dublin; in 1839, after nine more convents of her order had been established in Ireland, the first English convent of the Sisters of Mercy was established in Bermondsey, London. A year later, at the other end of the church spectrum, the Quaker philanthropist Elizabeth Fry founded a Protestant, non-denominational 'Institution for Nursing Sisters' at Devonshire Square, London; its members, although not an 'order' in any formal sense, were sometimes referred to as Sisters of Charity. The inspiration for this Institution had been the nursing work of the Church Order of Deaconesses at Kaiserswerth in Germany, which Mrs Fry had observed in the spring of 1840. Pastor Fliedner had revived this ancient form of church organisation for women in 1836, having himself been inspired by the example of Mrs Fry's prison visiting work.[14]

The High Church party in the Church of England was the next body to establish charitable sisterhoods. The Sisterhood of the Holy Cross was set up under the influence and guidance of the Rev. Pusey in 1845, and the Sisterhood of Mercy of Devonport and Plymouth was established by Pusey's friend Priscilla Lydia Sellon in 1848. Members of both orders nursed in the homes of the poor in the Plymouth cholera outbreaks of 1848, 1849 and 1853, and they merged into a single order in 1856. Finally, in 1848, the St John's House Training Institution for Nurses was founded by a High Church group including such dignitaries as the Bishop of London, the Rev. F.D. Maurice, and W.E. Gladstone MP. This was the first sisterhood within the Church of England to be designed exclusively as a nursing order, and it played a particularly important role in the Crimean expedition.[15]

Like other foundations of this period, St John's House was initially established to provide home nursing for the sick; but unlike them, it was also seen as a potential vehicle for the reform of hospital nursing. It was to achieve this by providing a better quality nurse for hospital work. Spiritual rather than medical improvement was the goal: it was not just a question of replacing drunks and drabs with competent cooks, cleaners and poulticers, but of steering patients towards salvation, and improving the general moral tone of the wards. Since it was impossible to dispense with the purely practical and domestic side of ward work, the two-grade system of nursing was seen as essential, and invested with even greater significance than hitherto, since only head nurses or sisters could be expected to have time for pastoral duties.[16]

The constitution of St John's House faithfully reflected this philosophy of Marthas and Marys. Members, who wore uniform but did not take religious vows, were divided into three distinct groups. Probationers and nurses received wages, and were trained for private and hospital work; they were also required to 'assist in such domestic duties of the house as may be assigned to them'. Sisters, who accepted no salary, and paid for their own board and lodging, trained and supervised the probationers, and visited the sick and aged poor in their homes. There was also a class of Associate Sisters, whose home ties did not permit residence, but who supported the work of the House generally.[17] A very determined confusion of the notions of social and spiritual superiority was in operation here. Women of means were automatically assumed to be more spiritually endowed than working women, and were also deemed qualified to instruct the latter in the proper duties of a hospital and private nurse, without themselves having to undergo any practical probation.

It is worth asking – as Florence Nightingale was to ask, in exasperation, many times in the 1850s and 1860s – why a group of women of independent income and religious inclination, but without formal training of any kind, should have been considered competent to perform these functions.[18] The answer lies at least in part in the side-effects of the industrial revolution, which produced leafy suburbs and comfortable middle-class households as well as satanic mills; and which increased the number of female domestic servants and of their leisured female employers, as well as giving birth to an industrial working class. Much has been written of the middle-class cult of domesticity in this period, and of the special role of women within it. The leisured woman, who neither accepted nor was educated for paid employment, was an important symbol of her family's new-found economic and social status; her confinement to domestic responsibilities was invested with a higher significance by the Evangelical movement within the Church of England, which stressed the value of family worship and religious teaching in the home. Women were seen as the guardians of spiritual standards, which were to inform the actions of their male relatives in politics and the marketplace; but they themselves were also seen as potential carriers of those standards beyond the household.[19]

In particular, women's relations with their servants were seen as models for the extension of middle-class influence on society at large. Within their homes, 'ladies' were supposed to exercise moral supervision over female members of the lower classes, teaching them cleanliness and discipline, and respect for their employers' way of life. Many of the reforming clergy thought that this experience of household management qualified ladies to exercise a beneficent influence over the homes of the poor, and over the inmates of public institutions such as prisons, workhouses and hospitals.[20]

In 1852, the Rev. Butler, chaplain of the Anglican Sisterhood of St Mary's, Wantage, which had charge of a house for penitents (former prostitutes), insisted that 'the discipline, so necessary to aid the work of the Chaplain in their repentance, must be carried out by those who can unite firmness with gentleness. . .' Such qualities were 'hardly to be found, except in those of gentle birth and education.'[21] In 1855 a Rev. J.S. Brewer enthused:[22]

> If then it were possible, in this or in the great manufacturing towns of this country, for the ladies of England to extend that influence over all classes of the poor which, for the great good of this country, they are extending over one large portion of the classes below them, I really believe the blessing to this nation would be inestimable.

Both these statements referred to the mistress-servant relationship. The paradigm applied to hospital nursing, with its heavy domestic component, more than to almost any other sphere of public and philanthropic work. The comparison between the work of nurses, under-nurses or ward-maids and that of ordinary housemaids was obvious. The role of the sister, head or upper nurse, being still in an early stage of development at many hospitals, could be assimilated to that of the supervisory mistress of the middle-class household. The nursing sister of St John's House was unwaged within the hospital, as she would have been in her own home. This indicated, not idleness and amateurism, but the disinterested and spiritual character of her work, as well as her fitness to exercise authority. The desiderata here were not so much medical cures as the tidiness, obedience and religion of the sick poor, and the humbler of their nurses; and women of the leisured classes, rather than male chaplains or medical officers, were seen as the crucial agents of social and spiritual transformation.

It is against this background that the special contribution of Florence Nightingale to nursing reform must be evaluated.[23] Her enormous influence on the development of hospital nursing as a profession was due not merely to her distinguished family connections and remarkable intellectual gifts, but to the fact that in her person she appeared to unite all the different strands in the movement for reform. She was passionately interested in social statistics of all kind, and was an enthusiast for sanitary reform; and as a follower of Edwin Chadwick and the anti-contagionist theory of disease, she insisted on the primacy of environmental factors in the spread of infection. Through a programme of reading and hospital visits in England and on the Continent, she made herself an expert on the newest theories of hospital management and design. But with all this, she was a refined gentlewoman, who from her seventeenth birthday had felt called to God's service, and who subsequently worked without remuneration.

Florence Nightingale was concerned with nursing as an aid to the prevention and cure of disease, not as a means to save souls. She did not believe that either a genteel pedigree or the desire to offer spiritual consolation were in themselves qualifications for nursing. Her own religious sense was highly individual and unsectarian: the laws of health were the laws of God; to reveal and follow them was to do his will. Caring for the sick was an act of self-sacrifice and charity which was not to be exploited in any competition between sects or creeds. Her personal experience of nursing before the Crimean War was relatively slight, consisting of two short stays with Fliedner at Kaiserswerth in 1850 and 1851, and twelve months as lady superintendent of the Institution for Invalid Gentlewomen at Harley Street, London. Nevertheless, she considered herself 'a real Hospital Nurse'[24] in comparison with many other well-meaning women who often had much more practical experience of dealing with the seriously ill, but who lacked her scientific interests and motivation. Being tarred with the same brush as other 'lady philanthropists' infuriated her, even though – perhaps because – it was one of the conditions of her public acceptance and success.

In practice, the different elements in the nursing reform movement often converged and complemented each other. Florence Nightingale certainly possessed a religious sense of vocation; and the nursing sisterhoods did not resist new ideas in hospital practice. But ultimately they competed for recognition by hospital governors and medical practitioners, and for the funds of the charitable public. When the Crimean War broke out, and the idea of a female nursing expedition was mooted, it was perhaps inevitable that animosities should have come to the surface. Each group needed to prove the superiority of its arrangements. None had ever anticipated that they might collaborate in an emergency, military or otherwise. Nor had any of them looked on the army as a potential field for their labours before 1854. The army hospital system, and its disasters in the Crimea, were pegs on which to hang their own, often rancorous, claims to recognition; and they had a vested interest in portraying the army hospitals' organisation, staff, and previous history in the bleakest possible light.

THE ARMY HOSPITAL SYSTEM

During the long period of peace in Europe which had followed the ending of the Napoleonic Wars and the Congress of Vienna of 1815, the British army had maintained a very separate existence from the mainstream of civilian society. It was not a conscript force, but a paid body recruited through voluntary enlistment, and largely occupied with colonial garrison functions. As far as health questions were concerned, the home battalions had not been the source of any major scandal in this period. During the cholera epidemics, indeed, the sanitary discipline established in barracks was such that mortality had compared very favourably with that among the population at large.[25]

An unemployed man who took the Queen's shilling at the beginning of 1854 gained access to a far more comprehensive medical organisation than would have been available to him in civilian life.[26] In theory at least, the state could not afford an army of sick soldiers. Each regiment, therefore, had its own medical officer, who officiated at daily sick parades, and attended the men in the regimental hospital. Malingering was as much the object of investigation as illness. For this reason, hospitalisation played a vital, and somewhat punitive, role in the army medical system. It was considered destructive of morale for sick soldiers to remain in barracks; hence the mildest illness or disability which prevented a man from carrying out his normal military duties was the occasion for his removal to hospital. (Officers were, of course, exempted from this regime of compulsion.)[27] If his disease or injury had not been contracted in the course of performing his duties, the bulk of a soldier's daily wage was deducted for the duration of his stay. This measure, known as 'hospital stoppage', was directed principally, though not exclusively, at men who had contracted venereal disease: at the beginning of the nineteenth century, between 20 and 25 per cent of all military hospital admissions were venereal cases.

Within the hospital, the soldier was cared for by ward orderlies seconded from the regiment. These men received no training in nursing, but often acquired some medical knowledge through long service. They undertook cooking and cleaning as well as nursing duties. They may have been clumsy, but they were not unkind to their patients, since these were also their regimental comrades. The

24

sick soldier was cared for as well as his civilian counterpart in many voluntary hospitals, and infinitely better than the pitiable inmates of most workhouse infirmaries.

The army medical system certainly had its defects, but these had little to do with the calibre of nursing staff, and were, in fact, not easily visible in time of peace. As in the British army as a whole, there was very little central organisation. The decentralised, regimental system was well suited to minor skirmishes and essentially policing duties in far-flung imperial stations (and, occasionally, at home); but it did not fit either the medical or the combatant wings for major military engagements. In 1853, one year before the Crimean War, the army held its first ever peacetime camp of exercise; brigades of infantry and cavalry combined for training with battalions of artillery and engineers. This was an enormous innovation, and a belated recognition of the need to bring British military organisation up to the level of the Continental powers through greater co-ordination of planning and resources. By this date Dr Andrew Smith, Director-General of the Army Medical Department, had begun to argue, against fierce resistance from his own staff, that medical officers should also have a stronger central organisation, and that fewer of them should be indissolubly attached to the regiments. This would certainly prepare the Department more effectively for going on to a wartime footing.[28]

Because the vast majority of medical officers were attached simply to their own regiments, they dealt with limited numbers and classes of cases – perhaps no more than thirty patients at any one time – and had little opportunity to gain wider professional experience. There were only three military general hospitals, situated at Chatham, Dublin and Cork; these held two or three hundred patients suffering from serious disease or injury, or needing long-term care. At larger stations, such as Aldershot, Shorncliffe and Portsmouth, it was still the practice for regimental hospitals to combine to occupy the same buildings, but to be administered and staffed independently.[29] In consequence, the regimental medical officers were deprived both of opportunities to advance their medical knowledge, and of experience in administering large units. They did not learn to work with professional colleagues, or to anticipate the problems involved in prescribing, dispensing, catering and nursing on a major scale: all skills which would have been invaluable in the Crimea.

Military medical officers belonged to the civil department of the army. They did not qualify for commissioned rank, and had, therefore, no power of command over combatants. As ward orderlies fell into this category, the situation in the hospitals was highly anomalous. The problem was glossed over in the regimental hospitals, where the medical officers were placed in authority over both ward staff and patients; in the general hospitals, however, the full separation of powers was enforced. The general hospital medical officer might instruct an orderly as to the care of the sick, but he could not give him orders as such, nor could he punish him for dereliction of duty. Disciplinary power resided with the military commandant of the hospital, and was exercised by the wardmaster or hospital sergeant.[30] This practical divorce between medical expertise and military authority did not threaten the day-to-day working of the system in peacetime; but when strangers were forced to work together under the pressures of war, the situation was pregnant with disaster.

What role, if any, did women play in the pre-Crimean military hospital system? Records from the mid-eighteenth century show women being paid, not only as nurses, but as head nurses, to accompany a military expedition abroad; whether they were army wives, or recruited direct from civilian hospitals, is not known. British army wives served as nurses, cooks, cleaners and laundresses in the military hospitals of the American War of Independence. Soldiers' wives are said to have been employed as nurses in regimental hospitals up to 1838. After that they were forbidden to attend male patients except with the previous sanction of the Secretary of State at War; but they were employed to attend sick regimental wives and children to whom a dozen beds were now allotted in every regimental hospital.[31]

It is clear that the practice of female military nursing was not, in fact, sharply discontinued at this point, but evidence on the question is extremely fragmentary. At least three applicants for war nursing posts in 1854 claimed military nursing experience. Mrs Bull, the widow of a major of militia, was said to 'understand gunshot wounds'; Mrs Anderton, the widow of a colour sergeant of the Royal Artillery, was said to have been 'accustomed to nurse soldiers at Spike Island'. Mrs Blakey, the widow of a soldier who had died on his way home from India, was 'five years Hospital nurse of the 5th Regiment', 'though generally employed in the women's ward'. It is more than likely that women who nursed soldiers' families would also nurse in the men's wards if the workload was heavy there; it is also likely that a hospital sergeant's wife might be asked to act as a nurse.[32] As late as 1856 there were female nurses at the Woolwich Artillery Hospital. They were 'in a wretched state – ill paid, under no system, neither fed nor clothed (& only nine of them lodged) in the Building', and the Director-General was in the process of replacing them with his newly created, and all-male, Medical Staff Corps.[33]

It can at least be stated with some certainty that between 1815 and 1854 the number of female nurses in military hospitals was declining. The practice of employing army wives, widows and camp followers as nurses probably reached its peak during the Napoleonic Wars. With the coming of peace there was a sharp contraction in the demand for their services; and with the dispersion of regiments among colonial garrisons, there were fewer opportunities for wives and children to accompany the men. Permission to marry was only granted to a small proportion of the regiment – between 6 and 10 per cent of the men – whose families were thereby classified as 'on the strength', and entitled to welfare provision.[34] The harsh conditions, and lack of employment, in some colonial stations, may have discouraged 'unofficial' wives from following their husbands.

There were other reasons for the declining female involvement in army life in these decades. In times of peace military support services, such as transport and supply, could be brought more completely under the direct control of the army. Soldiers were housed in barracks where once they had been billeted in towns. Food, drink, forage and clothing were provided by civil departments of the army. As military life became more self-contained, it became more male. Women who had moved freely in and out of army society as sutlers, cooks, nurses and seamstresses were now excluded; henceforth their relations with soldiers were restricted to the personal, and they were visible only as wives, daughters, widows and prostitutes.[35] The female presence in camp – 'on the strength' families apart – was almost by definition disreputable. It is likely that this process was responsible for the disappearance of female nurses from military hospitals.

The decision to staff military hospitals exclusively with male orderlies does not seem to have arisen from any new ideas of medical organisation as such. Little thought was given to the development of military nursing work in this period. Although it was recommended as early as 1811 that orderlies be treated as permanently assigned to their hospital duties, it was not until after the outbreak of the Crimean War that any necessity was seen for constituting them as an official, permanent corps, requiring appropriate training.[36]

Anyone in full possession of the facts would surely have shrunk from the enterprise of re-introducing female nurses into army hospitals in 1854. The circumstances were not favourable for 'feminising' a masculine occupation, and 'civilianising' a military institution. The vast majority of military medical officers resented their non-combatant status – many of them, after all, would be expected to take tremendous risks under fire – and they did not want to emphasise the civilian character of their service. They were unlikely to respond to arguments that a new female nursing corps might be vitally needed to bring army hospitals up to date with the latest civilian developments. They would see, instead, the problems involved in employing 'unattached' females – in an environment where this description carried indecent connotations – to perform highly personal services for male patients. They would not welcome the challenge of bringing new approaches to nursing, and a new body of hospital staff, into the labyrinthine organisation of the military general wards. The army medical system on the eve of the Crimean War was for the most part a regimental, colonial and masculine club. No one could have predicted the cataclysm which might lead to its penetration by religious sisters, refined gentlewomen, or 'superior family servants'.

CHAPTER 2

++++++++++++++++++++

THE CRIMEAN EXPERIMENT

++++++++++++++++++++

Most of our knowledge of the nursing of the Crimean War comes from the biographical (and often hagiographical) literature on Florence Nightingale, which deals with the subject largely in terms of a heroine's struggles with her opponents.[1] But this is 'political' rather than 'labour' history. It takes the achievements and qualifications of the Nightingale expedition very much for granted. It assumes that the arrival of the female nurses was an unmixed blessing; that nursing care, or the lack of it, was crucial to the health or misery of the troops; and that the female nurse was by definition superior to the male. All these assumptions deserve to be questioned. If we re-examine the Crimean episode from a different viewpoint, asking not who was on Florence Nightingale's side, but who the nurses were, and what they actually did, a very different history emerges. By giving other sources, especially the memoirs of other women, equal weight with Nightingale records, we are able to discover a great deal about the nature and limitations of hospital care in the mid-nineteenth century. We are also able to make the acquaintance of an extraordinarily varied group of Victorian women, whose achievements strongly influenced their female contemporaries and, as will be seen, inspired future generations of women and girls to become war nurses.

MEDICINE AT WAR

Female nurses were, quite literally, the last thing the sick and wounded soldier needed in the Crimea. His troubles originated with the inflexible structures of military bureaucracy, and the relative helplessness of medical science. The newspaper-reading public of the day focussed first its indignation, and then its philanthropy, on the final stage of his journey from the front; but the medical problems of the British military expedition actually began long before its first engagement, at Alma, on 20 September 1854.[2]

To begin with, cholera and other serious enteric disorders had hospitalised 20 per cent of the entire strength of the expeditionary force between June and August. Nearly one thousand lives were lost before a shot had been fired. Hospital supplies were rapidly exhausted, and replacements delivered to the wrong locations. When the military campaign finally got under way, Lord Raglan, anticipating a brief and mobile engagement, ordered the medical officers to accompany their regiments to the front without the major part of their stores. The army moved from Kalamita Bay towards the port of Sebastopol without a single hospital bed or marquee. The aftermath of the battles of Alma, Balaklava and Inkerman deluged the hospital ships and the base hospital at Scutari with casualties, both of the fighting and of a renewed outbreak of cholera.

Within the hospitals, precedents were lacking for co-ordinating the medical services for several regiments. Medical officers, as we have seen, had no official managerial authority, and no control over medical transport and supplies. In London, the Director-General of the Army Medical Department struggled with the Treasury, the Admiralty, the Department of Ordnance and the Commissariat for vital supplies, often in vain.[3] One particularly scandalous consequence of this dispersal of responsibilities was the failure to provide an ambulance corps. No plans had been devised for the transport of the sick and wounded before the spring of 1854. After Alma, the task of moving the British wounded three miles to the coast was accomplished only with the help of the navy, and of the French military ambulance service. A British ambulance corps had, indeed, arrived in the east on 20 July; it was composed of a hundred men, mainly army pensioners, who rapidly succumbed to

BULGARIA

Kalamita
Bay

Crimea

Sebastopol

Balaklava

Sea
of
Azov

Varna

Black Sea

Constantinople

Koulali

Gallipoli

Scutari

Sea of Marmora

Renkioi

TURKEY

0 50 100

miles

Ismeer/Smyrna

——— Site of British military hospitals
employing female nurses.

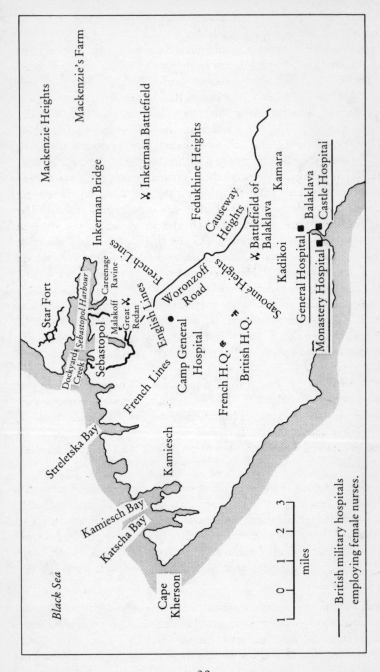

Black Sea

Mackenzie Heights

Mackenzie's Farm

Inkerman Battlefield

Inkerman Bridge

Feduhkine Heights

Kamara

Castle Hospital

Balaklava

Causeway Heights

Battlefield of Balaklava

General Hospital

Monastery Hospital

Kadikoi

Balakoi

Star Fort

Carenage Ravine

Great Redan

Malakoff

Sebastopol Harbour

Dockyard Creek

Sebastopol

French Lines

English Lines

Woronzoff Road

Sapoune Heights

Camp General Hospital

French H.Q.

British H.Q.

French Lines

Streletska Bay

Kamiesch

Kamiesch Bay

Katscha Bay

Cape Kherson

miles

1   0   1   2   3

—— British military hospitals
employing female nurses.

cholera and drink. The ambulance waggons proved unsuitable for the type of horses locally available.

Even under optimal administrative conditions, medical officers might yet have proved helpless in the face of the cholera epidemic. Between 1849 and 1854, research carried out by Drs John Snow and William Budd had established that the cholera infection was transmitted through water. Although their findings were initially rejected by the College of Physicians, they influenced many of their fellow practitioners. But military medical officers do not appear to have taken note of this research either before or during the war. Although trained alongside their civilian colleagues, they were very much isolated from them once they embarked on their army careers, particularly as most of their service was spent abroad. The official campaign reports of both the army and navy medical departments point to impure air as the chief agent in the spread of cholera; and practices in camp and hospital tended not to depart from the traditional.[4] Men were ordered to smoke in the wards, and their doctors experimented with chloroform, dosed them with brandy and ice, and had their stomachs and cramped joints rubbed with mustard or turpentine. It was thought that cholera could develop from other stomach infections, and might be brought on by an over-acid diet, or simply by an attack of panic. Most treatment was futile.[5]

The failings of nursing staff were, thus, almost the least of the handicaps under which the medical officers laboured. Surgeons in the field, still working within the regimental framework, were in fact fairly satisfied with their orderlies. They reported as much to the Parliamentary Commission on the state of the military hospitals:

> These men are, of course, fitted for their capacity, or they would not be retained. . . . They are men of good character and well fitted for their duty, otherwise they are immediately dismissed. . . . The men are exceedingly attentive to the onerous duties they have to perform. . . . All are willing to do their best. . . . All good steady old soldiers, and well suited to the purpose.

The scale of regimental hospital work was not too great for the existing organisation of staff; and the orderlies, however medically inexperienced, were at least among familiar faces. Like their general hospital colleagues, the regimental surgeons complained of losing good men through illness or military postings. But their greatest complaints still related to scarcity of equipment, and inadequate communication with the base.[6]

At Scutari, however, nursing problems were more in evidence. The orderlies were detailed to the hospital from regiments in the vicinity. They were chosen, not on grounds of previous experience in regimental hospitals, but because they were unfit for active service. As it was, no prior experience could have prepared them to cope with the shocking state in which the sick and wounded arrived, and had to be packed together in wards and corridors. One Anglican nursing sister thoughtfully observed:[7]

> it is either unduly depressing or hardening and demoralising for the wild buoyancy of youth to be thrust into such scenes. I have . . . caught them even at leap-frog along the feet of a row of sufferers, some in anguish, some in the awful stillness of death; and if reproved, 'We can do them no good, poor fellows; we must keep up our own spirits a bit,' was the answer.

The Scutari orderlies could undoubtedly be faulted on many grounds; but they were victims, not only of traumatic circumstances, but also of very poor management. The justification of the general hospital system was that it made possible all kinds of economies of scale; but there was no economy of effort in the way that orderlies were deployed. In order to feed 'his' patients, a ward orderly had to obtain that day's diet sheet from the ward medical officer, queue outside the Purveyor's office until the necessary raw materials had been supplied, then queue at the kitchen until the raw materials had been cooked. He had then to distribute the food to his patients. The same performance was repeated for the patients' second meal of the day. For the supply of medicines, a similar procedure was followed. These procedures, perfectly adequate to a regimental establishment catering for thirty patients, amounted to black farce in a hospital complex accommodating over 3,000. In a letter of 8 January 1855, Florence Nightingale described the existing system, and proposed its radical overhaul: one commissariat officer, for example, could be appointed to receive all the medical officers' diet sheets, and present them, with the necessary ingredients, directly to the kitchen orderlies, who could then proceed with a rationalised bulk order.[8]

It was perhaps an outsider's eye which was needed to single out

the failings of the system. This particular outsider had written a
year earlier, on taking up her first post as hospital superintendent:[9]

> The indispensable conditions of a suitable house are, *first*, that
> the nurse should never be obliged to quit her floor, except for
> her own dinner and supper, and her patients' dinner and supper
> (and even the latter might be avoided by the windlass we have
> talked about). Without a system of this kind, the nurse is
> converted into a pair of legs.

Under the Scutari system, the ward orderly was in fact little but a
pair of legs, although in principle his hands were also required to
care for his patients: to distribute food and medicine, spoon-
feeding it if necessary, at times which were appropriate to the
individual patient's needs; to wash the men, shift their position in
bed, and change their clothing and bed-linen; to dress their
wounds and attend to them during surgical operations. Hands
were also needed to sweep and clean the wards, and empty the
lavatory tubs. 'Of course', wrote the Anglican nursing sister
quoted above, 'men whose hands were hard and horny through
labour – hands used once perhaps to the plough, and more recently
to the firelock – were not fitted to touch, bathe, and dress
wounded limbs, however gentle and considerate their hearts might
be.'[10] The relative roughness or smoothness of a nurse's hands were
not as significant as the time in which he or she was allowed to use
them; but the finer points of military hospital organisation were
not the stuff of which popular clamour was to be made.

LOOKING FOR NURSES

The call for female nurses did not arise in the Crimea itself, nor
did it come from medical circles in Great Britain. The tirades of
The Times war correspondent, W.H. Russell, were directed
towards a middle-class public which responded chiefly in terms of
its own religious and charitable concerns and ambitions. Two
newspaper letters which appeared shortly after Russell's vivid
descriptions of the sufferings of the sick and wounded after Alma
and Balaklava seem to have been particularly influential. One, in
The Times of 14 October, asked with reference to the apparently
superior hospital arrangements of the French army,

Why have we no Sisters of Charity? There are numbers of able-bodied and tender-hearted English women who would joyfully and with alacrity go out to devote themselves to nursing the sick and wounded, if they could be associated for that purpose, and placed under proper protection.

Another, in the High Church *Guardian* of 18 October, declared,

It is more than ever a reproach on our Church that the faith of her members is not exhibited by the presence there of Sisters of Charity. . . . If the heads of the few sisterhoods we have . . . would spare two or more each, . . . I would see what could be done towards sending them out.

Between the publication of these two letters took place a now celebrated exchange of correspondence between Florence Nightingale, the Secretary at War Sidney Herbert, and his wife Elizabeth. Florence Nightingale wrote to the latter on 14 October, offering to command 'a small private expedition of nurses . . . for Scutari' and asking whether Sidney Herbert could give her letters of recommendation, or would advise her to apply to the Secretary for War for further authorisation. On 15 October Sidney Herbert wrote to Florence Nightingale saying that he had already received 'numbers of offers from ladies to go out' and begging her to organise and superintend such a scheme.[11]

There is, of course, no single explanation for the enthusiasm generated for nursing, or sending others to nurse, the sick and wounded soldiers in the east. But a predominant role must be ascribed to the ambitions of rival groups within the Church. The different sects wished to clothe themselves with the mantle of patriotism; their members did not seek fame and glory for themselves so much as respectability for their collective enterprise. The movement to establish sisterhoods had aroused considerable hostility and suspicion within the Church of England: its leaders were accused of destroying women's primary loyalties to their families, and of setting them on the road to Rome. The sisterhoods wished to prove on the most public stage that theirs was the best possible form of organisation for medical and other missions to the poor; and where better to rebut the charge of being 'un-English' than at the bedsides of Her Majesty's troops?[12]

The Catholic Bishop of Southwark hoped by the same means to

1 Florence Nightingale. (Bodleian Library)

dispel Protestant prejudice against the convents of the Sisters of Mercy now established in Britain:

> Let the nuns who are so fiercely assailed proceed at once to the battlefield. There their daily life, seen by the whole world, and their devotedness to the cause of charity, will be the best answer to the vile calumnies uttered against them.

He was so ambitious for this project that he made sure that five members of the Bermondsey convent set off for Turkey in advance of the main government party.[13]

Florence Nightingale's party of nurses consisted of 38 women in all: 8 sisters and 6 nurses from Anglican orders; 5 nuns from each of two Catholic Convents of Mercy; and 14 secular hospital nurses.[14] The task of selecting the latter she delegated to three friends: Mrs Bracebridge, who accompanied her to Scutari, Mrs Herbert, wife of the Secretary at War, and Mary Stanley. Lizzy Herbert and Mary Stanley were both High Church enthusiasts with strong leanings towards Rome. Mary Stanley was the daughter of the Bishop of Norwich, and a strong supporter of the St John's House philosophy of nursing reform.[15] Earlier in 1854 she had published a little book, *Hospitals and Sisterhoods*, in which she expressed the view that the sick patient was a spiritual opportunity, and nursing a pastoral calling. She believed that the ideal nurse belonged to 'a class of persons which remains to be created, and which will never be created except by education, and that not by desultory experiments or individual efforts.' The real article filled her with distaste. Of the paid nurses whom she selected for the first nursing party, she wrote:[16]

> I wish people who may hereafter complain of the women selected could have seen the set we had to choose from. All London was scoured for them. We sent emissaries in every direction to every likely place. . . . We felt ashamed to have in the house such women as came. One alone expressed a wish to go from a good motive. Money was the only inducement.

One of the Anglican sisters wrote with more sympathy and insight of the same women that many were widows, struggling to support large families; they were willing to risk death from contagious disease, cholera in particular, in the hope that the government would then make proper provision for their children.[17] As the paid nurses for the first two parties were hurriedly recruited in the space of barely six weeks, it is hardly surprising that they should have included a large quota of the financially desperate. Working women who had a secure livelihood might think twice before sacrificing it for dangerous employment of uncertain duration. But financial desperation need not preclude other sentiments. Mary Stanley must have been of a very fixed cast of mind to have been unmoved by this application from Matilda Norman:[18]

> I am Soldgers Wife and my Husband is just gone out to the East . . . the Colonel been well satisfied with my Carertor thought I should be very useful in the Regt but having heard that was being Nurses sent out I would do any thing to go for I there might be able to help him in is dieing moments I am Young and Strong and do not mind what I suffer should Sir you not think me Experienced I will try and get into a Horespitll for a time I really do not recorse to fly to. . .

The records which survive on the paid nurses selected do not entirely bear out Mary Stanley's strictures. Mrs Roberts of St Thomas's, for example, whom South had so highly praised for her surgical nursing, won equally golden opinions in the east. Elizabeth Smith, another St Thomas's nurse of six to seven years' standing, was also highly praised at the end of her service. Mrs Robbins, recommended on the basis of four and a half years' work in the female accident ward of Queen's Hospital, Birmingham, worked satisfactorily at Scutari for the whole duration of the war. Mary Ann Noble's competence at Scutari was rewarded by her appointment as head nurse of three female medical wards at the Westminster Hospital in January 1856. Neither E. Grundy, who had nursed seven years at the Middlesex Hospital, nor Mrs Tuffell, who had been a surgical nurse at King's College Hospital for two years, nor E. Hawkins, who had spent two months as a night nurse at Guy's, gave any cause for complaint; and a St John's House nurse, Mrs Lawfield, who was 'too much of a fine lady to be a good Nurse' and 'fonder of *sketching* than of poulticing' would hardly have been an offensive presence in Mrs Herbert's house.[19]

Florence Nightingale and her helpers may in fact have had very little close contact with nurses in British hospitals before the outbreak of the war.[20] They were quite unprepared to meet the nurses on their own terms. The candidates for the east did not match the standards of deference and submissiveness which they could have expected, say, in women seeking domestic employment. Thus, in March 1855 Mrs Davidson, the experienced head nurse in the surgical ward of a Dr Simpson in an Edinburgh hospital, was 'sent home for disobedience to orders' and 'lightness of behaviour'. Another nurse with 'very good medical and private certificates' was 'sent home for being out without leave in bad Company'. The nurses inspired alarm and distrust in their female employers. Florence Nightingale referred to them as 'the most slippery race in existence'. Mrs Bracebridge, her companion and amanuensis at Scutari, wrote of Mrs Jane Gibson, a St Thomas's surgical nurse, that she was 'sent home for intoxication has since proved a Thief' – but made a second note that on subsequent evidence this charge proved groundless. Mrs Mary Young, a Barts's surgical nurse, was 'sent home on strong suspicion of very gross misconduct'; the conduct of Mrs Newton, a nurse at the London Hospital for Women, caused scandal 'though nothing was proved'.[21] The main charge against all nurses dismissed, however, was intoxication, and this does pose problems of interpretation. Could so many women, highly recommended by responsible physicians and surgeons, really have been hopeless drunks? It is possible that in this respect a hospital nurse behaved more like a male employee than a female servant; and that what shocked a lady superintendent into shipping a nurse back to England might not have provoked the same reaction from a male doctor.*

After the formation of the first nursing party, Lizzy Herbert and Mary Stanley were left with the task of interviewing the seemingly

---

*One of the more interesting candidates for a nursing post to be turned down by Florence Nightingale and her helpers was Mrs Mary Seacole. She was born in 1805 in Jamaica, the daughter of a Scottish soldier and a black boarding-house keeper and herbal 'doctress'. Deeply disappointed that her familiarity with tropical enteric disorders and passionate wish to serve did not gain her admission as a government nurse, she raised her own funds and set up in the Crimea as cantiniere and dispenser of folk remedies. Her commercial services and her kindness to the wounded were greatly appreciated. We may speculate that she was rejected in London because she was neither a hospital nurse nor a domestic servant – but because of her colour she was not, despite her respectability, perceived as a 'lady'. 'Mother' Seacole appears not to have handed down her medical skills and recipes. See *The Wonderful Adventures of Mrs Seacole in Many Lands*, eds Z. Alexander and A. Dewjee (London 1984).

2 [Right] Fanny Taylor, one of Mary Stanley's 'lady volunteers', wearing the 'badge' of Koulali hospital; she rejected the rest of the uniform assigned by the War Office to ladies and nurses alike. (Bodleian Library)

3 [Left] Catharine Leslie Anderson, another 'lady volunteer'. She was sometimes mistaken for Florence Nightingale, and her husband later suggested that many war anecdotes about Nightingale (who did very little personal nursing) might have been a case of mistaken identity. (Bodleian Library)

4 [Right] Elizabeth Davis, a former domestic servant and hospital nurse, and the only paid nurse of the Crimean War to publish her memoirs, which were often critical of Nightingale. She is also the only paid nurse of whom we have a portrait – very far removed from Sairey Gamp and Betsy Prig. (Bodleian Library)

endless stream of applicants for nursing posts, and, where appropriate, arranging for them to receive hospital training in London. Many of the candidates were ladies volunteering to nurse on a non-stipendiary basis. Florence Nightingale herself had not accepted any such candidates from outside the sisterhoods, but she encouraged at least one, Jane Shaw Stewart, to gain experience at Guy's and Westminster Hospital while she was on the waiting list.[22] Florence's friends may have felt that 'lady volunteers' were the solution to the problem of the shortage of suitable paid nurses; but in this, and in other matters, they misread the workings of her mind.

DISPERSION AND DISCORD

In his letter to Florence Nightingale of 15 October Sidney Herbert had written:[23]

> It would be impossible to carry about a large staff of female nurses with the army in the field. But at Scutari, having now a fixed hospital, no military reason exists against their introduction.

He implied that it was the fixed position which made the whole expedition feasible, both from a managerial point of view, and from the point of view of propriety. The experiment was to have nothing in common with the traipsing of wives and camp followers who had been the chief female nurses of the Peninsular War against Napoleon. But Herbert was being unrealistic. Scutari was already overcrowded, and a second general hospital was just being re-opened at Balaklava, in the Crimea. Within three weeks of Florence Nightingale's arrival, the War Office was looking for further hospital accommodation in Turkey; this was found at Koulali. If female nurses were considered useful in Scutari, it was likely that reinforcements would soon be required, and would be employed wherever they were needed. The form of agreement presented to the nurses acknowledged this possibility: nurses' expenses were to be paid for journeys 'to or from the present, or any future Hospital that may be appointed for the accommodation of the Sick and Wounded of the said Army'.[24]

Florence Nightingale had arrived in Scutari to a mixed reception from the army medical officers. Some were hostile to, others contemptuous of the female nursing corps; above all, her privilege of direct communication with the Secretary at War – despite her nominal responsibility to the Principal Medical Officer, Dr Duncan Menzies – and her association with *The Times*, through the shared administration of its 'comforts' fund, aroused defensive suspicion. Sensitive to all these stirrings, she was horrified to learn in December that Mary Stanley and Elizabeth Herbert, without first ascertaining her wishes, had despatched a second nursing party, with Mary Stanley at its head. Ten of its members were 'ladies', without experience of paid employment; and fifteen were Catholic Sisters of Mercy from Ireland.[25] She was convinced that the Herberts and Mary Stanley had been intriguing behind her back, both to strengthen the influence of the kind of philan-thropic, non-professional gentlewoman whom she considered out of place in a hospital, and to reinforce the potentially controversial Catholic presence. She would have been doubly horrified had she known that the Reverend Mother Bridgeman, of the Kinsale Convent of Mercy, had been officially recognised as sole superioress of the Irish sisters outside the hospital wards, and as the only medium of communication between the sisters and Florence Nightingale; and that the sisters were to form a separate and undispersed community at all times.[26]

Much has been made, in the biographical literature, of the upset caused to Florence Nightingale by the arrival of Mary Stanley's contingent. Her gift for the sharp phrase has fixed them in our vicarious memory as given to 'spiritual flirtations', 'scampering about the wards', and 'wandering about with notebooks in their hands'.[27] Most of them, however, were seriously interested in nursing, and dedicated to the work as they conceived it; two of them died at their posts.[28] Frances Margaret Taylor, for example, was a far from inconsiderable person. She was the daughter of a rural clergyman and, at twenty-two, the youngest of Mary Stanley's ladies. At the age of sixteen or seventeen she had visited the (Sellonite) Anglican Sisterhood of Mercy of Devonport and Plymouth, of which her elder sister Charlotte, who also went to the east, was one of the first members, and worked with them in the homes of the poor during the cholera outbreak of 1849. She did not join the sisterhood, but went to live with her widowed mother in London, where she worked in hospital wards, visited the poor in their homes, and helped to found a Ragged School. She underwent a period of hospital training after being selected as a military nurse. Like Mary Stanley, she was received into the Catholic church while in the east. After the war, she wrote a number of books, which successfully plugged a temporary gap in the family fortunes; became proprietor of *The Lamp*, a Catholic monthly periodical; and finally became Mother Magdalen Taylor, the foundress of an order called the Poor Servants of the Mother of God.[29]

Another of the ladies was Kate Anderson, the daughter of 'a Master in the Royal Navy'. She too was an associate of the Sellonites, and acted as a visitor to workhouses and slums in Devonport. She had nursed cholera patients – as, indeed had most of the ladies in her party – and learned invalid cookery before applying to nurse in the east. She nursed at the naval hospital at Therapia, at Scutari, and at Koulali. There she became engaged to be married to an army chaplain. He wrote of this engagement after her death, thirty years later:

> The decision was not lightly made, with which her work had no slight concern – how that might be affected – . . . she really changed in nought, save the merely outward phases of being; keeping ever her own individual life largely, apart but never alien to mine, nor ever diminishing in pity and care, or ceasing to keep the vision of poverty, ignorance, and suffering before her, and 'going forth to her work and to her labour until the evening' and the Master's call.

If Florence Nightingale had such a one in mind when she wrote that 'the ladies from Koulali and Smyrna have little other idea than that of riding out with the Chaplains and Officers and none at all of work', she was being less than just.[30]

Florence Nightingale's assertion that the new arrivals were surplus to requirements has been widely accepted. It is clear, however, that the second party arrived at precisely the moment when hospital provision was being expanded. Their presence was to be genuinely welcomed by the doctors setting up overflow accommodation at Koulali – in marked contrast to the situation at Scutari, where some doctors remained unreconciled to the Nightingale nurses, and appear never to have called on their services.[31] At first, however, the majority of the Stanley party were told that there was neither room nor work for them, and were obliged to cool their heels in lodgings at Therapia.[32] In late January 1855 some were invited by John Hall, the Inspector-

General of Hospitals, to nurse outside Turkey, at the General Hospital at Balaklava; others were established in the new hospitals of Koulali.[33]

These migrations did not end the dispersion of the female nursing corps. By March Martha Clough had left Balaklava to take charge of the regimental hospital of the Highland Brigade. She was the only female nurse to work in a regimental hospital, going at the request of Sir Colin Campbell and against the wishes of both Florence Nightingale and Mary Stanley. Jane Shaw Stewart left the Balaklava General Hospital to introduce female nursing staff at the Castle Hospital, Balaklava; in 1856 she moved again, and established female nurses at the hospital of the Land Transport Corps, also in the Crimea.[34] By autumn 1855, Inspector-General Hall had, indeed, decided to concentrate most of his hospital provision outside Turkey: the work of Koulali was wound up, and Mother Bridgeman and the Kinsale nuns transferred to the Balaklava Hospital.[35] Many miles south of Scutari, at Smyrna and Renkioi, female nurses, recruited and equipped uniformly with those in the military hospitals, were also employed in hospitals established on civilian initiative.[36]

By the spring of 1855, therefore, the female nursing experiment had expanded beyond anything originally envisaged by Florence Nightingale. By the beginning of March she was asking the War Office for more nursing staff;[37] and she had admitted to Sidney Herbert, now out of office, that she was no longer in control of the female nursing corps as a whole. She still appointed the nurses of Koulali and Balaklava, but was leaving the management of their work in their hands, subject to the authority of the medical officers.[38] She cannot have found this a satisfactory resolution of her difficulties, and it was certainly not an official one. On 5 March she wrote to Lord Panmure, Herbert's successor:

> I beg to be distinctly instructed what authority I am deemed to have over the Scutari Hospitals, as regards the Sisters and nurses generally, as well as over the Hospital at Balaklava and those at Koulalee.

On the same day Herbert was writing to tell her that the independence of the Koulali ladies was about to be officially sanctioned.[39] In what appears to have been an attempt to recover the initiative, she wrote again to the War Office on 2 April: she asked to be relieved of responsibility for the Koulali hospitals, on the grounds of Mary Stanley's refusal of co-operation. On 20 April the War Office formally agreed to her request. It was perhaps not a coincidence, given the intense animosity which Florence Nightingale felt for her former friend, that her letter of resignation was not written until the day that Mary Stanley left for England.[40]

These developments completely undermined Florence Nightingale's position as 'Superintendent of the female nursing establishment in the English General Military Hospitals in Turkey'. Her original commission had been effectively withdrawn within four months of her arrival in the east. Both the War Office and the voluntary organisers in London had grown tired of all the wrangling. The support of pious and enthusiastic lady philanthropists, committee members and hospital visitors to whom she had before the war shown, at best, a breezy and patronising condescension, could no longer be taken for granted.[41] Lady Stratford de Redcliffe, whose earlier efforts with her husband, the British ambassador at Constantinople, to give assistance at Scutari had provoked scathing comments from the Lady Superintendent, was now put in charge of all arrangements and appointments at Koulali, and was in constant communication with the British Military Commandant in the Bosphorus.[42] As for the other nursing parties, those at Smyrna and Renkioi were already under the direction of civilian doctors; the Kinsale nuns' first obedience was to their Superioress; and most of the nursing staff who had gone to Balaklava placed themselves in direct communication with Inspector-General Hall and Lord Raglan and, taking a literal reading of the terms of Florence Nightingale's appointment, disputed her claim to have any superintending authority outside Turkey itself.[43] The bulk of the female nursing work of the Crimean War was, therefore, done outside Florence Nightingale's jurisdiction, and without reference to her ideas of proper professional practice.

Only in the spring of 1856, as the war drew to a close, was she able to reassert a position of control. She had since 27 April 1855 been officially designated Almoner of the Free Gifts in all British hospitals in the Crimea, and had visited the Crimean hospitals in 1855 and 1856 on the pretext of checking distribution. Through press reports, and through the publicising activities of her family and friends, she managed to capture the public imagination at home. The military hospital organisation was now contracting; Koulali and Smyrna were closed, and the ladies and nurses who did not return to Britain came to nurse under her at Scutari.[44] After protracted wrangles with Inspector-General Hall and Mother Bridgeman, she finally extracted a declaration from the War Office on her official position:

> It appears to me that the Medical Authorities of the Army do not correctly comprehend Miss Nightingale's position as it has been officially recognized by me. . . . Miss Nightingale is recognized by Her Majesty's Government as the General Superintendent of the Female Nursing Establishment of the military hospitals of the Army. No lady, or sister, or nurse is to be transferred from one hospital to another, or introduced into any hospital, without consultation with her. . . . The Principal Medical Officer will communicate with Miss Nightingale upon all subjects connected with the Female Nursing Establishment, and will give his directions through that lady.

The declaration was communicated to the Commander of the Forces on 25 February 1856, and issued as a General Order on 16 March. *The Times* printed it on 1 April,[45] two days after the peace treaty was signed. Florence Nightingale has monopolised the public imagination, and blotted out most of the history of Crimean War nursing, ever since.

WOMEN AT WORK

What needs were in fact fulfilled by the arrival of the female nurses? Since their coming was, literally, uncalled-for by those on the spot, did they find their own work or was it found for them? Did they perform tasks which could be characterised as 'female', in contrast to 'male' functions performed by the military orderlies? And can the concept of 'female' work be clarified by considering it in relation to the class composition of the nursing parties, and the divisions of labour within them? It is time to follow the female nurses about their work; and as we do so, we shall gain a clearer insight into what was meant by 'care' and 'cure' of the sick in the mid-Victorian period. The parallels between nursing and domestic service as occupations for women have already been remarked upon. What the nurses' war memoirs reveal is the closeness of the relationship between good housekeeping and medical science in 1854, and the fragility of the distinctions between 'care' and 'cure'.

When the first nursing party arrived at Scutari the immediate priority appeared to be not in the sphere of medical or surgical nursing as such, but in that of domestic management. The patients were not merely Sick and Wounded. They were also badly and inefficiently fed, and their unwashed bodies lay in filthy sheets or blankets in equally filthy and foul-smelling wards. There was little point in attempting nursing work until these very material non-medical conditions had been dealt with. Hence the exchange between Florence Nightingale and one of her party on approaching Constantinople:

> 'Oh, Miss Nightingale, when we land, don't let there be any red-tape delays, let us get straight to nursing the poor fellows!' 'The strongest will be wanted at the wash-tub.'

The laundry work was in fact farmed out to soldiers' wives, and the bulk of the cleaning continued to be done by the orderlies, after the arrival of the Nightingale expedition. But it was done at Florence Nightingale's insistence, and often with equipment procured by her.[46] A medical officer wishing to ensure cleanliness in and around his patients' beds had to give instructions to the orderlies; if these were not followed, he had to inform the purveyor; if the purveyor was unable to get the instructions carried out, appeal was to be made to the Principal Medical Officer, and in the last resort to the military commandant of the hospital.[47] This was hardly an efficient method of keeping the wards of a large and overcrowded hospital clean. Someone needed to be permanently on the spot to see that the work was being done. Just over a fortnight after her arrival, Florence Nightingale was available for the task. 'She scolds sergeants and orderlies all day long,' wrote one of her companions. The ladies and nuns at Koulali were equally brisk at licking the orderlies into shape.[48] Ironically, Florence Nightingale's domestic work, rather than her claims to nursing expertise, may have done most to reconcile the doctors to the presence of ladies in a military hospital. If there was one form of work in which ladies were fully qualified, whether hospital-trained or not, it was in giving directions to domestic servants: and this was a chore of which many medical officers were only too glad to be relieved.

In attending to their patients' dietary needs, the female nurses entered an area which seemed to be more simply 'women's work', and in which any special qualities of 'ladies' were largely irrelevant.

The staple diets of the hospitals were always prepared and served by the male orderlies. The sheer size of this catering operation, and the cumbersome and inefficient method of distributing meals to individual patients, meant that the provision of 'extra diets' – which often were of greater value in stimulating appetite and morale – was very unsatisfactory. Small helpings, intended to be tempting or revivifying, of e.g. arrowroot, beef-tea, port wine, lemonade, jelly and rice-pudding, were either badly prepared and served at inappropriate times, or not distributed at all. At Scutari Florence Nightingale set up her own 'extra diet kitchens' and supplementary boilers where these items alone were prepared and, on medical requisition, issued to ward orderlies. Mary Stanley after two days at Koulali wrote of the as yet incomplete organisation of the new hospital, and the 'messes of lemonade, arrowroot, beat-up eggs, rice pudding, etc., going on in every room.'[49]

After the war, Florence Nightingale wrote, with a note of regret:[50]

> Practically, it is of little avail to superintend, ever so carefully, the issue of extras to the sick, unless there is permission and opportunity to pour the nourishment, perhaps in continual drops, down the throat of reluctant agony, or delirium, or stupor.

From cooking to feeding was indeed a logical sequence, if the ratio of nurses to patients was adequate. During the war, however, Florence Nightingale was strongly critical of what she considered the overstaffing of those hospitals where the female nursing was not under her control: she predicted that the men would be overindulged and the medical staff alienated by extensive female interference; she claimed that moral dangers existed, since most of the men were not '*really* sick', but convalescing until fit for combatant service; in May 1855 she wished she had fewer nurses herself. The ideal ratio was 2½ to 3 female nurses per 100 severely sick men. Koulali now had about 43 female nurses for 500 patients.[51]

There is no evidence that the medical officers outside Scutari shared Florence Nightingale's reservations. When the Koulali hospitals were opened, it was explained to Mary Stanley that her party was chiefly required for cooking and administering the patients' diets, and watching and feeding the medical cases. They seem also to have been given more responsibility in the matter than the nurses at Scutari:[52]

> The doctors are worn out, and simply say, 'With such a diet you may use your own discretion: he must be fed, get down all you can.'

The extent to which these functions were appreciated was shown again towards the end of the war, when the staff-surgeon responsible for the civilian Land Transport Corps put in a request for twelve female nurses,[53]

> As there is a large amount of sickness in the Corps, and of a nature requiring nourishment carefully prepared and administered with discretion, as well as great attention to personal cleanliness and comfort of the sick, and as these ends are not obtained by the class of hospital orderlies sent from the Corps.

While it may seem that the female nurses were appreciated more for their domestic than their medical capacities, the classifying line between the two functions was necessarily blurred. Cleanliness, and the encouragement to eat, were recognised as aids to recovery in a situation where no certain medical antidotes to infection had been discovered. After the war, one surgeon wrote:[54]

> Those who remember the cooking for the sick which prevailed at Scutari before, and that introduced after the kitchen department underwent the 'female revolution,' will be able to appreciate the difference which attention to this point must make on the results of treatment. . . . It was in the management of those cases of such frequent occurrence in the East, where a lingering convalescence – most liable to relapse – had succeeded to a wasting flux or debilitating fever, that the 'extras' from the 'sisters' kitchen' came to tell in the treatment. Nourishment, properly and judiciously administered, was the sole medication on which we could rely in such cases. It was often of itself sufficient to cure, and it was in attending to this that the female nurses saved so many lives.

It was for the medical officers a small step from entrusting the female nurses with administering diets to patients, to entrusting them with administering medicines, and supervising severe

50

cases.[55] In a confidential report on the nursing system in the Crimea, prepared at the end of 1855, Deputy Purveyor David Fitzgerald waxed particularly lyrical over the qualities displayed by the Sisters of Mercy:[56]

> the Medical Officer can safely consign his most critical case to their hands; stimulants – or opiates – ordered every five minutes, will be faithfully administered, though the five minutes' labour were repeated uninterruptedly for a week.

At Scutari, by contrast, much to Florence Nightingale's chagrin, the female nurses' work in this area was actually curtailed. The arrival of the newly created Medical Staff Corps in the second half of 1855 seems to have provided the occasion for this:[57]

> The existence of the old regulations and the arrival of the new ones, about the Medical Staff Orderlies, were made great use of against our work, by some of the Medical Officers, after the heavy pressure of the war was over. So, at Scutari, a Principal Medical Officer took away and would not restore the practice of the nurses giving medicines, in which he was borne out by an existing rule. . . . The existence of these Regulations proved also a great stumbling-block in the Castle Hospital.

The final indication of the value placed on the services of the female nurses, especially outside Scutari, was the practice of night nursing. If the nurses really had been superfluous to requirements, or required for housekeeping duties only, there would presumably have been strong arguments, or grounds of propriety, against allowing them in the wards at night. Florence Nightingale did not allow her nurses in the wards after 8.30 p.m. She alone (with an occasional companion) was allowed to figure as the Lady with the Lamp.[58] At Koulali, night nursing was introduced after the arrival of the first reinforcements from England in the spring of 1855. In the autumn, when the Kinsale nuns transferred from Koulali to Balaklava, there was a cholera outbreak, and

> The Sisters were up every night. . . . Rev. Mother did not allow the Sisters to remain up at night, except in cases of cholera, without a written order from the doctor.

At Smyrna, some of the ladies sat up all night, on a voluntary basis, if a patient needed special care; eventually this became official practice.[59]

The female nurses' other main contribution fell in the category of small personal attentions for which the orderlies had little or no time. Fanny Taylor recalled cooling Koulali fever patients with a large feather fan, putting ice on their brows, or in their mouths at five-minute intervals. Margaret Goodman at Scutari included in her list of 'womanly attentions' moistening the lint over inflamed wounds, helping patients to turn in bed, and placing a cologne-filled handkerchief next to a stinking post-operative limb. At Smyrna a lady shaved a patient's head to get out the vermin.[60] Owing to the constraints of sexual propriety, only a very small proportion of the body's surface area could be washed or cooled by the nurses. Sister Doyle recalled that at Scutari 'aromatic vinegar . . . was the greatest refreshment the poor patients got. When a little of it was put into water, and they were sponged with it over and over, they used to hold out their poor hands for more.' Disarmingly, the same writer commented: 'Rarely, very rarely, did any remedy succeed.'[61] The one area where the female contribution seems to have been slight was in surgical nursing. At Scutari medical students, and at Koulali regimental dressers took care of the soldiers' wounds; however, Florence Nightingale is said to have attended operations at Scutari, and the Kinsale sisters did so at Koulali.[62]

It is difficult to escape the conclusion that the further the female nursing corps moved from Scutari and Florence Nightingale, the more they were appreciated by the doctors. Florence Nightingale's dire forecasts that the ladies would prove incompetent, and the Catholic nuns interested in little beyond proselytisation, were not borne out by events. It would have been galling to have to admit this, and even more infuriating to have to concede that the nurses outside her control found more favour with 'their' doctors than she had with the medical officers at Scutari. Instead, she libelled the ladies and sisters at every opportunity; the power of her pen is such that the accusations of incompetence, spiritual interference, filth and neurosis are still current in the literature. This said, however, it cannot be claimed that all was sweetness and light within the non-Nightingale ranks. There were difficulties involved in creating a unified corps out of women of very different social origins. The relations between the non-Nightingale corps and 'their' doctors may have been excellent; but relations amongst themselves were another matter.

NURSES OR LADIES?

At the beginning of December 1854, the second party of nurses had been assembled at the house of Sidney Herbert, Secretary of State at War, to hear a solemn address on the dangers and difficulties of their undertaking. 'If you behave yourselves well,' Herbert warned the very variegated group of women before him, 'there will be a provision for you; if not, it will be the ruin of you.' He further impressed upon them 'that we all went out on the same footing as hospital nurses, and that no one was to consider herself as in any way above her companions.'[63] Herbert's first warning was directed at the paid nurses in the party. The second was intended for the 'lady volunteers'. It was a startling remark to address to individuals such as Kate Anderson, Fanny Taylor and Jane Shaw Stewart. Not only had they been taught since infancy to regard themselves as in many ways superior to other women; they had also been encouraged by church reformers to think of their social superiority as a spiritual asset. Nursing was for them part of a mission to the poor, in which they identified themselves as moral preceptors – not as fellow workers. But what appeared to be a bizarre access of egalitarianism on Herbert's part was in fact a response to the practicalities of nursing work which awaited Mary Stanley's party. Army institutions were not a promising environment for the exercise of many of the ladies' long-cherished pastoral ambitions.

In particular, it was not feasible to divide the women going out to Scutari into the two grades of nurses familiar in many civilian hospitals. Civilian patterns of work could not be replicated in military wards. In the latter, where all heavy domestic tasks were assigned to male orderlies, there was no room for a low grade of female nurse hired to perform the same functions. Nor would it be possible to create a supervisory rank of nursing sisters which could simply replace or supplement the work of the ward sergeants, for the latter's duties were purely administrative and disciplinary; they could not be assimilated to the role of the head nurse or sister, since they did not take charge of serious cases, or instruct the orderlies in other than domestic duties. As Florence Nightingale later recalled, 'no General order or Warrant was ever issued as to the duties of the nurses',[64] and the hastily improvised female corps had no official grading within the military hospital structure. The female nurses were expected to supplement existing nursing provision in an *ad hoc* fashion, according to the differing wishes of individual doctors, and priorities to be decided by the latter on the spot. Clearly, it would only complicate matters if they had to be distinguished from the outset according to rank and function. Florence Nightingale had, of course, dealt with the problem of equal grading by engaging no 'lady volunteers' in her original party.

'Fancy one's receiving people', wrote Martha Clough from Balaklava, 'in such a costume as a pepper and salt, dirty-looking, dressing-gown sort of a dress, a night cap, a blue *checked apron*, and a hospital badge across one's shoulder! Yet I feel as proud of my humble costume as many of those men are of their orders.'[65] Her attitude was unique among the ladies going to the east, who were utterly dismayed to discover that the consequence of taking up government service was to appear to all the world as domestic servants. One of the nuns in Mary Stanley's party reflected, 'That ladies could be found to walk into such a costume was certainly a triumph of grace over nature.'[66] In most cases the triumph was exceedingly short-lived. Martha Nicol, who was sent out to nurse at Smyrna, felt the inconveniences of the uniform before she had even left European soil, when she heard one of the orderlies 'accost one of the ladies of our party with the greatest familiarity, shouting with laughter, when she instinctively drew back, evidently thinking she was assuming a superiority which did not belong to her. I shall not repeat his conversation, which was coarse, and excessively free and easy; but it ended by his telling her, "He supposed she was hungry, and that there was a slap-up dinner waiting for her at the hotel!"'[67]

The enormity of the offence lay not so much in the orderly's indirect reference to the lady's innards, but in his addressing her at all. Members of the servant class were not supposed to initiate conversations with their superiors. Domestic servants were not, indeed, supposed even to address each other before 'the ladies and gentlemen of the house' unless it were a matter of urgent necessity, when it should be 'as shortly as possible, and in a low voice'.[68] Fanny Taylor, too, felt the distress of the situation long before she reached Turkey: 'The ladies had suffered by it through the journey, for having no authority to restrain the hired nurses they were compelled to listen to the worst language, and to be treated not unfrequently with coarse insolence.'[69] Nevertheless, according to

Martha Nicol 'the real evil was done to the nurses, who fancied that according to our descent in the social scale, was to be their ascent, . . . the seeds of discontent and dissatisfaction were sown by their being told that we went out on the same footing.'[70]

More than *amour propre* was at stake. The Stanley party was, as we have seen, refused admission to Scutari and forced to seek lodgings elsewhere, where they had not been expected, and where arrangements for domestic service had not been made. Rashly, as it might appear to a twentieth-century eye, 'Miss Stanley refused assistance from the English hotel in Therapia, thinking it best to employ the paid nurses in the household work which was to be performed.'[71] This might have worked in St John's House, where nurses were expected to perform such tasks for sisters, but here it aroused among the paid contingent 'a strong inclination to strike work. "We are not come out to be cooks, housemaids, and washerwomen", and they dwelt considerably on Mr Herbert's words about equality.' The next morning, after a 'kind address' by Mary Stanley, on the need for ' "serving one another by love", each assisting to the best of her power in the work of the house as she should allot to them', 'some few of the nurses worked hard and willingly for the public good', 'most of the paid nurses performed their work with an air of infinite condescension' and one maintained her strike to the bitter end. The Smyrna ladies experienced the same revolt when they established their living quarters: 'On the nurses first being asked, if they would come and work for us, they all refused, with the exception of Mrs Gunning and Mrs Butler; saying, "they came out as nurses, not to do housework." '[72]

The ladies considered the issue one of urgent physical necessity as well as social principle. Mary Stanley was on record as 'lamenting her inability to carry a coal-scuttle or lift a pail of water.' Fanny Taylor was amazed when one of her own rank in the party joined the group of nurses whom Mary Stanley subsequently appointed to do laundry work for the naval hospital at Therapia: 'There would be few ladies whose health would have enabled them to undertake such a labour.' It was a relief to find that not all the nurses had been contaminated by the notion of equality. Some were 'hard-working, respectable and obliging'; and at Smyrna there was even a 'treasure':[73]

We had now seventeen nurses one of whom, Mrs Suter, acted as cook at our quarters. . . . Not only was she kind and obliging as a servant, but she was one who thoroughly knew her place, and was never above doing anything to assist us, or add to our comforts in any and every way.

However, the ladies did not wish to remain dependent upon the mere goodwill of their social inferiors. Promptly and energetically they set about altering the relative status of ladies and nurses on the spot, and redefining the conditions of the nurses' employment as laid down in London.

A simple first step was to cease wearing the same uniform. The Smyrna ladies kept to their grey dresses, but left off their 'badges', the strips of brown material bearing the name of the hospital embroidered in red. The Stanley party changed their dress. When a new party of ladies and nurses arrived at Koulali early in April, all clad alike in the noxious weeds, the welcoming ladies expressed 'our surprise and vexation' at the fact that 'the home authorities had not thought well to learn experience from those who had to struggle with difficulties on the spot'. They soon persuaded the new arrivals of their own class to follow their example in the matter of dress.[74] More far-reaching measures followed, to establish distance between the classes. The nurses were not allowed in the wards except under the ladies' supervision. This was explained with reference to the medical needs of the patients: 'not a single one, except Mrs Woodward, could be trusted alone. They would give things to favourite patients without the surgeon's leave, or omit to carry out his orders unless they were made to do it.' However, this measure did also bolster the ladies' own authority over the patients; 'the more external indications of our position were kept up, the more influence we had with them.' Other non-medical considerations – the prevention of too much familiarity between nurses and male patients of the same social class – provided a further powerful impulse for control. At Scutari, the nurses were forbidden to speak to the patients except through the Sisters of Mercy; they were also forbidden to speak to the patients at Balaklava.[75] Mary Stanley was, if anything, even more conscious of the difficulties of disciplining the nurses into impersonality in their relations with the sick and wounded than was Florence Nightingale.

A system of supervision was devised for the nurses at Koulali which covered all their waking, as well as their working hours:

At the ladies' Home we assembled at eight o'clock for prayers, read by our superintendent, then followed breakfast. At nine the bell for work rang. We all assembled; each lady called the nurse under her charge to accompany her to her ward, or kitchen, or linen stores (we never allowed the nurses to go out alone, unless with special permission). . . . At half-past two we dined, the ladies in one room, the nurses in another, with a lady at the head of their table. The ladies took it by turns, a week about, to superintend all the meals of the nurses. At half-past four the bell summoned us to return to the hospital. . . . At seven we returned to tea; then one lady – we took it in turns – went out with the nurses for a walk; now and then, for a treat, in caiques, to the sweet waters, or Bebec. At nine the chaplain of the Church of England came and read part of the evening service. Those who wished for it took some supper ere they went to their rooms.

There were, it is clear, times when the ladies rather regretted the duties they had laid upon themselves:

It was often very fatiguing, after a long day in the wards, to escort the long train of nurses for an evening walk. They were rather exigeant in their wishes as to where they should go. Some wished to climb the hills to catch the breeze, while others declared they could only walk along the shore, while the oldest of the party (and rather a character amongst us) had yearnings after a krogue as she termed a caique.

Mary Stanley had characterised her nurses, long before they could be tested in the wards, as being 'like troublesome children', and one has the strong impression that some of them were acting up to her expectations for all that they were worth.[76]

These controls, and the behaviour required of the paid nurses were not, perhaps, too dissimilar from the working conditions of a domestic servant resident in a middle- or upper-class household; but the Koulali regime also bore irresistible comparisons with the one, described by Mary Stanley in *Hospitals and Sisterhoods*, which was practised at St Mary's House, Wantage. Of this small sisterhood's house for former prostitutes she reported:

these poor persons required constant watchfulness. Whenever two or more are engaged in any work, some one in authority should be present, to see that the work is properly done, and to prevent improper conversation, quarrelling, or other misconduct. It is moreover at their work, and in their hours of recreation, that their various tempers are manifested: and then the watchful eye and ready word are needed, to check the evil, or foster the good feeling, as it is drawn forth. All this requires, not only many supervisors, but great tact and peculiar qualifications. It must be carried out by those who can unite firmness with gentleness, who will be faithful to their charge in requiring obedience, while they enforce it in the spirit of love.

Since a mistress–servant model had not held good for relations between ladies and nurses, the supervisor–penitent model was introduced to replace, or strengthen it – with equal maladroitness and lack of success.[77]

While the ladies certainly believed themselves innately qualified to exercise spiritual authority over the nurses, they also acknowledged, at some level at least, that they derived this authority from the lower classes' recognition of their social and political power. If this recognition were not forthcoming, then a position of superiority could not be maintained within the institution (household, hospital) in which work was being carried out, and spiritual influence would evaporate with disconcerting speed. 'The real mischief of the equality system', Martha Nicol asserted, was 'done . . . to the nurses, who felt themselves aggrieved at being displaced from their fancied position of "ladies" . . . and their insolent bearing made it impossible for us to be of that help to them which we otherwise might have been.'[78] In consequence, the Wantage methods of firmness, gentleness and the spirit of love needed reinforcement with something stronger: the threat of dismissal with a bad character.

Almost half the nurses at Koulali were dismissed in less than eight months, and 'to our profound astonishment we found that our sending home so many gave great umbrage to the authorities at home.' A request for individual particulars produced vague references to 'loose character and immoral habits'. The ladies did not imagine that 'the authorities would require details which were often too terrible to dwell on.' Nowhere in these particular memoirs (Fanny Taylor's) is any more specific delinquency named than drunkenness, and one declaration of atheism. However, it certainly seems as if many nurses found ways of escaping their warders. They must surely have needed a greater degree of relief from unpleasant and dangerous work, and from the contemplation of continuing, irremediable human misery, than was afforded by Mary Stanley's pious routines. These might, indeed, have been expressly devised to spark off the desperate conduct which the ladies so deplored. Florence Nightingale was convinced that some nurses in the east misbehaved deliberately, in order to be dismissed; she thought the prospect of a better situation provided the inducement, but the desire to escape the ladies' control was an equally plausible motive. For all their assumed spiritual superiority, the ladies made little allowance for the pressures acting upon their presumed weaker and more childlike sisters.[79]

Florence Nightingale, too, had her disciplinary problems. She claimed, often without justice, that failings among her paid nurses reflected their lack of previous experience, and blamed the selectors at home. Lady Canning agreed that nurses had often been engaged without appropriate previous experience. She begged the War Office to finance two or three weeks' training for more nurses at St John's House; at present she could obtain only four or five free admissions for training. The cost would not be greater than that of sending out and bringing home unsuitable nurses. Her anxiety over training stemmed from her dislike of hospital nurses as a class:

> From experience we learn to mistrust regular hospital nurses and very few of them should be engaged. There is no doubt but that household servants and private nurses after a little teaching answer best.

In short, she sympathised with the ladies' desire for lower-class women who knew their place.[80]

By the summer of 1855, Mary Stanley was back in England, and Florence Nightingale had direct control of female nursing in Scutari only. It was at this time that the ladies' view of the proper relationship between voluntary and hired nurses began to find official expression. In July an official circular 'To the Nurses about to join the Army Hospitals in the East' was printed,[81] whose preamble stated: 'that the Nurses who have gone to the East, complained of being subject to hardships and rules of which they were not previously informed, and of having to do work different to what they expected,' and which warned 'that none should undertake this duty who are not prepared and willing to perform every branch of work which lies within a woman's province, such as washing, sewing, cooking, housekeeping, house cleaning – all these have been in turn required from those who have already gone out, and may be again.' It would seem, however, that this warning was by itself insufficient to raise the standard of deference to authority, for in December a far lengthier set of Rules and Regulations were issued, which were more explicit on the subject of ladies and nurses.[82] Along with clauses on uniform, expeditions outside the hospitals, dismissals, etc., there was now an expanded clause on domestic work which included a reference to 'the cleaning of her own and the ladies' apartments' and, in case any misunderstandings should remain, clause fourteen stated:

> It having been found that some of the nurses have believed they were to be on an equality with the ladies and sisters, it is necessary they should understand that they will remain in exactly the same relative position as that in which they were in England, and under the authority and direction of the lady superintendent or the persons acting under her.

A BALANCE SHEET

'Would you or some one of my Committee write to Lady Stratford to say, "This is not a lady but a real Hospital Nurse," of me? "And she has had experience."' (Florence Nightingale to Elizabeth Herbert, 14 October 1854.)[83]

Florence Nightingale considered it essential that she should be seen in professional, functional terms, and that her staff should come to be accepted as integral parts of the hospital machine. If they were in any sense to be regarded as 'extras', they were to be like the dietary 'extras', making all the difference between regress and recovery. They were not to be decorative or emotional extras, like lady hospital visitors, nor were they to double as chaplains' auxiliaries. Two very different philosophies animated Florence Nightingale and Mary Stanley; but the Crimean experience did not provide evidence that the Nightingale methods produced a definitively superior service. The mortality figures published in the Parliamentary report on the state of the army hospitals of 1854–5, and the report of the Sanitary Commission of 1855–6 leave the relative and absolute efficacy of the different nursing systems very much in doubt.

Tables on mortality indicate no significant decline in the rate at either Scutari or Koulali before March 1855. The decline in deaths which is then recorded is attributed in the hospitals' report to the onset of milder weather; this permitted freer ventilation of the wards, and of course had 'other beneficial influences', presumably reducing the physical misery and weakness of convalescents, and of troops in the field.[84] The sanitary report produced figures for the period from the end of February to the middle of November 1855, giving clear evidence for a decline in mortality after 17 March – the date at which the Commissioners' recommended cleansing works began to be put into operation (see Table 2.3) Neither report mentioned changes in nursing as a contributory factor. The suggestion that 'The improvement in the sick may, perhaps, be attributed in some degree to the improved condition, sanitary and otherwise, of our hospitals' and the fulsome tribute paid to 'the benign influence of that other ministering agency which has added a new name and a fresh glory to the annals of female heroism'[85] indicate a slightly patronising attitude towards the whole experiment.

Table 2.1 Monthly report from Dr Cumming to Dr Smith, 28 April 1855

February	Remained	Admitted	Discharged	Died	Remaining
Scutari	4,165	1,895	2,139	1,027	2,895
Koulali	434	795	65	302	861
	4,599	2,690	2,204	1,329	3,756
March					
Scutari	2,895	2,385	2,475	421	2,384
Koulali	861	450	362	134	815
	3,756	2,835	2,837	555	3,199

In: *Report upon the State of the Hospitals of the British Army in the Crimea and Scutari*, pp 1854–5, XXXIII, p. 407.

Table 2.2 Abstract of weekly states of sick and wounded from October 1 to January 31

Date	Officers					Men				
	Remained	Admitted	Discharged	Died	Remained	Remained	Admitted	Discharged	Died	Remained
1854										
1–7 October	70	3	–	1	72	2,277	61	403	67	1,868
8–14 October	72	23	9	2	84	1,868	307	295	46	1,834
15–21 October	84	12	20	–	76	1,834	386	151	29	2,040
22–28 October	76	8	47	1	37	2,040	350	370	56	1,964
28 Oct–4 Nov	37	11	2	1	45	1,964	952	384	52	2,480
5–11 November	45	34	10	–	69	2,480	850	469	36	2,825
12–18 November	69	49	4	3	111	2,825	1,045	557	94	3,219
19–25 November	11	9	–	–	102	3,219	438	144	67	3,446
26 Nov–2 Dec	102	10	5	–	107	3,446	436	315	70	3,497
3–9 December	107	–	12	–	95	3,497	263	388	70	3,302
10–16 December	95	–	8	1	86	3,302	299	521	85	2,995
17–23 December	86	–	2	1	83	2,995	1,321	402	130	3,784
24–30 December	83	1	35	1	48	3,784	1,091	770	108	3,997
1855										
31 Dec–6 Jan	48	16	6	1	55	3,997	1,044	367	249	4,425
7–13 Jan	55	18	13	–	60	4,425	727	444	277	4,431
14–20 Jan	60	16	8	1	67	4,431	667	346	270	4,482
21–27 Jan	67	29	30	1	65	4,482	1,243	984	274	4,467
28–31 Jan	65	29	16	1	78	4,467	619	127	165	4,794

From: PMO's office, Scutari, 1 February, 1855   In: *Report Upon the State of the Hospitals. . .* p.257.

Table 2.3

Twenty-one days ending	(BARRACK			SCUTARI GENERAL			PALACE)			KULALIE		
	Remained and admitted	Deaths	Deaths to sick per cent	Remained and admitted	Deaths	Deaths to sick per cent	Remained and admitted	Deaths	Deaths to sick per cent	Remained and admitted	Deaths	Deaths to sick per cent
March 17	2,482	186	7.49	1,227	144	11.73	686	51	7.43	1,127	133	11.80
April 7	2,495	99	3.96	1,011	60	5.93	460	15	3.26	1,094	66	6.03
April 28	1,988	65	3.26	801	21	2.62	399	11	2.75	875	30	3.42
May 19	1,574	33	2.09	691	18	2.60	268	4	1.49	895	16	1.78
June 9	1,180	19	1.61	567	17	2.99	183	8	4.37	627	5	0.79
June 30	1,408	15	1.06	524	8	1.52	242	2	0.82	610	4	0.65
14 July to 10 Nov 1855	4,759	87	1.82	1,607	58	3.60	1,149	22	1.91	1,555	36	2.31

from *Report . . . of the Proceedings of the Sanitary Commissioners dispatched to the seat of War in the East 1855–6*, PP (Accounts and Papers [2]) 1857 IX, p. 324.

Mortality rates at both Scutari and Koulali began to decline after the former centre had enjoyed the benefits of female nursing for five months, and the latter for three. According to most accounts based on Nightingale records, Mary Stanley operated with staff and methods inferior to Florence Nightingale's, and with inadequate supplies and finance. One implication of the figures, therefore, is that Mary Stanley was not a significantly worse nursing superintendent than Florence Nightingale. Another is that both women's efforts were largely irrelevant to the soldiers's welfare. No cast-iron case for the superiority of the Nightingale system can be made. It could be argued that the Koulali mortality rate should, in fact, have been lower, and fallen much sooner, than that at Scutari; the former centre dealt with fewer patients, and at this period, the larger the number of patients, the greater the spread of cross-infection. However, one cannot be certain of comparing like with like. At Koulali, the doctors did not reject the services of female nurses; the female system there could, thus, be said to have been fully tested. At Scutari, on the other hand, many surgeons declined female help; so the mortality rate there is the rate under a mixed nursing system. Are Scutari's merits or defects to be attributed to its male or female staff? One can hardly accept Florence Nightingale's opinions on the question as definitive.

It is perhaps the crowning irony of the Crimean episode that Florence Nightingale was unable to prove her claims for the superiority of well organised female nurses over the existing corps of male orderlies. She could and did make assertions as to the irresponsibility and indiscipline of Mary Stanley, the slovenliness of the nuns, or the drunkenness and incompetence of the military staff – but she could not prove beyond dispute that her methods saved lives. Her strictures on the purveying system, and her enthusiastic collaboration with the Sanitary Commissioners, whose assumptions and methods were so close to her heart, were indeed influential and constructive. But when it came to the actual business of nursing, she could only fall back on revelations of the sensational horrors which she had found upon her arrival, and aspersions upon her female rivals. She was indeed a moral, as much as a practical force, in the care of the sick; she, who wished so much to distance herself from amateur philanthropy and mere kindness, had in fact made her chief contribution through the rousing of public opinion and the improvement of morale. The voice might be the voice of Chadwick, but the hands were still the hands of Lady Bountiful.

What cannot be proved at this date about Florence Nightingale's work was not believed at the time by the officers of the Army Medical Department. The experience of other military medical services, moreover, would have confirmed many of them in the view that female nursing was a luxury rather than a necessity. The navy, for example, employed a few lady nurses at its fixed hospital at Therapia, but otherwise relied, at sea or ashore, on untrained male sick-berth staff. The relatively favourable mortality rate in the navy was thought to reflect more effective methods of victualling and supply in general. The French military medical service, on the other hand, was much admired for its nursing system: it employed trained and permanent corps of *infirmiers*, supplemented by Sisters of Charity; but, probably owing to sanitary deficiencies, it was unable to bring down the mortality rate among French soldiers after the spring of 1855.[86] What the Crimean War experience had clearly demonstrated to the Army Medical Department was the case for better supplied regimental hospitals, and better communications between dressing stations at the front and general hospitals at the base: for the application of the most up-to-date ideas on hospital and camp sanitation; and for a new and better method of organising the non-nursing work of general hospitals. As for nursing itself, doctors argued first and foremost for a stable labour force, not a motley crew of men on brief secondment from combatant service; and secondly for a corps appropriately trained for its duties.

On 12 May 1855 Lord Raglan had written to Lord Panmure requesting the creation and despatch from England of a new corps of hospital orderlies. The Medical Staff Corps arrived in Scutari in autumn 1855, and were not universally welcomed. They had received no hospital training, and seem not to have achieved notable standards of sobriety. This hastily improvised corps was disbanded at the end of the war. But its failings had done nothing to persuade the army medical authorities of the need for a female nursing service. Instead, a year later, a new Army Hospital Corps was created. This was to be recruited from volunteers from regiments of the line, who were to be literate, and men of good conduct. They were to be graded as privates, sergeants, company sergeants or sergeant majors, and allocated to either the medical branch or the purveying branch of a hospital. They would receive an initial training and, as they were to be permanently appointed, it could be assumed that their instruction would continue in the course of their hospital work.[87] It was this corps which was considered the most promising model for the development of army nursing; and any post-war proposal to incorporate female staff would find it uphill work to gain acceptance. It is to the fate of such proposals, and their lobbyists, that we must now turn.

CHAPTER 3

LADY INTO NURSE:
JANE SHAW STEWART AND THE
PUBLIC SERVICE, 1859–70

It is in many ways surprising that a female army nursing service should have been established after the Crimean War, let alone that it should have survived to the end of the nineteenth century. Even if plans had not been afoot for the reform of the male orderly system, there were many redoubts of antagonism to the popular heroine who had calumniated the Army Medical Department. Florence Nightingale's sponsor, Sidney Herbert, was no longer in office; and she herself had obligations to many other causes. Nevertheless, thanks to Florence Nightingale and her friend and colleague, Jane Shaw Stewart, the first official female service of the Victorian army was inaugurated in 1861. The story of its first seven years veers between tragedy and farce; and it ends in disaster. It is an episode which has been hidden from history, partly because Jane Shaw Stewart had a horror of publicity, and partly because it reflected poorly on Florence Nightingale's judgment.[1] Like the fracas between the ladies and nurses of Mary Stanley's party in the Crimea, it is far more than a tale of personalities: indeed, it portrays in miniature the conditions and constraints under which women of the leisured classes first attempted the transition from domestic to public spheres of action.

ESTABLISHING THE SERVICE

The war and its aftermath spawned a huge number of official inquiries in connection with army health.[2] Female nursing occupied only a very small part of these deliberations. That it found its way into them at all is largely due to Florence Nightingale's collaboration with a number of army officers, and military and civilian medical men, who shared her other enthusiasms for statistical surveys and sanitary reform.[3] In April 1857 a Royal Commission of Inquiry was instigated into the Regulations Affecting the Sanitary Condition of the Army, the Organisation of Military Hospitals, and the Treatment of the Sick and Wounded; its report was published in January 1858. The sanitary reform of barracks, the creation of an Army Medical School and Statistical Department, the reconstruction of the Army Medical Department, and the revision of the Hospital Regulations were dealt with by four sub-commissions.[4] The last of these broached the question of introducing female military nurses. No immediate change was envisaged. Female nursing was recommended only for military general hospitals, preferably in wards holding twenty to twenty-five sick. Accommodation at the three existing general hospitals at Chatham, Dublin and Cork was considered inadequate for the innovation; and it was generally assumed that female nursing would not be introduced until the completion of the grandiose new hospital planned for a site at Netley, near Southampton Water.[5]

The army nursing service was only one of several projects competing for Florence Nightingale's attention at this time. Her passion for planning, for behind-the-scenes influence, and for major public health initiatives was finding satisfaction in the work of the four sub-commissions. She was also under pressure to decide on the best application of the Nightingale Fund. This was a sum of £44,000 which had been raised by voluntary public subscription as a tribute to her war work. It was invested in a trust to finance 'an Institution for the training, sustenance, and protection of Nurses and Hospital attendants'. The Fund offered her the best opportunity to put into concrete form her dissatisfaction with existing patterns of nursing, and to train disciples who would in their turn transform other institutions. When the Nightingale Training School was eventually established at St Thomas's Hospital

5 The Royal Victoria Hospital Netley on Southampton Water, constructed after the Crimean War. (Bodleian Library)

in 1860, its pupils were expected to receive systematic training from their matron in observing and tending the sick, and managing the hygiene and general order of a ward; they were also to attend special lectures given by doctors, and to be tested in their knowledge at the end of a year's instruction. Since their expertise was not to be limited to the work of one ward and the methods of one doctor, they would in principle become fit to work, superintend and train in all areas of medical and surgical nursing; they would also establish a secular model for women health workers of all kinds.[6]

There were, nevertheless, spurs to action on the military hospital front. One was the spate of women's war memoirs issuing from the presses. Elizabeth Davis, Fanny Margaret Taylor and Martha Nicol published accounts of their experiences as 'English Nurses in Eastern Hospitals' which not only made it clear that Florence Nightingale did not enjoy a monopoly of female heroism and philanthropy, but also cast aspersions on her management of hospital work and workers. Another was the burgeoning growth of the sisterhood movement. The sisterhoods had, indeed, done well out of the war, and were the immediate beneficiaries of the public enthusiasm it generated for improvements in nursing. St John's House took over the nursing at King's College Hospital, London, in 1856; the All Saints' sisterhood moved on to the wards of University College Hospital, London, in 1860. At the end of 1856 a new Catholic hospital was opened in London to utilise the Crimean experience of the Catholic sisters.[7] Compared to the champions of these nursing orders, Florence Nightingale was a commander without troops. Her concept of nursing was of an occupation to be refined through improved training, wages and status; it was in danger of being over-shadowed by the sisterhood movement's claimant advocacy of increased moral and spiritual standards in nursing, its glorification of the value of unpaid work, and its denigration of the class of woman who came into hospitals 'only' for mercenary reasons.[8]

The sisterhood movement was particularly threatening, because its influence extended to the Army Medical Department. Florence Nightingale wrote in something like panic to Lady Cranworth in December 1856 that 'Dr Andrew Smith tells me he wishes to see female nursing in the Victoria Hospital near Southampton but done by *Nuns*!!! (He is a Roman Catholic convert – and wants to have Mrs Bridgeman).' Lady Cranworth agreed on the necessity of 'keeping all thought of these dreadful Nuns out of even Dr. A. Smith's head.'[9] It was more realistic to fear that an Anglican order might win the prize of the new general hospital. Referring to the future arrangements at Netley, Deputy Inspector-General Mouat opined[10]

> that women, as a rule, can only make good and useful nurses when led to the adoption of this most trying and disagreeable of occupations from strong moral feelings, in fact, feelings of devotion or affection; when adopted from sheer necessity or for mere mercenary considerations, as will in all probability be the case in a great majority of candidates, the risk of failure will be great and success the exception. A great moral change must come over this class, and Protestant Sisters must form an integral portion of the community, for the express purpose of supplying the necessary assistance on this head; and anyone who succeeds in effecting so great an object will deserve well of their country, and confer a lasting benefit on the nation.

Florence Nightingale's influence in public health policy sprang from her supposed pre-eminence in the field of hospital nursing and war work, and she could not contemplate being toppled from this position. With the Training School scheme in its infancy, her only weapon was the pen: alongside the flood of work on other topics engaging the sub-commissioners' attention in 1857 and 1858, a steady stream of texts on female military nursing appeared under her name. Four were of particular importance: a lengthy memorandum to the Secretary of State for War in May 1857;[11] written evidence to the Army Sanitary Commission in mid-1857; a short book, *Subsidiary Notes as to the Introduction of Female Nursing into Military Hospitals in Peace and in War*, printed in 1858; and, in mid-1858, the section on 'the Duties of Officers, Attendants, and Nurses' in the War Office's draft regulations for military hospitals.[12] These texts maintained her reputation, and effectively mapped out the boundaries within which the subject of military nursing could be discussed.

Her tenacity was certainly put to the test by officialdom. In January 1858, the War Office opposed the Army Sanitary Commission's proposal for a female nursing service.[13] Undeterred, the sub-commission formed to draw up hospital regulations continued with its work, and in July 1858 submitted model regulations to the Secretary of State, once again recommending a female nursing service.[14] This proposal was in turn shot down in February 1859 by a committee representing the medical, purveying and ordnance departments. No substantial grounds were given for deleting 'all directions and instructions for the guidance and control of female nurses' from the proposed new regulations, beyond the bald statement that 'we are of opinion that nursing by means of a properly organised and trained hospital corps of male attendants must always be attended with many advantages over a system of female nursing, and many possible inconveniences attendant on the latter will be avoided thereby.' Special instructions could always be prepared if the situation changed.[15] This delaying tactic did not work for long. A new ministry returned Sidney Herbert to the War Office in June 1859; the 1858 Hospital Regulations were promulgated under his signature, with their original nursing section, the following October.

Just over a year later, Herbert assembled a committee to report on the Army Hospital Corps and to consider the possibility of establishing new general hospitals at Woolwich, Portsmouth and Plymouth. At the end of February 1861, the committee reported that the garrison hospital at Woolwich could be converted more quickly and cheaply than the others. It was recommended that AHC orderlies be employed there in the proportion of one to every ten sick, and that a minimum female staff should include a superintendent, four nurses, and one linen nurse. Cases should be divided between medical, surgical and venereal wards; female nurses were not to work in the latter.[16] Conversion work went ahead promptly, in contrast to the long-drawn-out process of construction at Netley. At the end of July 1861 an AHC party replaced the regimental orderlies at Woolwich, and on 1 August the new regulations for general military hospitals came into operation.[17]

In October 1861, the female nursing service was inaugurated when Jane Shaw Stewart, as Superintendent, established a staff of six nurses at Woolwich.[18] In the spring of 1863, Netley finally opened. 'Mrs. Jane Shaw Stewart' was designated 'Superintendent-General of Female Nurses at the General Hospital at Netley (not commissioned)', and, with this appointment on 6 March 1863, a woman's name for the first time appeared on the British Army List. She seems to have taken five nurses to Netley.[19] In October 1866, when the construction of a new general hospital at Woolwich, the Royal Herbert, had been completed, she returned there to establish a staff of eight nurses. She was back at Netley with five female staff when, in May 1868, an inquiry was launched into the 'state of the nursing service', and she was obliged to resign.[20]

JANE SHAW STEWART AND FLORENCE NIGHTINGALE

Who was Jane Shaw Stewart, and why has the name of this pioneer in women's public work been almost totally blotted from the record? In July 1868 Florence Nightingale's amanuensis, Dr John Sutherland, wrote to her:[21]

> I should act as if the late Superintendent-General and her nurses had never existed. We now know that the whole affair has been so much below your standard and that of the regulations, that even to remember it tends to keep one from seeing one's way clearly to future proceedings. . . . The past establishment has been like Sisera, struck dead through the temples by a second Jael.

He wrote as if Jane Shaw Stewart was merely a disciple who had failed her mistress. But she was very much more than this. She was the joint creator, as well as the Superintendent, of the first official corps of female army nurses. Many of her ideas were, indeed, lifted word for word from her private letters and memoranda onto the printed page of the Hospital Regulations and Florence Nightingale's other writings on military nursing. From the first Jane sought the obscurity which, she felt, best suited her position as a Christian and a gentlewoman. After her efforts were crowned with failure she most certainly took her lack of celebrity as a blessing.

Jane was the daughter of Sir Michael Shaw Stewart, sixth baronet of Ardgowan, Renfrewshire. The family's wealth was drawn from properties in Scotland and the West Indies; its influence was mainly confined to Scottish affairs. Her brother, Michael Robert, the seventh baronet, represented Renfrewshire in the House of Commons from 1855 to 1865. Her uncle, Sir Houston Stewart, was at the time of the Crimean War the Rear-Admiral appointed second in command of the Black Sea fleet; his son, William Houston, also held a Black Sea command; both finished their careers as admirals. The Shaw Stewarts do not appear to have been distinguished as philanthropists, though the Houston Stewarts involved themselves in the work of naval benevolent societies, and the management of Greenwich Hospital; Jane's younger brother John Archibald was perhaps the relative with whom she had most in common, as he worked with the Oxford Tractarians to found Keble College, with Gladstone to establish a market refuge and industrial school in Soho, with the Metropolitan Asylums Boards, and as a manager of St George's and Guy's hospitals.[22] However, her surviving letters do not refer to members of her family, or indeed to any relationships outside her own female world of religion, philanthropy and hospital work.

She first met Florence Nightingale while the latter was superintendent of the Invalid Gentlewomen's Institute in Harley Street, 'on a certain, to me, memorable, Oct. 18/54'.[23] She was a year younger than Florence, and relatively free from family ties: her widowed mother had died two years previously, and her younger brothers were all of age. It would seem that this meeting fired her to take up hospital work with great seriousness, though she may well have had an earlier interest in it, and determined her to be among Florence Nightingale's reinforcements in the east. It was in the Crimea that she and Florence Nightingale met for the second time. Working in Balaklava, away from the hospitals in Turkey, Jane had remained apart from the bagarre with the Stanleyites; and a common enemy, the War Office, now drew the two women closely together. Both saw themselves as suffering servants. The War Office had deprived Florence Nightingale of the bulk of her command; it was now commissioning, from Deputy-Purveyor Fitzgerald, a confidential report on the hospitals, which was to comment adversely on Jane Shaw Stewart's methods of drawing and distributing stores, and to cast doubt on the competence of all female nursing staff other than Roman Catholic nuns.[24] The circumstances created a bond of intense sympathy between them and, on Jane Shaw Stewart's part, intense devotion; she felt that she and Florence Nightingale were one in religious dedication to a 'coarse, repulsive, servile, noble' work which the world at large misunderstood.[25]

Jane Shaw Stewart was a deeply religous woman – her specific commitment to the Church of England was one which Florence Nightingale did not share – and she might have been expected to sympathise with the aims of the nursing sisterhoods. However, although she respected the sisterhoods, she also distanced herself from them. This was partly due to her admiration for Florence Nightingale, to whom she wished, in principle, to subordinate all her plans and wishes, writing that 'when I say we – remember always it is as mistress and maid' and 'I shall serve you until you wish my service ended, or until I die'. As the post-war controversy deepened between Florence Nightingale on the one side, and Mary Stanley's ladies and the sisterhoods on the other, Jane placed herself unequivocally in the former's camp. But she had already begun to work out her own ideas as to the religious vocation in nursing, which she was, ultimately, to defend as stoutly against 'My dear Mistress' as against the Anglican nursing orders.[26]

Applying to be one of Mary Stanley's nursing party, Jane had declared 'This is not a note from a lady to a lady, but from a candidate nurse to Miss Stanley.'[27] For her, the call to hospital work signified the sacrifice of worldly status in the joyful acceptance of the role of God's servant. Given her social background, this was a conviction which was to tie her in knots for the rest of her professional life. In the first place, however, it made her sceptical of the sisterhood method of organisation, in which a community of ladies with private incomes employed a group of women, both as hospital and private nurses acting under their supervision, and as their own domestic servants. After the war, she wrote that 'the improver must live among those she endeavours to improve and to train, one of, tho' superior to them.' If women of the class to which she and Florence Nightingale belonged wished to work in hospitals, it should be 'under the same rules, and on the same strict footing of duty performed under definite superiors. . . . The real and faithful discharge of the duties of the wards of a General Hospital, whether with reference to superiors, companions, or patients, is incompatible with the status, as such, of ladies.' The concept of leaven appealed to her greatly. A small element could transform the whole, and, moreover, should do so privately and silently.[28]

Jane Shaw Stewart's Crimean experiences confirmed many of these convictions. Fitzgerald's confidential report had never been shown her, but its contents, alleging extravagance on her part, had been leaked, and had caused her great anguish.[29] More than ever she made the anonymity of the nurse her personal goal, rather than the distinction – and the exposed position – of the lady superintendent. She considered the publication of contentious nursing memoirs of the war exceedingly distasteful, and inimical to the future of the service: 'it is impossible to let Her Majesty's Nurses subside too soon into perfect quiet.' She was wholly content to work unseen and unsung, at Florence Nightingale's disposal, gathering information and composing memoranda for her to present to the Queen, to Lord Panmure, and to the Army Sanitary Commission, for, she wrote, 'it has ever seemed to me that the action of women in public matters . . . can be but two-fold: either individually, as Sovereigns or Regents; or else mediating, by convincing or influencing men: i.e. by inducing them to adopt and act upon our own views.'[30] She became increasingly distressed as Florence Nightingale's activities appeared to deviate from these ideals.

In the matter of nursing reform Jane agreed with the statement in Mary Stanley's *Hospitals and Sisterhoods*: 'It is in fact a class of persons which remains to be created.'[31] She saw the task as one of social modelling by personal example, for which the setting up of the Nightingale Training Fund was no solution: 'For many long years, at the least, the want in English hospitals will probably be women, not money.' Florence Nightingale should have nothing to do with 'the committees of bracelets and tea-pots'. They were useless, self-congratulatory distractions from the real work of reform: 'there is but one real way of doing so − to spend one's life in hospitals, . . . in silent, quiet, as well as laborious and trying work, in governing, training, and organizing the women who nurse in hospitals.' By definition, this was work which could not be done by any man, but only by a woman, and one whom God had marked out with 'the glorious talent of action, of female action and direction, which you have received'[32]

Unfortunately, Florence Nightingale showed no sign of being content with those spheres of action to which, in Jane Shaw Stewart's opinion, heaven, social class and gender had assigned her. She had come to prefer a life of political intrigue, pulling the strings of commissions, to the hurly-burly of a hospital ward. Moreover, she was not wholly satisfied with working anonymously and unseen: she was prepared to put controversial opinions on nursing and public health matters into print. Her friend's protests against such a course of action met with a poetic denouement in 1858, when Florence printed and circulated, under the title *Subsidiary Notes as to the Introduction of Female Nursing into Military Hospitals in Peace and in War*, the bulk of Jane's confidential memoranda and letters to her of 1856 and 1857,[33] together with several chapters of her own composition.

The text was published anonymously, and, to a twentieth-century eye, contained very little that need have embarrassed its joint author; it was, however, written in a more pungent tone than ladies of Jane Shaw Stewart's class might be expected to use, and contained slightly condescending remarks on the St John's House sisterhood, with which she wished to maintain good relations. Above all, the enterprise was a betrayal of trust. It unleashed a torrent of criticism of the former idol: she had no personal knowledge and experience of India, and no business making recommendations concerning the health of the Army there; she had 'never had the experience of acquiring real science' and should not make pronouncements about contagion; was it not more than possible that the deference of 'professional men who see you – who have obtained advancement through you – is due to your influence with the War Office rather than respect for your scientific knowledge?' But mingled with the abuse was the plea for the idol to return to her pedestal, to put aside the excuse that exhaustion and over-work made it impossible for her to resume the active superintendence of nurses: she must now give up men's work, rest, and restore herself to a physical state in which she could do her duty.

It is not known what replies, if any, were returned to these entreaties.[34] Florence Nightingale made it abundantly clear that she would engage in public service on her own privileged terms. She would continue to feel free to publish, both anonymously and under her own name, precisely because, unlike Jane Shaw Stewart, she would never expose her person: she would live in seclusion, communicate with most human beings in writing, see others briefly and by appointment only in her own home, and deepen her retreat by invalidism and continuous hints that she was about to depart for the next world. Her own obsession with privacy was idiosyncratic, but originated in the world of convention which she inhabited jointly with Jane Shaw Stewart and the women of her class.

SUPERINTENDENCE AND SEGREGATION

Jane Shaw Stewart's ideas on the future structure of the female nursing service were encapsulated in her letter to Florence Nightingale of 22 October 1856:[35]

You were Super.t Gen: of Nurses – a distinct office, a part, altho' a new one, of the Military Medical System, and in the nature of things under the Chief Surgeons. But *you also had powers* and duties assigned, which made you in a certain sense independent of, and in a certain sense superior to, those Chief Surgeons. That you accomplished far more good than you could have done had you not had these independent powers is most certain.

Both women had drawn the same moral from the Crimean War. The peacetime Superintendent-General should not have to endure either the resistance of medical officers, the interference of Inspectors-General, or the humiliation of 'confidential reports'. The privileged relationship with the Secretary of State for War should be maintained, and bolstered with regulations supporting an inviolable position within the hospitals.

The hospital regulations published in 1859 specified that the new Superintendent-General was to select the nurses for each general hospital, as and when required by the Director-General of the Army Medical Department. No appointments or removals were to take place without her sanction. Within each hospital, the Superintendent of nurses had to be consulted before the medical officers made any changes in ward duties, and misconduct by nurses had to be reported directly to her. The downward chain of authority thus linked Superintendent-General, Superintendent and nurse, and excluded both the military Governor and the Principal Medical Officer of the general hospital. The upward chain linked the Superintendent-General directly to the Secretary of State for War, replicating Florence Nightingale's wartime privilege of direct communication with Sidney Herbert. She was to report annually to the Secretary of State, and to receive 'copies of all reports, confidential or otherwise, . . . regarding the Nursing Establishment'. More pithily, Jane Shaw Stewart had written on an earlier occasion: 'the humble boon, granted to pickpockets, of being informed of accusations laid to their charge, must be extended to the Superintendent of the nurses.'[36]

The downward chain was, perhaps, a constitutional necessity. Individual soldiers in this period could enlist only by entering a regiment and agreeing to accept the rules and punishments administered by regimental officers. Female nurses had no regiment; and arrangements for punishment, suspension and dismissal had therefore to be devised outside the official framework. The upward chain, however, could not fail to re-awaken wartime resentments. The Superintendent-General was not even under the authority of the Director-General of the Army Medical Department: any conflict between them had to be submitted to the Secretary of State for arbitration. But she was expected to work in general conformity with his wishes, and he was to communicate with her if any change in nursing arrangements was needed. The system could only work with great good will on both sides, a commodity which the regulations themselves seemed likely to diminish in a very short space of time.

The new military general hospitals would thus contain staff responsible to three separate chains of command. Male orderlies were subject to the discipline of the Military Governor, exercised by Wardmasters and Captains of Orderlies: medical officers were also subject to the Military Governor, and responsible to the AMD Director-General: female nurses were responsible to the Superin-tendent and the Superintendent-General, who communicated directly with the Secretary of State for War. The medical officers were already frustrated by their lack of direct authority over male orderlies: they were now equally powerless to discipline female nurses. Nevertheless, the regulations compelled them to be accompanied by a female nurse on their rounds of the wards. To complicate matters further, the regulations also stated that the orderlies should conform strictly to the nurses' requirements and instructions.[37]

It would be almost impossible to devise a system of hospital management more pregnant with confusion and dispute than this one. And it was more than a desire to settle old scores which was reponsible for its complexities. For all their dissent from, or rivalry with the sisterhood movement, both Jane and Florence were deeply imprinted with many of its assumptions: the arrangements proposed for military hospitals were strikingly comparable to those which the sisterhoods were introducing into London civilian hospitals at this time. In King's College Hospital, for example, St John's House undertook the nursing duties under a contract system. The sisterhood took charge of the hiring, firing and disciplining of nurses, and was accountable, not to the physicians and surgeons attached to the hospital, but to its lay management. Neither the medical officers nor the managers found the arrangement wholly satisfactory, but it was tolerated because

St John's offered a comprehensive and efficient service.[38] In a military hospital, where female nurses were a novelty, constituted a very small proportion of the nursing staff, and could on both counts be regarded as dispensable, the new service would be much more vulnerable to criticism.

The independent, self-contained, self-disciplining female nursing corps was a phenomenon of the 1850s which was only very gradually superseded. Its conscious rationale was a religious one: the nursing sisterhoods were formed to improve the moral and spiritual quality of ordinary hospital care by providing nurses with devoted Christian guidance and supervision. If hospital governors or medical officers attempted to mediate between nurses and sisters, they would be subverting the original purpose of the organisation. However, beyond the religious rationale, this form of organisation had another, crucial significance in facilitating the entry of middle- and upper-class women into public life. The status of 'lady' was susceptible of a variety of definitions, but two qualifications were essential: freedom from the necessity to seek paid employment; and power to employ and direct as domestic servants that class of women who did not enjoy such freedom. This power was exercised without masculine or any other outside interference; the manner in which it was financed was indirect and, so to speak, invisible: women were not seen to be salaried by the husbands or other male relatives who supported them. Jane Shaw Stewart's ideas were inseparable from this context. Like Florence Nightingale, she never worked for remuneration. Her conception of authority derived almost exclusively from the relations of domestic service. She could not even describe her own devotion and respect for her friend without using the expression 'as mistress and maid'.

Under no normal circumstances, Jane's religious idiosyncracies notwithstanding, would a lady tolerate being visibly placed on the same footing as a non-lady, as the adventures of Mary Stanley's party at Koulali, and Martha Nicol and her friends at Smyrna, amply demonstrated. The danger could be obviated if, on entering public service, the lady retained the sole right to discipline the non-lady, relating to her as mistress to servant, while on her own account enjoying a separate relationship with an altogether higher body. Any other arrangement would powerfully suggest that both classes shared a common subordination to, and dependence upon, a male employer – one who might even enjoy a lower status than the lady in her private life. Ladies were highly unlikely to enter public service if they were thereby deprived of their domestic prerogatives. The maintenance of an independent female chain of authority, with privileged access to a governing body, may, therefore, have been the essential condition on which the leisured class of Victorian women extended their philanthropic work beyond the domestic and non-contractual sphere; and the absence of such a condition may have been a bar to their taking up many other apparently attractive careers.

Co-operation between men and women employees in work outside the domestic sphere was certainly not a novelty in the 1850s; but it was conventionally considered, by those not obliged to seek their livelihood in factories, mines or farms, to pose great moral dangers, especially for women. Even voluntary work among the genteel of both sexes posed its problems, according to a plaintive reviewer of Mary Stanley's *Hospitals and Sisterhoods* and Mrs Jameson's *Sisters of Charity*:[39]

> as all know, who have ever been on committees, or attempted to carry on any measures requiring the co-operation of men and women, because there is apt to be an undefined, obstructive want of confidence on both sides; and this again we believe arises from sheer awkwardness, ignorance of one another's minds, and the novelty of the junction.

Florence Nightingale and Jane Shaw Stewart believed the military hospital to be a particularly sensitive case. Female misconduct would prove more pernicious there than in a civilian hospital. For all the praise lavished on the noble, uncomplaining and disciplined Crimean soldier, it was clear from their writings that the sick soldier could not be regarded as a uniformed seraph unless he were one hundred per cent incapacitated. Because military patients were obliged to remain in hospital until they were fully fit to rejoin their regiments in the field, most of them were not bed cases. They were, in fact, too healthy for the possibility of sexual misconduct with female nurses to be ruled out. It followed that there should be only a small number of female nurses in a military hospital, who should confine their attentions to severely sick patients.[40] It also followed that these women should be imbued with the highest possible standards of morality. Many a war nurse whom Florence Nightingale was prepared to recommend warmly for civilian hospital employment was nevertheless 'wholly unfitted by the impropriety of her manners for a Military Hospital'.[41]

Florence Nightingale proposed to tackle this problem by engineering nursing morality both through concrete structures and appropriate conditions of work. Hospital nursing should become as impersonal a task as possible. Small wards were 'decidedly objectionable, because unfavourable to discipline, inasmuch as a small number of men, when placed together in the same ward, more readily associate together for any breach of discipline than a larger number.' Even in a large ward a nurse 'ought always to be *on duty*, never sitting down to her own personal work, or making *one of the party*. A good hospital nurse is a sentry on duty, within sight of the enemy's lines.'[42] A far cry indeed from the sentimental picture of the war nurse whose passing shadow was kissed upon the soldier's pillow, and whose soothing ways were a reminder of the affections of home and hearth! The particular vehemence with which Florence Nightingale advocated large wards was due to her belief that they were easier to ventilate as well as to administer; she was furious to learn that wards for fourteen, twelve, nine and even as few as two patients were being planned for the Royal Victoria Hospital, Netley, and she strove in vain to halt its construction and to have the building converted into a barracks.[43] Further barriers to misconduct would be provided by a scheme of rigid residential segregation. She exercised more influence over the lay-out of the new general hospital at Woolwich than she had at Netley, and was able to work out her ideas very thoroughly. No orderly was ever to be permitted to enter the nurses' quarters. Not only the nurses' quarters, but also the nurses' female servants' quarters, their infirmary and linen rooms were placed behind a single door communicating with the rest of the hospital. Coal and other necessaries were to be supplied by a lift.[44]

As might have been expected, Jane Shaw Stewart was less obsessed with architectural constraints than with the character of the women to be employed. They should be women of head nurse calibre, aged between thirty and sixty years, who would receive a starting salary of £20 per annum. The former inmates of reformatories, penitentiaries and the like should be barred. A first offence of dishonesty, and a third, at most, of drunkenness, should be punished with dismissal. Nurses would have to accept the authority of a Superintendent who would 'keep a constant watch over their moral conduct', 'see that their dress, cleanliness, and personal habits are properly attended to', and reprimand 'any neglect of duty or impropriety of conduct'.[45] Were such paragons easily to be found? Not until 1860 did the Nightingale Training School accept its first probationers; and by 1859 Jane Shaw Stewart was convinced that the military nursing project was premature. She recommended deferring the experiment until the general standard of civilian hospital nursing had improved. If delay were impossible, and the pressure on her to take up the Nightingale baton and renounce her own plans for being merely a nurse were to prove irresistible, then she would take office without a salary; and she would stipulate that all the nurses should be Anglicans. Although such a discriminatory policy applied nowhere else in the army, this wish was granted by a dying Sidney Herbert, to the intense annoyance of her former 'dear Mistress'.[46]

To the last Jane Shaw Stewart fought against taking office in the new service, and in June 1861 Florence Nightingale went over her head, sending Colonel Clark Kennedy, Commandant of the Military Train, a formal letter recommending Jane for the post of Superintendent of Nurses in the Woolwich General Hospital; at the same time she asked him, in a private letter, to forward Jane's name directly to the Secretary of State for War without enquiring as to her willingness to accept the post. It was 'important that the new organisation should all begin at once': Jane's well-known preference for work in the humblest and least visible ranks of the service was dismissed from consideration. So was her recent recommendation that 'an "officer's widow", who has never been found' be appointed as Superintendent. Florence Nightingale concluded breezily 'I have recommended the Secretary for War to offer her the appointment for one year – putting it to her in this light: – that she may train some lady ("officer's widow" or otherwise) for the permanent appointment – '[47]

Jane Shaw Stewart's ideas for alternative candidates were based on more than a personal desire for self-effacement. She had begun to realise that the powers granted the Superintendent and Superintendent-General would provoke a hostile response from medical officers. This might be partially disarmed if such posts were filled by the widows of army officers or surgeons. She explained to Sidney Herbert:

> your lordship, still more a successor indifferent to the work, *must* estimate the Superintendent's being able to do her duty,

and the usefulness of the Service of which she is the responsible head, in great measure by her doing it quietly, without, at least with very rare, appeals and reclamations to you. And the Governor *must* consider her being able to work in good concert with the Medical Officers as an essential part of her duty. . . . The Medical Officers, with whom the Superintendent has necessarily a great deal to do, must and *will* have a much better understanding with her on matters of duty and business, if she is of their own class, than of another. . . . To add jealousy of order to jealousy of office would in truth overweight this difficult work.

She also argued that it would be wrong for her to take up a post which would afford an honourable livelihood to a poorer woman than herself.[48]

Jane's prophecies suffered the classic fate of being totally ignored. She allowed her sense of duty to transcend her better judgment, and agreed to superintend the first female nursing staff at Woolwich. She was trapped in a device of her own making: the Superintendent and Superintendent-General were creatures made in her own image. They were women who would be in a position to wield considerable authority over lower-class men; who would exercise authority over women employees in almost complete independence of professional male colleagues; and who would enjoy a privileged channel of communication with a Secretary of State. In the Victorian army, grading alone was not enough to command authority and respect. Even after the abolition of the purchase of commissions, an officer had to be a gentleman. The nature of the 1859 hospital regulations required the appointment of a gentlewoman as Superintendent or Superintendent-General. As and when a medical officer's widow replaced Jane Shaw Stewart, it would signal important changes in the hierarchical relations between the sexes in army hospitals.

THE CAMPAIGN AGAINST THE SUPERINTENDENT-GENERAL

On 26 May 1868 Lieutenant-General C. Hay received War Office instructions to institute an inquiry into the conduct of the Superintendent-General of Nurses at the Royal Victoria Hospital, Netley, and to discover 'how it is that after a period of six years the establishment of nurses is in so unsatisfactory a state; and that you will record the opinion of the Committee on the future prospects of the nursing system under the present management'. The setting up of the inquiry was the culmination of the continuous series of claims, counter-claims, accusations and recriminations, which had accompanied Jane Shaw Stewart's career in military general hospitals. In the opinion of Colonel Wilbraham, the military Governor, she had almost from the first exhibited a violent temper, and a manner 'often imperious and calculated to provoke a spirit of opposition'. This had led to complaints from nurses, orderlies, medical officers, and even from patients.[49]

The Governor's own discontent had soon become known to his superiors. He found the segregated chain of command totally unacceptable, and looked for opportunities to undermine it. Florence Nightingale was inclined to believe Jane's hints that some of Wilbraham's resentments originated outside the hospital: he had been most put out when the aristocratic Superintendent-General declined to socialise with his sisters or accept their vague offers of help on the wards.[50] Covert inquiries were initiated, and at the end of 1864 a War Office report was produced which was communicated in full neither to Wilbraham nor to Jane Shaw Stewart. Instead, each received private letters of reprimand from Lord de Grey. According to Florence Nightingale, 'the scolding being to be administered to Mrs S.S. not to call it a threat (which it was) without asking whether she had anything to say. (If she had resigned upon this, which she was quite certain to have done, and her brother had read this letter in the Ho: of C., it would have been a slur on the War Office's justice for ever and a day.)'[51]

Many of the differences between Wilbraham and Jane Shaw Stewart were exacerbated by the fact that from April 1863 she combined in one person the posts of Superintendent-General of all female nurses, and Superintendent of nurses at Netley. One consequence of this was that, in practice, a nurse lost her right of appeal against dismissal – a serious matter which would prevent her from ever re-entering the service, and might deprive her of her pension rights. (Wilbraham was known to be partisan in such cases, and according to Florence Nightingale gave references to dismissed women 'not fit to be the commonest nurse'.)[52] The Governor, meanwhile, was not empowered to suspend a Super-intendent from office except 'in cases of flagrant neglect or misconduct', and had no right to dismiss her. This could take place only by decision of the Superintendent-General – who was in any case the same woman, and over whom he had, of course, no powers whatever.[53]

Between Jane Shaw Stewart and the orderlies there were many areas of dispute. The regulation that subordinated orderlies to female nurses implied at the least that the latter were more expert in sick care. But the men who cleaned and scoured the wards for the nurses were often sufficiently able to gain promotion within the Army Hospital Corps, through its own scheme of nursing training. If, as will be seen, the superiority of the female service was not immediately obvious, this new hierarchy would understandably give rise to resentment.[54] Moreover, the demarcation of labour was often unclear: for example, despite the appointment of a 'Linen Nurse', female nurses were responsible only for distributing linen within the wards, and not for supply and cleaning.[55] It was not long before Jane Shaw Stewart was convinced that orderlies were stealing from the linen department, and she was incensed at Wilbraham's refusal either to call in the police, or take any disciplinary action of his own. In May 1863 a War Office memorandum forbade orderlies carrying bundles or parcels from leaving hospital grounds without an authorised pass.[56] This vindicated Jane's position, but can hardly have increased her popularity with the men concerned.

More serious, in the long term, was the Superintendent-General's failure to reach a *modus vivendi* with the medical officers. Within a month of her installation at Netley they were defying the regulations and refusing to allow nurses to accompany them on their rounds. She remonstrated on the subject and obtained official support in March 1866; but as soon as she went to install female staff at the new Royal Herbert Hospital at Woolwich, the Netley medical officers defied the regulations as before. She had done little to help her case when, in late 1865, she had chosen to pick a full-scale quarrel with a Dr Fyffe. She denounced him both to the Inspector-General of Hospitals and to the Director-General of the Army Medical Department, for the alleged crimes of sitting with his feet on a table, and his head covered, in the room of a sick nurse whom he was attending.[57]

The Fyffe incident showed that Jane Shaw Stewart could not tolerate any invasion of her own territory. Unfortunately she was incapable of recognising the same desire for privacy and segregation among her male colleagues. Indeed, the symmetry of needs and claims may have made negotiation and sympathy impossible. The entry of a more educated class of woman upon hospital work in the 1860s was resented by many civilian doctors, who feared anything resembling professional interference or competition. Moreover, the 'lady nurse' threatened more than male professional exclusiveness. When the *Lancet* reported 'in military hospitals especially, attempts made by well-intentioned ladies to do the actual nursing, instead of superintending the inferior nurses, have proved embarrassing to the surgeons, and distasteful to the patients' it was not just throwing up a smokescreen to protect a monopoly. There were social as well as professional boundaries marked on the map of the military hospital, to which the diarist Arthur Munby offers a guide:

> To the lady, you are all deference and smiles: you smooth your phrases and put away all allusions to things coarse or common, you do things for her, you would not hear of her doing things for you. To the servant, you are civil, indeed, but you speak plainly and frankly to her about things which may not be mentioned to a lady; you call her by her Christian name though you never saw her before and expect her to call you Sir in return.

If co-operation between ladies and gentlemen on charitable committees presented problems, how much more difficult must it have been to work in an institution in which the social conventions were being turned on their heads.[58]

This social-sexual embarrassment was almost certainly not what Jane Shaw Stewart had had in mind when she wrote of the danger of adding 'jealousy of order to jealousy of office.' She had merely sensed that the medical officers would resent the official privileges of the Superintendent and Superintendent-General, and that this resentment would be heightened if the women in question were also their 'social superiors'. As discontent within Netley grew, Jane's opponents began to express themselves along precisely these lines. Wilbraham wrote to the War Office that the Superintendent's post[59]

> would be filled with greater advantage by a woman of the middle class. I cannot but think that the difficulty of finding a suitable person is over rated. All that is required is a sensible and right minded woman of active habits, such as may be found, for example, in so many of our large national schools.

The medical press, when Jane Shaw Stewart finally resigned, announced[60]

> We trust that the successor of the late Superintendent-General may be elected solely on the grounds of personal qualifications and we should be glad to learn that the appointment had been given to the widow of some deserving Medical or military officer possessing the necessary tact and knowledge, to whose income the salary attached to the office would be an acceptable addition.

These views carried considerable weight because by this date army hospitals for wives and children had been established with quite different staffing arrangements from those of the military general hospitals.[61] A committee of officers' wives was given an important role in selecting the matrons from among deserving military widows and spinsters.[62] The medical officer in charge of the new female hospitals, as they were called, had control over all nursing duties, and dealt with matters of discipline in collaboration with his ladies' committee.[63] This was indeed a far cry from an aristocratic Superintendent-General communicating directly with the War Office, or an independent lady superintendent in sole charge of her female employees.[64]

The War Office's confidential inquiry into the female nursing service in 1864 had proved inconclusive; and it seems highly likely that the discontented medical officers of Netley, despairing of any decisive victory over the Superintendent-General within the constraints of the regulations, began to 'leak' their story to the press and to their military and civilian colleagues, in order to subject the War Office to the pressure of a minor public scandal. This was now made easier by the fact that Jane's brother had lost his seat in the House of Commons in 1865. Rumours began to circulate early in 1866 that the patients at the new Royal Herbert Hospital were having female nursing 'thrust upon them contrary to their desire'. *The Times* of 17 October also reported patients' complaints: 'it appears to be generally considered that the introduction of the lady nurses is an innovation from which no benefit can possibly be derived.' In 1867 the *Lancet* reported that 'the invalids in one at least of the military hospitals have petitioned Government to exchange the present lady-nurse system for the old plan of orderly attendants on the sick.' The *Medical Times and Gazette*, repeating this report, applauded the news that the

Government of India had just rejected a scheme to introduce female nurses into the British military hospitals there.[65]

On 9 May 1868, an article in the *Lancet* entitled 'A Visit to Netley Hospital', claimed that all was well with the Army Hospital Corps, but that it was otherwise with the female nursing service. Since military discipline silenced the medical officers themselves, it was for their civilian colleagues to speak out on their behalf, and for the good of their patients:[66]

> Female nurses might prove altogether beneficial if they were completely under the control of the medical staff, or at least if their own superintendent were amenable to the authority of the medical officers. It will easily be understood that there are many cases in which the immediate presence of a woman is neither requisite nor desirable; and particularly when, as is often the case, the patient has an insuperable objection to her presence. Under these circumstances, the surgeon would gladly dispense with the nurse, and let her be attending to other duties; but here the lady superintendent steps in, and *orders* the nurse to follow the medical officer closely in all his rounds. The lady superintendent, though no doubt a well-intentioned person, is the *bête noire* of the establishment. When we say that we believe, from the General at the head of the establishment to the most junior candidate, there is but one feeling of dislike to her constant interference, it is probably time that the public should inquire why a whole public establishment is sacrificed to please a lady of aristocratic connexions.

At about the same time that this article was being prepared for the press, Jane Shaw Stewart was informed that all correspondence on the subject of her post was being referred to the Secretary of State, and she ceased going into the wards. Throughout most of the previous year she had been in the Royal Herbert Hospital, her position daily becoming more isolated and vulnerable. Nurses came and went at a rapid rate. Medical officers refused to find time to see her, and she was reduced to communicating with them by means of lengthy memoranda which alienated their sympathies even further. The policy of segregation now seemed to apply to her alone: her chain of command was breaking down. The nurses told tales on her to the medical staff, and laid formal written complaints against her to the Principal Medical Officer. She became increasingly hysterical and violent in front of nurses, orderlies and patients.[67] When the committee of inquiry was announced, it was on terms which pre-judged the central issue, since they stated flatly that the nursing service was unsatisfactory. No material was assembled to show whether the regulations for military hospitals had been complied with by all parties concerned. No provision was made for a discussion of the merits and flaws of the Hospital Regulations as they stood. The many different issues raised by Jane Shaw Stewart's stormy tenure of office were to be boiled down to one – the turnover rate of nurses. The awkward and temperamental outsider, whose presence had exposed many of the problems and difficulties of the new system, would also serve as a convenient scapegoat for them. Her imminent resignation from the service was a foregone conclusion.

'AS MISTRESS AND MAID'

At the commencement of the Netley inquiry, it was stated that no less than forty-one nurses had passed through the Royal Victoria Hospital since 1863, and that this too-rapid turnover had brought too many inexperienced nurses into the service.[68] It is tempting to see in this figure the transposition to the public arena of a well-known domestic phenomenon – the mistress who could not handle her servants well, or keep them long. The periodical literature of this time is full of articles on 'the servant problem' from which it clearly emerges that bad relations between 'maids and mistresses' were the norm rather than the exception.

Mistresses, it was said, imposed too exacting standards on inexperienced girls: 'We have no doubt that you are always right; but do not forget that this makes it all the more uncomfortable for the person who is always wrong.' Moreover, many mistresses, unobserved by outsiders for the most part, resorted to verbal and even physical abuse of their servants: 'I never yet could understand why a lady should cease to be one, when she is required to discharge the duty of reproving her servant.' The right to chastise servants physically was only legally abolished in 1861, and it is reasonable to assume that the practice continued, in private at least, in the following decade.[69]

The hospital regulations allowed for the private reprimand of nurses by their superintendent. Jane Shaw Stewart's male colleagues were shocked to hear, or hear of, shouts and even blows in the wards. In 1866 the Superintendent-General admitted to having beaten one of her nurses. This was officially condemned by the medical officers and privately disapproved of by Florence Nightingale. Jane promised that the incident would not be repeated; but it seems likely that she found it difficult to consider the hospital wards as anything but her own private domain.[70] The medical officers were, after all, only occasional visitors there, and the orderlies were, like good servants, expected to accommodate themselves to the wishes and instructions of female superiors. The idea of shared public space, and the practice of being overseen were foreign to women of the Superintendent-General's class; and very little in the regulations was designed to encourage this new consciousness.

Particularly severe strains were imposed on the mistress–maid relationship at Netley in consequence of Jane Shaw Stewart's idiosyncratic views as to her vocation. She believed that nursing could be improved only by personal example: 'Gentlemen and ladies know nothing whatever about these things. They do not live with their subordinates, they ought not. A Superintendent living apart from her Nurses would be a very useless animal.' However, a consequence of this practice was that she could not view misdemeanours with detachment: 'it is not good that a Nurse who has just behaved, for instance, with deceit or with gross insubordination, should sit down to dinner with the Super-intendent.' Nurses were sometimes punished by being made to eat alone for up to a month. In retrospect Jane Shaw Stewart thought this punishment should have been limited to a week. More serious offences – the exchange of love letters with a patient, the discovery of empty gin bottles – resulted in instant dismissal without right of appeal.[71]

It is possible to dwell too much on Jane Shaw Stewart's temperamental failings and the peculiarities of her approach to a leadership role. For she was, in fact, being asked to make bricks without straw: the mistress may have been inadequate, but the maids were truly awful. All Netley and Woolwich nurses were described as 'probationers' on entry. This may have been Jane's designation of women of whose qualities she was unsure; but at least three, Mary Barber, Elizabeth Young and Frances Smith, were only probationers at St Thomas's when they arrived at Netley.[72] Medical officers remarked on the inexperience of the recruits, which perhaps reached its nadir when two nurses joined the surgical division who had never previously attended a surgical operation.[73] Yet the military hospitals were supposed to employ only the highest grade of female nurse. Making up the gaps in training placed a heavy burden of supervision on Jane's shoulders. Wilbraham claimed that she demanded 'entire abnegation of self' from her nurses, and 'sacrifices which the regulations never contemplated, and which few women would be capable of either morally or physically', but without giving concrete examples. One Frances Johnson was, apparently, highly aggrieved to be told that she must learn to administer enemas. It is a measure of the Superintendent-General's success, and also of the uncomfortable intensity with which she pursued her objectives, that no medical officer found fault with any nurse on grounds of inefficiency or unkindness.[74]

In most civil hospitals, the ward nurse learned her work by attaching herself to her ward medical officer; and in military hospitals the medical officers supervised such training as the orderlies received. But they had no remit to train female nurses: they objected to being accompanied by them on their rounds, and thought such attendance particularly inappropriate in a teaching hospital, serving the Army Medical School. Jane Shaw Stewart had, of course, so constructed the service that the medical officers were virtually without influence over the work of her nurses; by hermetically sealing off the service she effectively denied it, and herself, access to the only realistic training resource then available.

Just how bad the military nursing recruits were in this period is revealed in the correspondence of Jane's successor. Mrs Deeble and six other nurses completed a Nightingale training course at St Thomas's and installed themselves at Netley in November 1869.[75] In the first month, one sister nearly poisoned a patient by dosing him with liniment instead of cod liver oil. Shortly afterwards, she let the side down again:

> She was ordered to apply an Ether Spray to a quinsy patient instead of silently receiving the order and asking information from me she told Dr Maclean she did not know how to do it. I was the more sorry about this, as these Orderlies are well up to such things.

Two months later, Mrs Deeble reported:[76]

Sister L. was asked to take the temperature of a patient and she replied she did not know how, . . . Sister Clarke made a sad mistake in the application of leeches to the eye of a patient. She applied one so close to the inside of the eye as to cause hemorrhage (sic). . . . The Ward Orderly remarked to Sister Lennox next morning that if Sister C. had used the Eye-glass such a thing could not have happened. These glasses are always used here but Sister C. had never seen them.

Rebecca Strong, one of Mrs Deeble's original contingent at Netley, recalled of the training given at the Nightingale school in 1867:[77]

Very little was expected from us, as progress was slow in regard to organised teaching. Kindness, watchfulness, cleanliness, and guarding against bedsores were well ingrained. A few stray lectures were given, one I remember especially, I think it was on the Chemistry of Life, or some such title; . . . There was a dummy on which to practise bandaging, and some lessons were given, also a skeleton, and some ancient medical books, one, fortunately, on Anatomy for those who attempted self-education.

Perhaps, then, it should not be wondered at that the Nightingale 'graduates' were so inadequate to the needs of the military general hospital.

At the beginning of November 1869 Florence Nightingale had had her first meeting with Mrs Deeble. Born Jane Cecilia Egan, Mrs Deeble was the widow of an army medical officer, and it seems likely that her career in military nursing was promoted by her late husband's colleagues.[78] Florence Nightingale was profoundly unimpressed by her, but strove to be fair. She wrote to Dr Sutherland:[79]

she is brave, sincere, courageous – but she has no observation – she is quite incapable of understanding far less of making a Regulation or an organisation. . . . Any officer may turn her round his finger. She will be engaged in planning a *nice tea* for the Nurses, while she lets the Nursing go to ruin. . . . I have not approached the subject of the Regulations yet with Mrs Deeble. I doubt whether she has seen them. I doubt whether she is able to understand them. I doubt whether she has a glimmer of the fact that she is to have a personal relation with and report to the War Office.

An outsider might have seen the case very differently. The medical officers had secured the replacement of the aristocratic lady by a woman of their own class. Mrs Deeble's 'failings,' her homeliness, her lack of interest in constitutional rights and wrongs, were exactly the qualities which would ingratiate her with male and female colleagues alike; they were, indeed, what the medical press had been clamouring for since it had had the dismissal of Jane Shaw Stewart in its sights. Her appointment guaranteed the survival of the female nursing service, although not in its original form.

For many years the potential value of female nursing far outweighed its actual contribution to the military hospital system. If medical officers agitated for modifications in the 'constitutional' position of the female nursing service, rather than demand its abolition outright, it was because they perceived some of its inherent advantages over the Army Hospital Corps. They desired a permanent workforce, owing no overriding responsibility to combatant officers, which could not be withdrawn for non-nursing duties. The AHC was, however, 'liable to be employed, in any way that may be required, in the performance of any duties in the Medical and Purveyor's Departments.'[80] It was for this reason that medical officers were so disturbed by the turnover rate among Jane Shaw Stewart's nurses. In principle, a female service could be tailored to meet medical officers' requirements, especially once the anomaly of the female superintendent's 'parallel power' had been removed.

Modified hospital regulations, with a section designed specifically for the Netley nursing service, were issued to coincide with Mrs Deeble's appointment.[81] They represented one clear victory for the medical officers: regulation 46 stated that 'During the session of the Army Medical School, it is not necessary that the Sister should attend the Medical Officer while engaged in clinical instruction, unless permitted by him to do so.' The second victory was implied rather than stated: the office of Superintendent-General had quietly disappeared. Henceforth the Army List would refer only to the 'Superintendent of Nurses' at Netley. These changes in the letter of the law were small: the new regulations had in fact been drawn up by Florence Nightingale with Jane Shaw Stewart's assistance. The special relationship with the War Office still existed in principle, and the nursing sisters remained responsible solely to their Superintendent. However, between 1870 and 1885, as will be seen, these female prerogatives were to be completely eliminated.[82]

No one spoke of Jane Shaw Stewart in 1885, when a major revision of the military hospital regulations was published, and yet her preoccupations were still very much live issues. On the vexed question of selection of nurses Mrs Deeble, not normally critical of her male colleagues, made a bitter private complaint that 'men are not fitted to judge of a woman's capabilities'. She was in no doubt that there was a deliberate drive to reduce women's authority within the new system, 'as Sir Thomas Crawford himself told me that sooner than have a Superintendent General of Nursing he would vacate his Chair'.[83] Florence Nightingale also fulminated against the new arrangements for selection; and her objections were couched as much in the language of class as of professionalism or gender. 'Would Lady Crawford intrust you with the duty of selecting your housemaid or your cook? . . . How could the mistress of a household manage her household if she did not enquire personally into the character of her servants?' she wrote, after hearing that the Director-General had accepted some Nightingale trainees as military nurses without even taking up their references, let alone putting them through an interview.[84] The domestic metaphor undermined the validity of her criticisms; and this was symbolic of the administrative change which was taking place.

The remodelling of the Army Nursing Service in 1885 coincided with similar developments in civilian nursing. Doctors' complaints against 'segregation and superintendence' – the independent management of hospital nurses by external, female institutions – had been gathering strength throughout the 1870s and 1880s. They demanded greater control over the training and supervision of nursing in their hospitals, and by and large lay managers acquiesced. In 1885 the St John's House sisterhood left King's College Hospital, and four years later it gave up the management of the nursing at Charing Cross Hospital.[85] The entry into public service of the class of woman who did not necessarily require a salary, and who did not regard herself as an employee, was beginning to be blocked. Florence Nightingale and her peers had, in a sense, been undone by their own success. Philanthropic ladies had impressed both civil and military medical practitioners with their distinctive contribution to the welfare of the sick poor and the wounded soldier: but in the process they had created the demand for a new species of trained female employee, subordinate to the male medical officers of the hospital, rather than to 'the lady of the house'. Female nurses were retained within the army, but not on their own terms. They were no longer to embody the norms of an alien, female world of household management. The rest of the century would see them striving to become fully accepted as servants of the state.

CHAPTER 4

UNEASY TRUCE: HER MAJESTY'S NURSING SISTERS, 1870–1902

Throughout the 'post-Shaw Stewart' era the position of the female military nurses remained anomalous and, to them, highly unsatisfactory. Their problems were aptly summed up by a civilian doctor who volunteered for war service at the end of the century:

> The whole system of female nursing in the army appears to have been clumsily grafted on to the old system of nursing by orderlies, purely out of deference to public opinion and Miss Florence Nightingale. The graft has never taken root.[1]

Almost every impulse to expand the female service, to integrate it within the military system, and to regularise its position in war, came from outside the army. Between 1861 and 1882 the service was confined to the two general hospitals at Netley and Woolwich, and numbered little more than a dozen women. Pressure for change came from independent observers and philanthropic agencies: between 1879 and 1883, campaigns in South Africa and the Middle East placed unaccustomed strains on the army medical services and, as in 1854, created a lobby for employing more women nurses in war. Civilian demand prompted searching War Office inquiries into hospital provision, and new regulations were promulgated in 1885.[2] These extended the female nursing service to all hospitals with over 100 beds; and in 1893, the 100-bed restriction was rescinded. In practice, however, the service remained a very limited one. By 1890, a total of 60 army sisters were working in 16 military hospitals in the United Kingdom and abroad; in 1898, there were 72.[3] The regulations had stipulated a minimum of three female nurses wherever they were employed, but in many hospitals this was interpreted as a maximum.[4] When at the end of the century the crisis of the Anglo-Boer War found the army nursing sisters wanting, it was through little fault of their own. Indeed, it was largely because of the restricted recruitment of female nurses, and the curious pattern of their peacetime duties, that the British military medical system found itself unable to meet the demands of the battlefield.

'IN BUT NOT OF' THE ARMY

At the heart of the army sisters' discontents in the nineteenth century was the ambivalence of their status within a combatant establishment. For most of the period ambulance rescue and field hospital work were considered the most urgent requirements of military medicine in wartime. These functions were exclusively male: female nursing, confined strictly to base hospitals, was often thought of as a luxury. In principle, any male orderly might have to work under fire, which justified his classification as a combatant; female nurses could not, and thus remained outside the system. The medical officers themselves were not ranked on a level with their combatant colleagues until 1898, when the Royal Army Medical Corps was constituted. Army sisters had to wait until the Second World War to be granted officer status.[5] Their marginal position as merely medical workers was reinforced by the fact of their sex – or rather by the characteristics attributed to their sex by their male colleagues: the sisters' own opinions on war service were rarely canvassed. In 1900 an RAMC officer was able to inform the Royal Commission on the care of the sick and wounded of the Anglo-Boer War: 'In the army estimates we do not even provide theoretically for a single lady nurse.'[6]

Meanwhile, within the military hospitals of the peacetime establishment, the structures of segregation and superintendence so carefully erected by Jane Shaw Stewart were gradually being whittled away. Minor amendments to the Army Medical Regulations between 1878 and 1885 marked the erosion of the authority of the Superintendent of Nursing over the female staff; they also marked the weakening, and finally the disappearance of her privileged relationship with the Secretary of State for War.

In 1878 Mrs Deeble's exclusive power to 'select, and with the sanction of the Secretary of State appoint, the Sisters' was amended to her duty to select and dismiss sisters with reference to the wishes of the Director-General of the Army Medical Department, and in consultation with the Medical Officer of the hospital, and the principal medical officer of the district, concerned. In 1885, in a radical break with the past, it was laid down that the Director-General alone would 'nominate Superintendents and Nurses from a list in his office', and no dismissal was to take place without his sanction. In 1870, the sisters were still 'responsible solely to the Superintendent' who could dismiss and suspend them with reference to the military commandant and the Secretary of State for War; medical officers had to refer directly to her any complaints against her staff. In 1885, although the MO still had this obligation, he could, if necessary, 'direct the suspension of the nurse from duty, pending reference to the Principal Medical Officer, and if necessary to the Director-General.'

By the end of the century the Superintendent's cause, particularly in the matter of appointments, began to be pleaded in the columns of the nursing press; chiefly, as in the case of the *Nursing Record*, where editorial policy favoured the advancement of nursing through professional self-regulation and state registration. It was argued that the standard of nursing and nursing appointments in military hospitals was falling below that in civilian hospitals – a case for which, as will be seen, there was much justification – and that the remedy for this was greater control by female professionals. None of those writing on the subject in the 1890s were aware that twenty years previously, the Superintendent had enjoyed the very powers they were now advocating.[7]

Although the female nurses were ultimately subject to the authority of the medical officer, both in matters of discipline and in the organisation of their ward work, they themselves were given no official authority over the orderlies. They were thus placed in an extraordinarily difficult position in attempting to carry out their duties. The regulations made them 'responsible for the personal cleanliness of the patients in their wards; that all medicines, diets and extras, are supplied to the patients according to the instructions of the prescribing medical officer.' The sisters were not, however, given the necessary authority to enforce obedience

6 Mrs Jane Cecilia Deeble, Lady Superintendent of the Army Nursing Service 1870–89. An army surgeon's widow, she succeeded in repairing the damage done by the aristocratic Jane Shaw Stewart, and held office for a record number of years. (Bodleian Library)

on either patients or orderlies. If a sister met with misconduct or insubordination she had to report it to the wardmaster;[8] he alone had the right to compel the orderlies to obey the sisters and to treat them 'with every courtesy and respect'.[9] An anonymous army sister tartly observed that 'a British soldier is bound in subordination to one woman only, and he draws the line at every other'; and that the interpretation of the terms 'courtesy and respect' 'would vary with the early training and social standing of the individual orderly.'[10] Sisters complained both among themselves and to their civilian colleagues, but they were unwilling to use all the machinery open to them under the regulations. In the last resort, if the wardmaster did not co-operate, the sister could report him to the medical officer: not only was this a cumbersome approach to the problem of the unmade bed or the neglected patient, but it was one unlikely to improve her standing with any of her male colleagues. As another sister observed, 'It is a fatal mistake to report either orderly or patient unless absolutely obliged.[11]

WORKING CONDITIONS

An Army Sister . . . may do as little as she likes or she may work herself to death.'[12] This was the verdict of a civilian volunteer nurse during the Anglo-Boer War; her comment aroused predictable resentment within the Army Nursing Service, but it helps us to decode the often rather vague statements contained in the medical regulations. The first regulations for army sisters, published in 1859, required a considerable amount of personal nursing work, including 'the administration of food and drink to helpless patients, the application of leeches and blisters, poulticing and minor dressings, the administration of enemas, when required by the Medical Officer to do so, and the due warming and ventilation of the ward.' The 1870 amendment still obliged the sisters 'personally to take an active share in all nursing duties, both by night and by day', but did not instance specific duties. By 1878, detailed references to personal nursing work were omitted from the regulations, which increasingly confined the sisters to a supervisory role.

It is clear that the medical officers placed a high value on the supervision exercised by the sisters, for they attempted to make it a

MILITARY SISTER, NETLEY.

7 Military Sister, c.1890. (Bodleian Library)

twenty-four-hour function. The 1878 regulations prohibited night duty for sisters, presumably on grounds of propriety. The 1885 regulations allowed night duty where two sisters could be detailed for it together. In 1893 Helen Campbell Norman, Mrs Deeble's successor, resisted pressure to break this rule and allow sisters on night duty singly. But the medical officers did manage to establish the principle that a member of the female staff should be present in the wards throughout the day.[13] From 1894 onwards the sisters had to take it in turns to go 'on orderly duty' and be the 'afternoon Sister' supervising the entire male nursing staff, though they managed to retain their statutory afternoon break of between two and three hours.[14]

It was difficult for the sisters to arrange a satisfactory pattern of work for themselves. The orderlies were trained to replace them in time of war, and were in theory able to carry out duties identical to theirs. The regulations offered very little guidance on a division of labour. They laid down that the sisters were to be present at surgical operations when required, and – as the memory of the Shaw Stewart imbroglio began to fade – that they should accompany the medical officer on his rounds. For the rest, the sisters' duties evolved between the lines. They tended to assume such tasks as taking temperatures and pulses, and measuring and administering medicines, comforts and stimulants. In a severe case, they might abandon the supervisory role altogether. A sister might well insist on personally undertaking night duty, on preparing a special diet, on feeding and even washing and making the bed for a seriously ill patient.[15]

It remained true, however, throughout the century that an army sister could be clearer in her mind about what she should not do than about what she should. She was not allowed to nurse venereal or convalescent cases – only the helplessly, and innocently, ill. She was not responsible for the discipline of the ward, for the supply of linen, or for the distribution of meals. She neither fetched, carried nor scrubbed. But there is no doubt that many sisters chose, or felt obliged to do, far more work than was officially assigned them. Much depended on the numbers and workload of the female staff of a hospital at any given moment; much depended also on a sister's assessment of the abilities and attitudes of 'her' Medical Staff Corps. Certainly too much depended on the character of the individual sister, for the Regulations gave her, instead of concretely defined duties, a set of 'responsibilities' which were subject to a variety of interpretations. She might decide that the most satisfactory solution was 'for the Sister to do all the really important part of the work herself (*sub rosa*), and let the orderly take the credit for it with his superiors.' On the other hand, some medical officers thought that many sisters wanted the orderlies to do nothing but fetch and carry; and one orderly rather unfairly blamed the sisters for 'the influence their presence had on the orderlies, in creating an indifference to their duties seldom seen in a hospital wholly worked by Corps orderlies.'[16]

The male and female nursing staff functioned alongside each other in very different, and even incompatible ways. The sisters had trained in civilian hospitals which by the 1880s had established a strict hierarchy of nursing duties, and which increasingly allotted domestic work to non-nursing staff or untrained probationers. Orderlies, on the other hand, were not permitted to limit their duties to the care of the sick. The 1883 inquiry into the army hospitals services reiterated the multiple nature of their duties: military hospitals other than general hospitals were too small for a strict division of labour between medical, housekeeping and provisioning work to be economically feasible.[17] In consequence, orderlies could be[18]

> required to do all the work in connection with the hospital at which they are stationed. They may be, and they are, called upon to act as cooks, gardeners, clerks, window-cleaners, floor-scrubbers, store-keepers, servants to the medical officers, mess-waiters, anything and everything, in short, and finally, occasionally as nurses.

In this respect they recalled the civilian nurses of an earlier period, and justified the epithet 'Sarah Gamps in male attire'.[19]

The chief difficulty facing the sisters, however, to which a horde of Sarah Gamps would have been preferable, lay in the orderlies' status as soldiers first and nurses second:[20]

> the orderly nurse may be ordered out of the ward by the Non-Commissioned Officer on duty, to go on drill, or on parade, or to do coaling, or some other fatigue duty, and it is no uncommon occurrence . . . for the Nursing Sister to come on duty in the morning, and find her patients in bed, perhaps, but her nurses out on the parade ground.

The arrangements made for night duty were particularly extraordinary by civilian standards. Three orderlies were assigned for a night, 'each taking two hours in turn and being off four, as if on guard. . . . Different Orderlies come on each night for nearly a week, when the first trio reappear, a most trying arrangement for both patients and Sisters.'[21] Continuity of patient care was thus subject to disruption both by day and night.

Almost from the first, the female nurses had sought a role in the training of the orderlies. Their stated purpose was to improve the standard of ward work. At first, however, there was scant basis for their claim to professional superiority; and it is difficult to escape the conclusion that training was seen chiefly as an instrument of control to compensate for a lack of official authority. Mrs Deeble had spent one year at the Nightingale Training School and only a few months at Netley when she wrote of 'beating the Orderlies into shape' and 'making the Orderlies learn the practical part of nursing'. Given the medical gaffes of her first cohort of Nightingale nurses, this smacked of presumption.[22] The expertise of Mrs Deeble's later recruits to the Army Nursing Service was also rather meagre. Anne Caulfield, who later became Superintendent at the Herbert Hospital, spent only three months at King's College Hospital before entering the service in 1874. Most of the probationers sponsored between 1881 and 1885 by the National Society for Aid to the Sick and Wounded in War (later the British Red Cross) had received no training prior to their reception at Netley.[23] In fact, shortly after taking up her post, Mrs Deeble had realised that the only way to make good the shortcomings of her own nursing staff was to gain access to the scheme by which the orderlies themselves were trained. She requested permission to join their classes, along with five of the sisters; and she also spent much time reading the orderlies' manual of instruction to her staff.[24]

Until the late 1870s, the training given to the orderlies of the Army Hospital Corps was at least as systematic as that given to nurses in many of the voluntary hospitals of the metropolis. The 1870 syllabus covered general anatomy; bandaging, dressing and the treatment of fractures; administration of internal and external medicines; the uses of various surgical appliances; the observation of the sick, the nursing of the helpless, invalid cookery, and ward management. In addition, they were instructed in first aid, the transport of the sick and wounded, and the special demands of field hospital work. Their theoretical instruction was given over five weeks; the men studied for two hours a day, and were given weekly examinations. The full training lasted three months, followed by a final oral examination.[25] If the 1870 syllabus is compared with that supposed to be in force at the Nightingale Training School at this time, many similarities are evident, and it is possible that Florence Nightingale had drafted both. It would appear that the orderlies were trained more systematically than the St Thomas's probationers;[26] and the much-trumpeted failings of the orderlies almost certainly had more to do with the way they were deployed than with the level of their instruction. If they were, as was sometimes claimed, insubordinate to the army sisters, this may have had less to do with antagonism to women in positions of authority than with resentment at being supervised by persons to whom they felt in no way professionally inferior.

By the mid 1880s, it was less inappropriate for Mrs Deeble to insist on the training prerogative. She was now able to recruit nurses from several general hospitals which gave them a thorough all-round nursing probation;[27] at the same time, the quality of the orderlies had begun to decline. This was due not to any deterioration in the training given them, but to the introduction of Cardwell's short-service system as part of his programme of building up army reserves. Until 1878, members of the Army Hospital Corps served for twelve years: their terms of engagement were then altered to seven years' service, and five with the Reserve; a decade later, these terms became three years' service, and nine with the Reserve. Even Mrs Deeble regretted the disappearance of the old hands, whose experience was as valuable as their initial training.[28]

In response to her representations, the 1885 regulations required the sisters 'under the medical officers, to assist in training the orderlies, in the mode of handling patients, the application of dressings, and in the administration of medicines, diets and extras.' In practice this worked out at giving the orderlies half an hour's daily instruction for a month after they had received six months' theoretical instruction at Aldershot. By the end of the century this had been whittled down to ten minutes in some hospitals; and since many hospitals employed no female nurses, and others very few, for most practical purposes in-service training was in the hands of staff sergeants and wardmasters.[29] In any case, without greater official authority, the sisters could not train the orderlies as they wished: they could not assign individuals to specific tasks over a period of weeks as if they were civilian probationers, nor could they be sure that a pupil's progress might not be disrupted by a spot of square bashing or gardening.

During and after the Anglo-Boer War the army nursing service as a whole was stung by the comments on their style of work made by the civilian nurses and doctors who volunteered for service alongside them. Even such a colleague as Maud McCarthy, who passed through the wartime Army Nursing Reserve into the new Queen Alexandra's Imperial Military Nursing Service, and later became its Matron-in-Chief, found much to criticise, albeit privately, and recalled:

> No patients were thought of as requiring 'skilled' nursing however dangerously ill the patient might be. In fact, when preparing to attend them in this manner, I was told by an Army Sister that I should lose all prestige.

A male volunteer for orderly service wrote rather bitterly that 'the nurses visit the wards in the morning and evening, having the afternoon to themselves for expeditions to the lovely environs of the locality.'[30] The Anglo-Boer War saw a very high incidence of serious enteric disease among the British troops; where almost all hospital cases were severe ones, there was little room for a body of nurses with a purely supervisory function. The sisters' pattern of duties in peacetime was simply not appropriate to the desperate pressures of war. But no instructions were given to the sisters as to how they might modify their regulation roles. All was left to the discretion and initiative of individuals.

General Buller, in his evidence to the 1904 Royal Commission on the war, was extremely blunt in his verdict on the pre-war system:[31]

> I do not think our female nursing system is as good as it should be, because I think our nurses are above their work. Their training is more to do small odd jobs for the comfort of this or that patient than to nurse. . . . I do not for a moment suppose we ought to keep up in peace time an establishment of nurses that would be required in war, but I do not think we insist on the nurses we do keep performing duties which would make them able to take the position I think they ought to take in war.

The nursing press was soon full of indignant rebuttals of these criticisms from army nursing sisters, many of whose colleagues had, literally, worked themselves to death. The structure and conditions of work laid down for them, however, had clearly made abuses and derelictions of duty a possibility. What was indeed unjust was to blame them for an incapacity for war service which had been sedulously fostered by those in authority over them.

Less than half the nurses joining the Army Nursing Service in 1893 completed as much as three years' service, 'the casualties consisting chiefly of resignations'.[32] Reporting to the War Office Committee on the Army Nursing Service of that year, Lady Superintendent Norman confessed that she wished they would stay on longer: she did not think that many of them left to be married; and she thought the fact that some nurses went straight from their training hospital into private nursing while they were on the waiting list for the service ultimately unfitted them for the discipline of hospital work.[33] Of those who completed three years, few stayed on as long as ten. It was common for civilian nurses to move from one hospital to another after only one or two years' work. But army nursing might have been considered a more attractive option than most; certainly there was never any shortage of applicants for posts. The army nurse was offered shorter hours and, in principle, lighter duties than her civilian colleagues, with comparable pay and allowances. She was guaranteed the rank of sister on entry, and a pension on retirement – which few stayed long enough to collect. Many women must have been attracted by the certain prospect of foreign postings, the hope of 'station gaieties' and social life abroad, and the more remote possibility of active service in war. All army sisters had to complete five years of foreign service, allotted according to seniority. In practice, most entrants were too quickly discouraged by conditions of service in the home stations to qualify for these opportunities.

Why was the workforce so unstable? High on a long list of the service's disadvantages must have been its loneliness. The Netley chaplain reported in 1888 that the sisters 'cannot and do not enter much into general society';[34] and in hospitals employing only three or four female nurses their seclusion was almost conventual. From 1870 onwards the service regulations expected them 'to restrict their communications with officers, non-commissioned officers, orderlies and patients as far as practicable within the limits of their duties. They will endeavour to combine personal reserve with strict and respectful obedience to officers, and with courtesy and kindness to non-commissioned officers and men.' From 1888 onwards regulations were laid down to keep the sisters from the compensatory activity of talking too much to each other: they were not to enter each other's rooms after 10 p.m., not to talk in 'thoroughfare wards, corridors and stairs', and not to enter wards in which they were not working. Things must have been even more unpleasant at a station where the nurses did not even like each other enough to want to break these rules; and frequent postings interrupted many friendships. One cannot help sympathising with the occasional miscreant such as Mary Cole, who in 1889 lost her grade as Acting Superintendent, and was brusquely despatched from Aldershot to Canterbury, on being found 'to admit sick officers to the nurses' Quarters, and to indulge in card playing'.[35]

Army nursing work was not, on the whole, professionally satisfying. By 1891 the entry qualification had been raised to three years' combined training and service in a civilian hospital, with a further six months' probation at Netley – as high a standard as any required of nurses in this period. The three years' certificate was being urged, by those agitating for the registration of nurses, as a qualification essential to building up the calibre of the nursing profession. Army nursing, however, had little to offer the woman dedicated to professional advancement. The structural difficulties facing the military nurse in the organisation of ward work have already been discussed. In a civilian hospital nurses could certainly expect a more rational programme of work, and a better-trained and more reliable subordinate staff. They could also enjoy using more up-to-date equipment, and have the satisfaction of treating a wider variety of cases, particularly on the surgical side.[36] By the mid-1890s, an ambitious nurse could hope to earn a higher salary as a civilian Matron than as a military Lady Superintendent – and, of course, only one woman at a time could hold the latter post.[37]

Promotion was a vexed issue. It was a discouraging fact that the regulations allowed for appointments to the rank of Lady Superintendent and Acting Superintendent from outside the service.[38] Promotions from within the service depended heavily on the social bias of those in authority over the nurse. Although an army chaplain listened with amusement to 'the sisters calling themselves "seniors" and saying with pride that they are senior to So-and-So. I did not know, before meeting these sisters, that women ever desired to be considered senior,'[39] seniority did not always bring its hoped-for rewards. Annie Steele resigned in 1891 after seven years' service, having received the comment 'Satisfactory report on all points. Not being a lady, is unfit for promotion.' Elizabeth Dowse, a well-trained nurse from St Mary's Hospital, Paddington, on her entry into the service in 1885, was described as 'socially ineligible for promotion'. Thirteen years after entering the service she reached the rank of Superintendent, and in 1908 became a Matron in Queen Alexandra's Imperial Military Nursing Service. Few ambitious women would have been so patient.[40]

An army sister's commencing salary was set at £30 in 1870, rising by yearly increments of £2 to a maximum of £50. This figure remained unchanged until 1902. Promotion to 'Nursing Sister acting as Superintendent' entailed an additional £20 per annum. A Lady Superintendent's salary was fixed in 1884 as £150, rising by increments of £10 to a maximum of £200. An additional allowance of £50 per annum was allotted to the Lady Superintendent at Netley (the post of Lady Superintendent at the Herbert Hospital, Woolwich, was abolished in 1894) in recognition of her training duties. Throughout this period a ward sister in a civilian voluntary hospital commanded a starting salary of between £26 and £35, so the military nursing salary was not uncompetitive.[41] However, by 1897, when civilian nurses were being invited to enrol in the Army Nursing Service Reserve, their starting salaries were fixed higher than those of the regular service, viz., £40 for nursing sisters and £60 for acting superintendents. This suggests that army nursing salaries were beginning to fall below those in civil life. In 1902 a sister's starting salary in the new Queen Alexandra's Imperial Military Nursing Service was fixed at £37 10s. In addition to their salary, the army sisters received free fuel, light and quarters, and an allowance for clothing, board and washing, as they might have expected in most civilian posts. These payments in kind do not appear to have added to the allurements of their employment. Living-in accommodation was not provided in the majority of military hospitals, which was felt as a grievance; where it existed, it was euphemistically described as 'barrack-like in its simplicity'. No description survives of the food provided: but the rituals at Netley and Gibraltar were most unfavourably compared with those served to the nurses at the height of the Anglo-Boer War![42]

The great material bonus which should have distinguished army nursing from civilian nursing employment was its non-contributory pension. Retirement was at sixty, but, after 1894, a nurse could be asked to retire at fifty or earlier. If officially pronounced unfit, she could retire after ten years' service on a pension of 30 per cent of her salary; longer service entitled her to a sum up to 70 per cent of her salary. In principle this offered the nurse an unusual degree of security, but in practice the size of the pension, and even the likelihood of its award, were to a disturbing degree dependent on the opinions of a nurse's superiors. She could receive no pension if she were dismissed, or if she resigned without permission, no matter how long she had served. She might work long and hard and yet not receive the bonus for 'special devotion to the public service' which was instituted in 1870 and which could take a pension up to a maximum of £50 per annum. Thus Alice Briggs, who left the service after fourteen years in 1898, owing to ill-health, received a pension of £40 per annum; Emily Dew, leaving on the same grounds in 1897 after fifteen years' service, received only £28.[43] Such discrepancies did not escape the notice of the nursing press, which considered even the most generous sums awarded as derisory. The *Nursing Record* considered £78 to be a reasonable pension, rather than the current maxima of £35 per annum for nursing sisters and £49 per annum for acting superintendents.[44]

THE INDIAN ARMY NURSING SERVICE

The uncertain status, low salary levels and difficult working conditions which afflicted the members of the Army Nursing Service were reproduced and magnified within the sister service established separately for India in 1888. An experimental scheme for employing female nurses in Indian military hospitals had first been discussed as early as 1864; however, when the scheme was published in 1867 dissatisfaction with the Shaw Stewart regime was coming to a head, and was used as an excuse to shelve it.[45] The campaigns in South Africa and the Middle East, where female nurses worked in unfriendly climates and terrains, helped to dispose of arguments that they were unsuited to military hospital duties in India; and by the 1880s the success of philanthropic schemes such as the Zenana Mission, which employed British women to minister to the medical needs of native Indian women, had helped to swell expatriate demands for the benefits of trained British nursing for themselves.[46]

111

The appointment of Lord Frederick Roberts as Commander-in-Chief for India in November 1885 helped to accelerate developments: not only was he keenly interested in welfare facilities for the private soldier, but his wife, Lady Nora Henrietta Roberts, was particularly concerned to introduce trained British women into Indian military hospitals. In 1886 she published an appeal to establish a female military nursing system in India, and to raise money for rest homes for the nurses. She felt that skilled nursing was needed specially in 'those protracted and serious cases of enteric fever, &c., to which the young men who now-a-days come to India in largely increased numbers are peculiarly subject'. She also sounded a practical note which did not gain official currency until after the Anglo-Boer War: humanitarian considerations aside, the project should commend itself on utilitarian grounds, 'when one considers what an expensive article the British soldier is – costing the State, as he does, £100 on landing in India'. In wartime, these nurses could move to hospitals at the base of operations, 'setting free the able-bodied men whose time has hitherto been taken up in looking after the sick and wounded, but whose services would be of so much greater value to the State if employed at the front.'[47]

Lady Roberts's ideas found favour with the Military Department of the Government of India; and by the end of 1886 Deputy Surgeon-General Hamilton of the Lucknow Division published an alternative scheme, modelled on the lines of the Army Nursing Service.[48] Despite the objections of one India Office writer that the proposal to establish a female military nursing service was 'very extravagant . . . and . . . what may be termed sentimental expenditure',[49] both nursing projects were realised, and were to some extent complementary. Lady Roberts's nurses, who first started work in 1887, at an officers' hospital established by her fund at Murree, normally worked in stations to which the official Indian Army nurses had not been assigned, and were occasionally drafted in to make good the deficiencies of the official service.[50]

Deficiencies there undoubtedly were. The inaugural contingent of the Indian Nursing Service numbered 10:2 superintendents and 8 sisters. By 1893 the numbers had risen to 52 for all India; but, as Catherine Grace Loch, the chief superintendent, observed, 'this increase is a mere drop in the ocean, for the country is so vast that although Nursing Sisters are placed in a few only of the largest stations, they are scattered in twos and threes and even singly at

8 Catherine Grace Loch, first Superintendent, Indian Army Nursing Service. (Bodleian Library)

immense distances apart.' By 1903, when the Queen Alexandra's Imperial Military Nursing Service was established in India, the numbers had risen to 84.[51] The smallness of the service was justified, as in the United Kingdom, by the principle that the sisters were not to do the work of nursing in person, but were to supervise the work of others. However, the difficulties which were observed in Britain when translating these principles into practice were as nothing when compared to those in India, where the necessary substratum of subordinate hospital staff was almost entirely lacking. India had no Army Hospital Corps or Medical Staff Corps, no definite body of men who went through a prescribed period of medical training, and who might subsequently continue to receive instruction from the nursing sisters.[52] Instead the sisters employed native servants for domestic duties, and orderlies seconded from the regiments for nursing work. Troop postings made continuity and training of personnel, impossible: between January and October 1897, for example, Catherine Loch had experienced six changes of orderlies in one station, three of them in the space of two months.[53]

In the circumstances, the sisters were obliged to work extremely hard to maintain reasonable standards of patient care. They themselves were often down with local fevers, and Catherine Loch's health was completely broken when she was obliged to retire in 1902. The rigours of nursing during the hot season were vividly described in the *Indian Civil and Military Gazette* in 1892:[54]

> for the purpose of obtaining good nursing, numbers of typhoid and serious cases are crowded into the Sisters' ward, and a perpetual stream of such men are being sent, with hardly a break, into the same rooms, until the places become saturated with a typhoid atmosphere . . . the Sisters . . . are often 'dead beat' from . . . nursing twenty or thirty typhoid cases at one time. Inspections of Hospitals are made in the cold season – but visit a typhoid Ward on a July day, and see a Sister who has been on duty for twelve or fourteen hours over a Ward full of Sick!

It was estimated that typhoid attacked 1,400 soldiers in India annually, of whom 400 died. Medical officers as well as nurses called for the institution of a trained and stable male nursing corps for the Indian Army throughout the rest of the nineteenth century, but without success.[55]

While the sisters often found helpful allies among the medical officers in India, relations between them were not invariably good. Many MOs were, in 1888, quite unused to working with female military nurses: they were not interested in building up the professional quality of the service or maintaining its integrity as a corps. Moreover, given the very steep rate of admissions to military hospitals for venereal disease, the MOs could perhaps be forgiven for regarding the sisters as supernumerary.[56] Catherine Loch suffered intense frustration at orders and postings of sisters which were made entirely without reference to her.

In emergencies, unqualified women were engaged over her head. To add to her grievances, generals and even the Commander-in-Chief were capable of whisking the sisters away from hospital work altogether to deal with private cases.[57] Moreover, not all the sisters possessed the tact needed to deal with potential areas of conflict with medical officers. One wrote, albeit anonymously, of the Indian Army Medical Service as 'that happy hunting ground of impecunious Irishmen' where 'the average medical officer, when he is not absorbed in racing and polo . . . prefers . . . the happy-go-lucky method peculiar to the Eurasian apothecary . . . to a highly trained nurse.' Some MOs and assistant surgeons returned the compliment by blaming the high mortality from enteric on the Indian Army Nursing Service, and 'their gradually appropriated latitude of action, even to the extent of unauthorized medication'.[58]

Nora Roberts had wanted her own nurses to be 'devoted women', indifferent to any official salary which could be expected to tempt 'the ordinary run of *paid* nursing sisters'. The Military Department did not share her enthusiasm for religious nursing sisterhoods, but was emphatic that the new service should be composed of ladies: 'In this way the soldiers would learn to treat the nurses with proper respect, and complications, which might ruin the experiment, would be avoided.'[59] The arrival of the first army sisters at Rawal Pindi in 1888 was marked by 'A garden party, and the opportunity was taken of introducing them to the society of the cantonment, by way of demonstrating their social position as ladies.' They were 'generally invited to most of the gaiety that goes on in their station', and attached great importance to their social absorption into the higher officer class. Some of the sisters worried, indeed, that their service might become too attractive to social climbers and husband-hunters and that they, as 'gentlewomen in every sense of the word' might 'find themselves thrown out of their proper position in life on account of their colleagues.' Catherine Loch wished in vain that she, or at least a qualified female colleague (she had in mind Mrs Bedford Fenwick) could be consulted when the India Office selected candidates to be sent out from England; she felt that neither their moral nor professional backgrounds were sufficiently investigated.[60]

Catherine Loch also worried lest the 'station gaieties', in addition to attracting women to the service for other than the highest motives, might make bad nurses out of previously good ones. They might lose both energy and inclination for their professional duties: and gossip about private individuals would reflect badly on the reputation and cohesion of the corps. These fears led to a number of deeply unpopular measures. She decided in her first year against giving the sisters leave to go to dances; and she seems to have agreed with the Principal Medical Officer's ban on participation in station theatricals in 1893.[61] When these decisions attracted adverse comment in the English press, she defended her position vigorously:[62]

> I do not hold that a Nurse should be debarred, by reason of her profession, from all amusements appropriate to her friends, and to her own rank of life; . . . But the fact that they [the sisters] are young women, living without any protection from relations or friends, renders their position in some ways a difficult one. Instead of being more independent, they have practically less *safe* liberty of action than many a girl living in her father's house might safely enjoy. Nurses out here are far more prominent in the eyes of the community than Nurses in England. Everyone criticizes them; and should one of them, perhaps from mere thoughtlessness, 'get talked about,' as the saying is, there is no one to stand up for her or to vouch for her in any way.

Despite these arguments the restrictions were definitively rescinded in 1894.[63]

GROUP PORTRAIT

What sort of woman joined the Army Nursing Service? The records which might answer this question are extremely scanty. Those women who lasted less than three years have, with the exception of those sponsored by the National Aid Society between 1881 and 1885, vanished without trace; so have many of those for whom no pension was awarded. Those War Office registers which exist for the pre-1902 service do not list father's occupation, place of education, or nurse training school. Some nurses appear in the nursing directories which were published in the 1890s, and some can be traced through the larger metropolitan training schools, though the information contained in their registers is often disappointingly meagre. Nurses who saw war service, and were awarded the Royal Red Cross, were often described or interviewed in the nursing press. The picture which emerges from these different sources is necessarily partial.

Contemporaries were in no doubt as to which women were the favoured candidates for the service:[64]

So far as is possible, Mrs Deeble tries to employ none but officers' daughters. Not only do they understand better than civilians what discipline and routine is, but it provides in a measure for a class of ladies who are often sorely puzzled to know where to turn for a living, and the men appreciate their military pedigree.

When in 1885 the Army Medical Department dropped the National Aid Society's scheme for sponsoring military nurse training, Mrs Deeble's chief regret was the potential loss of livelihood to officers' daughters.[65] Suspicions of military favouritism seem to be more than justified by the proceedings of the War Office committee on nursing services of 1901. Surgeon-General Hooper stated flatly that

preference is always given to the relatives of Military Officers. It obtains in both Services, in the Army and in the Indian Service. I think we should provide that, or else the outsiders will swamp the Military candidates. It entails a good social qualification.

The civilian members of the committee baulked at the idea of laying down such a regulation for the new Nursing Board in cold print: agreement was finally reached on leaving it 'as a *lex non scripta*'.[66]

The surviving evidence on the pre-1902 service does not lend unequivocal support to these impressions of favouritism. It is true that the higher posts went, in the main, to 'military' women: Jane Cecilia Deeble, Lady Superintendent 1870–89, was the widow of a

Surgeon-Major in the army medical service; Anne Ellen Caulfield, Lady Superintendent at Woolwich from 1877 to 1894, was the daughter of a colonial official in Ceylon and the niece of the Bishop of Nassau, but there was also 'a long roll of soldier Caulfields'; Helen Campbell Norman, Lady Superintendent 1889–1902, was the daughter of Field-Marshall Sir Henry Norman; C.H. Keer, who entered the service in 1887 and was Matron-in-Chief, QAIMNS, 1906–10, was the daughter of 'an English officer in the Indian service'.[67] Many of the longer serving army nursing sisters, such as Alice Briggs, seem to have had a military background, as did several of the trainees sponsored by the National Aid Society.[68] However, Sidney Browne, first Matron-in-Chief of the QAIMNS, 1902–6, who joined the service in 1883, was the daughter of a civilian doctor; Catherine Grace Loch, first Lady Superintendent of the Indian Army Nursing Service, was the daughter of a QC.[69] It must, of course, be borne in mind that having a civilian father need not preclude the existence of military grandfathers, uncles, brothers and cousins whose influence, as in Anne Caulfield's case, might have been equally significant.

While Mrs Deeble and her successors may have placed great importance on the military background of their nursing staff, they attached equal if not greater importance to their social qualification as ladies. They felt that female nurses should of necessity occupy a higher social class than the patients and male nursing staff. Their authority was seen to derive as much from external social status as from any position they might occupy within a professional hierarchy. Mrs Deeble's ideal was[70]

A class of women entirely superior to that of the ward-master and the sergeants: because she must be a terror to the wrong doer. When a sister comes it must be 'Oh, here is sister;' she should be the shadow of the medical officer, and she should be superior to all the female relations of the patients if she is to have her proper influence.

Society at large subordinated women to the men of their own class, and to men in the classes superior to them; but not to those in the classes below. This fact was grasped by Mrs Deeble as the key to her own exercise of authority; the same fact had made it impossible for the aristocratic Jane Shaw Stewart to enjoy a successful working relationship with professional men. Mrs Deeble's judgment also involved considerations of decorum: it would be easier to maintain propriety within the wards if there were no temptation for the nurses to mix socially with orderlies and patients.

When new regulations were introduced in 1885, the influence of ladies outside the service was blocked by the abolition of the National Aid Society sponsorship scheme;[71] that within the service by the reduction of the Lady Superintendent's powers over the female staff. Nevertheless, 'the lady' managed to retain a toehold in the system through the new requirement that applicants to the service were to bring a letter of personal recommendation 'from a lady of position !!! in Society!!!'[72] The 1894 prospectus still stipulated 'a recommendation from a lady in society, to the effect that they are desirable persons to enter a service composed of ladies of good position.'[73] From 1888 onwards, however, the regulations were rather less exacting, and less tailored to the wishes of a particular class of women. Instead of asking that a nurse be a lady bearing a recommendation from another lady, they required only that 'some person of social position' testify 'that her family is one of respectability and good standing in society'.

In 1887 Mrs Deeble was reported to have said 'that the great drawback to many of her nursing sisters was, that they were *not* ladies but of the "shop girl class"'; and Anne Caulfield told the 1893 inquiry into the nursing service, 'I think we ought to have nobody but ladies in the military hospitals, they are not all of that class now.'[74] The failure of some nurses to achieve promotion on grounds of 'social inferiority', and the many laments of Catherine Loch and her colleagues in India, make it clear that the lady was by no means ubiquitous in the service. But social class remained an important criterion of promotion, and the lady now had her champions even among the medical officers: asked whether he preferred 'the "lady" class or the better portion of the domestic service class', Brigade-Surgeon Lieutenant-Colonel Harrison came down firmly in favour of the former: 'They have their heart in the work; they are a better class altogether, and they maintain a higher tone in the hospitals, besides which the men are more respectful to them.'[75]

The insistence of successive Lady Superintendents that the female service would fail if it were recruited from the same social class as orderlies and patients explains their resistance to suggestions that the wives of private soldiers and non-commissioned officers be trained to join the nursing staff.[76] Sir Edward Sinclair, a former army surgeon who was appointed

Professor of Midwifery at the Dublin Medical School, in 1869 devised a scheme for training soldiers' wives as midwives for the army's 'female hospitals'. He was assisted by the Lady Superintendent of Sir Patrick Dun's Hospital in Dublin. The scheme received the blessing of the Commander-in-Chief, and trained 400 midwives between 1869 and 1880.[77] War Office circulars in 1870 lent approval to this and similar schemes;[78] a scheme developed by Lady Strangford for training soldiers' wives as military nurses through the St John's Ambulance lectures was adopted only briefly in 1880–1.[79] By the 1890s, instruction in midwifery and general nursing was given at Aldershot and other stations to cater for the needs of the 'female hospitals' only.[80] In 1908, the *Nursing Mirror* printed the obituary of 'A Midwife of the Old School' who had received her training as an army wife, and on returning to civil life practised extremely successfully for twenty years in a colliery district in Derbyshire. She was completely illiterate, although the Army Medical Regulations recommended that training be given only to those possessing 'a fair elementary education'.[81]

Perhaps the only thing which can be said with absolute certainty of the army sisters is that the post-1885 intake were better trained than their predecessors. By 1888 entrants were required to have spent twelve months training in a civilian hospital where nursing was controlled by a matron and sisters, where adult male patients were treated, and where certificates in medical and surgical nursing could be obtained; they then spent six months on probation at Netley. By 1891 this requirement had been extended to three years' combined training and service in a civilian hospital. The age of the sisters at entry was to be between 25 and 35: there were no longer to be the variations of the 1860s and 1870s, when entrants might be as young as 21 or as old as 46.[82] Most entrants for whom records exist came from the metropolitan hospitals, especially Bart's, St Thomas's, the London, and King's College Hospital. One St Thomas's trainee, who eventually accepted an appointment in a civilian colonial hospital, recalled that in 1897 only 'specials' – paying probationers who had '"bought their commission"' – could hope for a sister's appointment at St Thomas's. She was content to be 'an "ordinary" nurse' there, because she had decided in advance that she wished to be an army sister.[83] Other hospitals in this period, the Middlesex and Guy's, for example, took in two classes of trainee – lady pupils and ordinary probationers – and made promotions to the rank of sister from

9 Miss Norman, Superintendent, with some of the Netley sisters.
1896/7. (Bodleian Library)

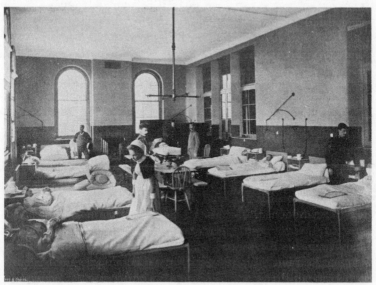

10 Ward scene, Netley Hospital, 1896/7. (Bodleian Library).

among the former only. It is possible that some middle-class women who made a career out of army nursing were those who wanted sisters' posts but could not afford the 'officer's entry,' as it were, into a civilian career.

What portrait, then, can be drawn of the individual army sister in the second half of the nineteenth century? F.E. Fremantle, a civilian doctor who volunteered for military medical service in South Africa, drew one in what he clearly thought were unflattering terms:[84]

> the Army nurse of some years' service, . . . a good nurse, mind you, as to knowledge and energy, but hard, hard as flint-stone, and with a contralto voice to match, and a devil-may-care spirit of independence, which seems to be fostered by the army life.

Catherine Loch wrote anxiously from India of the need to recruit army sisters 'who are content to live quietly and unostentatiously, without parading their independence.'[85] Yet none but the most independent-minded women could have been expected to survive the loneliness, and constant changes of post, involved in British military hospital work; and a sister had to be a sturdy soul to brave the discomforts of travel and foreign stations. She certainly leapt at the chance of war service, and, as will be seen, was jealous of the chance to earn distinctions in campaigns abroad. She seems as likely to have been a woman who had struck out on her own, away from all family traditions of work, as to have simply fulfilled the expectations of military or medical relatives. Although her professional, like her social life, was somewhat removed from that of her civilian colleagues, and she resented outside criticism of her corps, her attitude to her work, and its position within the army system, was not one of unthinking acceptance. She was likely to be a member of the Royal British Nurses' Association and, by the 1890s, increasingly adept at communicating to, and via, her civilian colleagues her grievances about selection, salary, combatant rank and service, and her criticism of the male orderly regime. For the most part, however, this small band of intelligent and hardy women remained unknown to their contemporaries, and must remain tantalisingly obscure to us.

PART II

A NEW VIEW
OF WAR

CHAPTER 5

PHILANTHROPY
AND THE BATTLEFIELD, 1854–78

The first section of this book has followed the path of women making important social transitions. Military nursing service took women from households to hospitals; from the status of employer to that of employee; from privileged seclusion and anonymity to the rigours of War Office inquiries and Army Medical Regulations. These transitions between private and public spheres of action have yet to be considered within their wider national and international context. We have seen the military nurses as 'women in a man's world'; now it is time to focus more sharply on that 'man's world' of European armies and wars in the mid-nineteenth century. It is a far from static picture. This period, so often presented as an 'age of equipoise', stability and optimism, was in fact plagued by military upheaval and change, as the political map of the Continent was redrawn through the unification of Italy and Germany. Military and social history are usually kept in separate compartments; and the decisions of generals and the dates of battles may seem to have little to do with the process of uncovering the texture of Victorian women's lives. But here we must insist on reversing the conventions: for the manner in which wars were waged between the end of the Crimean War in 1856 and the end of the Franco-Prussian War in 1871 transformed the relationship between soldiers and civilians, and hence affected women deeply. At first it seemed merely to afford them new outlets for old ambitions; ultimately it was to offer them a new role in the public sphere, and a new relationship to the political process.

'Total war', in which civilian involvement is virtually as complete as that of the military, is a concept associated with the twentieth century. But its foundations were laid in the decades of the wars of unification. Like all major historical trends, this development was uneven in its impact. No two wars are the same, no two national societies are alike, and no single national society is uniform. But an important shift in perceptions of war took place in strikingly similar ways in Britain, France, Italy, Germany, Austria and the United States between 1848 and 1870, and it is clear that each country observed and was influenced by the others. Essentially, war was becoming the business of the whole of society. It was ceasing to be a mainly delegated responsibility, a tiresome necessity for which the appropriate labour could always be hired. Changing civilian attitudes to war and soldiers were closely interconnected with new ideas of citizenship. Armies could be seen as symbols of society at large; the citizen perceived his identity in the soldier, and hers, it will be argued, in the soldier's nurse. Medical provision for soldiers became a particularly important medium for expressing the deepening relationship between war and civilian society: the Red Cross workers, the fundraisers, the committee organisers and the ambulance and nursing volunteers whose careers we are about to trace all played their part in preparing the ground for the mass mobilisations of 1914.

NEW HEROES

The military history of Britain, and the history of British attitudes to military service, owe much to the accidents of geography. Unlike most of her Continental neighbours, an island state had little reason to fear invasion, and every incentive to develop naval power rather than a large land-based army. The entire country could hardly put out to sea for extended periods, and the duty to defend the state was normally delegated, and discharged through taxation. The separation between arms and the citizen was accentuated by the development of a large overseas empire, policed by long-service professional troops. After Napoleon Bonaparte's final defeat at Waterloo in 1815, the British army withdrew from European theatres of war and became increasingly remote, both geographically and socially, from civilian society. Soldiering was a profession like no other, in which – among the mass of privates at any rate – violent forms of punishment, a lack of privacy in domestic life, and heavy indulgence in alcohol and whoring were condoned long after they ceased to be tolerated in 'respectable' civilian life.[1] On the eve of the Crimean War, and indeed for long after it, the British soldier was almost by definition a social outcast. Despite this, his failings were beginning to make him the object of philanthropic concern; and in many cases they were being idealised out of sight.

One symptom of this growing civilian sympathy with the army was, of course, the press outcry over the initial failings of the Crimean war hospitals. Accounts subsequently sent home by the female nursing volunteers and their supporters reinforced this sentiment. The sick and wounded private soldiers, portrayed in the most favourable light, were glorified as the finest types of their social class. In a sense, they were treated as a special category of the 'deserving poor'. As one of the Anglican sisters who nursed them recalled:[2]

> what made their heroism, as shown in endurance, so delightful to witness, was the simplicity and resignation with which their sufferings were accepted . . . we were also convinced that the discipline of military life is elevating to the character in a very high degree. . . . The army proves a school which can convert the disorderly, self-willed blackguard into an intelligent, self-controlled man.

It is not hard to detect in this statement a considerable degree of anxiety as to the goodwill and controllability of the average working-class citizen in his natural habitat. The army was, so to speak, valued for making the poor safe for society. But adulation of the military – 'scarlet fever' as it was sometimes called – was a more complex phenomenon than this. The officer class was also idealised in an extraordinary way. Catherine Marsh, the evangelical daughter of an Anglican clergyman, who had done missionary work among navvies in Kent, published *Memorials of Captain Hedley Vicars, 97th Regiment* in 1856; this was an account of a pious life, terminated at Sebastopol, which virtually conferred the status of a Christian martyr on an English officer. It was a massive best seller; and the crisis of the Indian Mutiny in 1857 reinforced its symbolism. The British soldier was the representative of his Christian race, the defender of empire against heathenism.

Symbolism apart, there was a greater need for his services now that less trust could be reposed in native Indian mercenaries. If Britain was to believe in the long-term future of the empire, then only the best could be believed of its guardians.

The British regular soldier did not become respectable overnight, but he was beginning to lose his outcast status. Given the embarrassing fact that the real article did not often match up to his noble stereotype, he was seen increasingly as a target for reforming effort, and a fruitful field for missionary labour. In the post-Crimean decade, both voluntary and official agencies busied themselves providing religious ministry and wholesome recreation facilities for the army.[3] Very often these were female initiatives: Mrs Daniell and Sarah Robinson, for example, organised welfare projects for the men at Aldershot; the Crimean veterans Mary Stanley and Catharine Leslie Hobson organised remunerative sewing circles for soldiers' wives.[4] Middle-class civilian society was re-fashioning the soldier and his family, if not exactly in its own image, then in accordance with its own clearly-expressed wishful thinking.

The movement to equate the soldier with the solid citizen received added impetus in 1859. The French Emperor Louis Napoleon was pursuing a strategy of intervention in Italy, supporting the national movement to withdraw from the Austrian empire. In Britain this raised again the spectre of aggressive Bonapartism, and revived memories of an invasion scare which had swept the country in 1803. Cross-Channel invasion certainly seemed a more realistic possibility now that the French navy had taken the lead in exploiting steam power and encasing its new ships in iron. The Volunteer Force – the Home Guard of Bonapartist days – was revived on a large scale. It now became, as never before, a truly national and popular movement; by the mid-1870s it embraced almost every class and region·of Britain. As the immediate panic subsided, the troops of so-called 'Saturday night soldiers' came for the most part to fulfil a sporting and recreational role rather than a patriotic one. But they kept in currency an acceptable face of soldiering – domesticated, decent, even politically liberal; and their presence served as a reminder that war might threaten the British Isles as well as its far-flung empire, and that the duty to bear arms might not always be restricted to a small professional force.[5]

Although women philanthropists played an important part in

missions to the regular army, the Volunteer movement offered women limited scope for action. A few ladies' rifle-matches were held, and an apparently unique female corps drilled weekly in Hartlepool in 1860; for the most part, however, women were confined to raising funds and providing continuous moral support. They flocked to special parades, inspections and sham fights, lending credence to the Volunteers' belief that they were drilling in defence of 'Home and Beauty'. At competitive events they presented prizes, subscribing for silver bugles and the like.[6] Otherwise, their role was largely passive, and they do not appear to have contemplated any training in nursing for themselves, as complementing the men's training in military drill. As we have seen, the regular army in this period was reluctant to allow even a very small number of female nurses on to the peacetime establishment, or to take them into account in its war mobilisation plans. After the Crimean War, British women had to look across the Channel if they wished to find models for female participation in war work.

SOLDIERS AND CITIZENS

The history of war in Continental Europe is, unlike that of Britain, one of invasion and repulse, of land-based armies, and of civilian awareness of the likelihood and atrocity of conflict. A tradition of universal male military service was well established, in France and Germany in particular, although those civilians who could would always buy exemption from their obligations. The pursuit of arms, which in the eighteenth century may often have appeared to be little more than the private business of quarrelling princes, took on a new significance as the century drew to its close. War was redefined as the struggle for cultural survival of entire populations: the conflicts of the period of the French Revolution, and their continuation in the era of Napoleon Bonaparte, popularised the concept of *la levée en masse* and *das Volk in Waffen*. In Britain, liberal opinion perceived the army as an engine of repression at home and of conquest abroad; conscription was considered almost synonymous with serfdom. In western European states, armies had a more defensive function, and conscription was seen as fully compatible with the ideal of a democratic polity. The concept of a liberal militarism, and of the army as an instrument of civic unity, survived the peace established in 1815, which abolished French hegemony over much of Europe only to replace it with that of Austria. It was an important element in legitimating the armed struggle to end Austrian dominance in Italy and Germany after 1848. The dashing red-shirted volunteer who fought with Garibaldi's Thousand may seem to have had little in common with the disciplined Prussian conscript, beyond the Hapsburg adversary; but there was a joint inheritance for them in the rhetoric of revolutionary nationalism.

The struggle for Italian unification and independence, the French Emperor Louis Napoleon's intervention in that struggle, and the aggrandisement of Prussia under Bismarck's leadership at the expense of Denmark, Austria, and finally France, recalled the wars of the Bonapartist era in the massive scale of the land engagements they occasioned. But the technology of the industrial revolution had in the intervening period transformed the character of warfare in many important respects. Thanks to the military use of the railway, troop movements took place with unheard-of speed. The invention and perfection of breech-loading rifles meant that the loading and firing of ammunition could also take place at greater speed than in the past; and accuracy of aim was much improved. Battles could be conducted more swiftly and decisively than ever before.[7] To contemporary observers, the number of troops involved was even more impressive than these technical innovations. At Solferino on 24 June 1859 Austria brought approximately 160,000 troops to encounter the same number marshalled by France and Italy; at Koniggratz in 1866 Prussia and Austria each brought 250,000 troops into collision. Inevitably, the increased number of combatants resulted in an increased number of killed and wounded: at the end of that one day's fighting at Solferino, approximately 42,000 dead and wounded soldiers lay on the battlefield, and many thousands who were able to walk away subsequently succumbed to their wounds and fatigue. In America between 1861 and 1865, the Civil War presented European observers with an even more gigantic spectacle of conflict, not to be matched until the First World War: over 600,000 lives were lost, a number which certainly dwarfed the catastrophes of the European wars.[8]

Not unnaturally, generals and governments on all sides concluded that victory depended upon larger and larger numbers of troops; but it was clear that no state could afford to maintain in peace the huge numbers necessary to fight a war, and simple conscription measures alone could not supply enough men to meet a military emergency. There was a need for reserves of men who had kept up their military training after their period of conscripted service was over; who were no longer a financial burden on the military establishment, but who were fit to be mobilised immediately war broke out. The system of building up layer upon layer of military reserves was perfected in Prussia, and was also important in Austria and France.[9]

These mass mobilisations, and the operation of a reserve system, meant that more and more classes in society were drawn into the catchment zone of military planning; more families had a personal stake in the outcome of battles. Of course, a war characterised as being in a patriotic cause, waged on or near the territory of the home state, was capable of mobilising mass support in a way that a war of conquest and colonisation might not have been. But the very methods by which war was waged defined it as the business of respectable citizens in uniform, not the dirty work left to ruffians and mercenaries; non-combatants were, indeed, anxious to be involved in the national struggle, and to contribute more actively than by sitting at home and allowing themselves to be taxed.

The chief form which this contribution took was the provision of supplementary medical aid for combatants. Voluntary societies, in which women played a vital part, were formed to raise funds for military hospitals; hospital equipment was supplied, and supplementary medical and administrative staff recruited. The societies also undertook welfare work among soldiers' families. From 1848 onwards, insurrections against Austrian rule inspired patriotic Italian women of all classes to volunteer as war nurses, and in the 1860s a Voluntary Sanitary Service co-ordinated all ambulance work. During the American Civil War, the Government Sanitary Commission co-ordinated the voluntary work of enormous numbers of women, some of whom nursed in hospitals or looked after welfare in military camps, but most of whom worked to supply millions of dollars' worth of hospital clothing, linen and food.[10] In Austria a Patriotic Aid Society was formed in 1859. In Prussia a Relief Society was formed during the Schleswig-Holstein war against Denmark in 1864, which collected funds and medical equipment; at the same time existing charitable organisations – Protestant nursing sisterhoods, and the Order of St John of Jerusalem – turned over to war purposes the hospitals which they were already staffing and maintaining in peacetime. Similar voluntary aid organisations were formed in France in 1864, and in Russia in 1867.[11]

The British popular response to these developments was not confined to alarms and fantasies about invasion from France. Deep political sympathies and antipathies were aroused among every social class and stripe of opinion, and not the least of their by-products was the growth of voluntary medical aid organisations on the Continental model. Liberal, republican and anti-Catholic support was rapidly forthcoming for insurrections against Austrian domination; in particular, the cause of Garibaldi and Italian unification aroused passionate enthusiasm. A 'Friends of Italy Association' was founded by radical MPs; 'Garibaldi Penny Funds' were organised all over the country; a tumultuous reception was accorded to the great man in Trafalgar Square when he visited Britain in 1864; and individual members of the Volunteer Force actually went out to Italy to fight with their hero's volunteers.[12] Many women were drawn into this movement, usually through liberal or radical family connections. Elizabeth Barrett Browning's network of friendships in Italy, and the poems which she published in England on such themes as 'The Forced Recruit, Solferino 1859', did much to awaken and heighten interest in the struggle. Jessie White Mario, a member of a radical dissenting family connected with the Friends of Italy, married an Italian supporter of Garibaldi, publicised his cause at home, and worked as a war nurse in all the unification campaigns between 1859 and 1871. Among her closest friends and associates was Barbara Leigh Smith, later Barbara Bodichon, a cousin of Elizabeth Browning's, who was already active in the cause of women's emancipation.[13]

After 1859, many British women expressed their solidarity with the Italian cause by organising medical aid for Garibaldi's troops. Jessie Mario was a leading figure in the 'Ladies' Association for the Relief of the Sick and the Wounded, Widows and Orphans of Garibaldi's Followers and the Sufferers at Palermo and other Places' which was founded in London in July 1860. Its president was Lady Shaftesbury, and its subscribers included the Duchess of Argyll, Lady Palmerston, Mrs Gladstone and Florence Nightingale. In 1866 another such committee was formed, whose members were not prominent public figures. Little is known of its president, a Mrs Chambers, who herself went out to Italy to supervise the distribution of items to the sick and wounded, working through an

English ladies' committee in Milan. After the battle of Bezzica, she and another Englishwoman gave personal nursing aid to the wounded. She again sent stores to the Garibaldini in 1870.[14]

British women of a rather different stamp were inspired to action in sympathy with the military struggle in Germany. The female members of German aristocratic and royal families were called upon to play a leading role in the organisation of voluntary medical aid; two of Queen Victoria's daughters, Princess Alice of Hesse and the Crown Princess of Prussia, were thus heavily involved in the work. Their activities were soon emulated in court circles in Britain. It was perhaps an embarrassment to the British court that expatriate relatives could not always be on the same side of a conflict. When Austria and Prussia went to war with Denmark in 1864, the Danish-born Princess of Wales led the movement to send assistance to the wounded of her own nation;[15] during the Austro-Prussian War of 1866, Hesse was allied to Austria in opposition to Prussia. It may have been this awkward fact which led to the founding of the first British organisation offering non-partisan aid to all combatants. This was a purely female initiative, a 'Ladies' Association for the Relief of the Sick and Wounded of All Nations engaged in the War'. Florence Nightingale was on its committee: both princesses had appealed to her for practical advice. (Significantly, the Crown Princess of Prussia had made her request a full three months before the outbreak of hostilities.) In correspondence with Thomas Longmore, Florence Nightingale claimed that the Ladies' Association had 'lasted just one fortnight' and achieved very little, because 'English people like to feel enthusiastic pity for Austria – or enthusiastic raptures for Garibaldi – But they don't like merely to do good (out of England.)' But she contradicted this when she wrote to the Crown Princess of Prussia that the committee had contributed money, 'comforts' and surgical instruments, and had refused the requests of 'many English ladies' to be sent out to nurse in German war hospitals.[16]

Florence Nightingale was certainly correct in her assumption that the voluntary aid movement in Britain was predominantly partisan. She may have been writing with one particular women's association which felt 'enthusiastic pity for Austria' in mind. In 1866, some of her female nursing 'rivals' of the Crimean War were associated with the 'Austrian Soldiers' Relief Fund'. The Fund claimed to be non-sectarian and apolitical, but many of its leading lights were Catholics or Catholic converts who considered the Italian unification movement hostile to the papacy. One of these was a Lady Georgiana Fullerton; five years previously she had worked with Mary Stanley, Fanny Taylor and Lizzy Herbert – all three, like her, converts to Catholicism – to establish members of the French nursing sisterhood of St Vincent de Paul in London. In 1866 Lizzy Herbert was a member of the committee of the 'Austrian Soldiers' Relief Fund'. Lady Fullerton and Fanny Taylor subsequently founded a religious community called 'The Poor Servants of God Incarnate'; their connection with the voluntary aid movement ceased, but that of Mary Stanley continued through to the establishment of the British Red Cross.[17]

THE BIRTH OF THE RED CROSS

In the present century the work of the international Red Cross is associated with impartial humanitarianism, and it is perhaps startling to find that its nineteenth-century origins were so highly politicised. But it was national military necessity which in the first place dictated the establishment of voluntary aid societies in Germany and Austria, rather than a wave of universal compassion; and genuine civilian sympathy for the casualties of battles and their widowed and orphaned dependants was bound up with a strong sense of identification with the nation state at war. Foreign sympathisers, as in England, generally picked their own side and cheered it on. It is true that the formal inauguration of the international war relief movement was the inspiration of a neutral. Henri Dunant was a Swiss civilian who by chance found himself a spectator of the battle of Solferino, and remained for some time in the vicinity to help the victims of the carnage. The experience led him to conclude that, as armies were now brought at great speed into massive confrontations, so medical help needed to be mobilised at equally short notice; that the scale of any war effort would make it financially essential for national military-medical establishments to be supplemented by civilian volunteers; and that all medical personnel and equipment employed in wartime should be treated as neutral.[18]

Largely as a result of Dunant's exertions, an international conference met in Geneva in 1863 and passed a series of resolutions, dealing with the formation of national voluntary aid societies. In August 1864 a second conference drew up the Geneva Convention: this conferred neutral status on the wounded and those who cared for them, and established the red cross as the badge of neutrality. By the end of the decade, all European governments adhered to the Convention. However, the Convention did not recognise volunteer aid other than that organised by government agencies; and subsequent efforts to obtain treaty protection for voluntary societies as such between 1867 and 1874 were without success.[19] A tension between the impulses of nationalism and impartial humanitarianism was thus built in to the early years of the Red Cross, and the struggle seems to have left little room for the emergence of a critique of war itself.

It should not be assumed that the formation of government-approved agencies resolved all conflicts within the movement. In 1866 Thomas Longmore, first Professor of Military Surgery at the Army Medical School at Netley, hinted at potential differences of opinion when he declared:[20]

> No government in the world could afford to maintain a medical staff, or to provide the necessary means of meeting the wants of such a battle as that of Solferino, in the way that the wants of the wounded are now expected to be cared for.

The key words here were 'now expected to be cared for'. The issue of voluntary aid involved civilian expectations and norms, and could not be reduced to a simple question of military numbers and finance. Strategic objectives might be easy to define, but military-medical objectives, and the budgets required to fulfil them, were harder to pin down. The function of military medicine in peacetime was to maintain the fitness of the troops for war; in war, it was to disencumber fighting forces of their non-effectives. More than this could not be promised: medical officers could not guarantee to save soldiers' lives after a battle, much less restore soldiers to full active service. When public opinion found fault with standards of patient care in wartime, it was not according to criteria of military efficiency. The standards applied were those of civilians, acquainted with the latest developments in civilian hospital accommodation. And very often, the standards were those of philanthropic women.

The organisation which first set itself the goal of forming a permanent British voluntary aid society on the Continental model was the Order of St John of Jerusalem, which was revived in London between 1841 and 1858. The ancient Order had its origin in the Crusades; in its nineteenth-century incarnation it was a semi-religious, semi-masonic body, which sponsored much philanthropic work among the sick poor.[21] We can perhaps speculate that ambulance and hospital work in wartime offered its members an appealing and dramatic modern-dress version of the activities of the Knights Hospitallers in the age of chivalry. The Order was undoubtedly also influenced by the example of its opposite number in Prussia, which by the 1860s enjoyed an enviable degree of social status and official recognition in wartime, and was represented at the earliest conferences of the international Red Cross. Many members of the English Order had military connections; in 1869 a Captain C. Burgess, together with John Furley, an enthusiastic figure in the Volunteer movement, attended the Berlin conference of the Red Cross, and immediately afterwards began conversations with the War Office, the Admiralty and the Army Medical Department on the practicalities of voluntary aid in Britain. The establishment had, however, no great enthusiasm for partnership with civilian agencies, and by June 1870 Burgess and Furley had only rebuffs to report.[22]

A few weeks later, however, in July 1870, France declared war on Prussia. Burgess wrote to *The Times* proposing the formation of a British 'Society of Help for the Sick and Wounded in War', which would raise funds and recruit personnel. The latter would be male and female: 'A number of gentlemen and gentlewomen possessing sufficient surgical knowledge to enable them to temporarily bind a wound and move, or attend to, the wounded until the military surgeons can apply the proper treatment.' It would be helpful if they could speak French and German, and they would need to be able to rough it 'and to spare the time and expense of thus employing themselves'. These volunteers would be expected to work close to the front, 'to gather men from the battlefield instead of leaving them to lie there, in horrible pain and thirst, unsheltered and helpless, for hours or days'. Three days later, another letter appeared in *The Times* which rather upstaged Burgess's; it was from Colonel Robert Loyd-Lindsay, a veteran of the Crimea, and son-in-law of the Governor of the Bank of England, who stated that he had already placed £1000 in Coutts Bank for war relief purposes.[23] On 4 August a public meeting convened by the Order of St John agreed to form a 'National

Society for Aid to the Sick and Wounded in War', with Loyd-Lindsay as Chairman.

This organisation, which later became the British Red Cross Society, soon covered itself with prestige. Queen Victoria was its patroness; her daughter Princess Christian was on the Ladies' Committee; so were Florence Nightingale and Lady Augusta Stanley, wife of the Dean of Westminster, and sister-in-law of Mary Stanley, who did much practical work behind the scenes. The (all-male) executive committee included the good, the great, and the very rich: the Earl of Shaftesbury, Baron de Rothschild, and Lord Overstone, Loyd-Lindsay's father-in-law. It also included two close associates of Florence Nightingale's, her cousin Captain Douglas Galton and her brother-in-law Sir Harry Verney. The Order of St John was represented on it by Furley, by Burgess, and by a Captain Henry Brackenbury.[24] The War Office, which was making its own arrangements for observing the military and medical organisation of both France and Prussia, welcomed the Society's initiative: it sold Loyd-Lindsay twelve ambulance wagons, allowed the Army Medical Department to direct their fitting out, and gave Thomas Longmore permission to accompany them to France. The project aroused the enthusiasm of medical professionals: ambulances were sent out staffed by volunteer surgeons from St Bartholomew's, and by American doctors with recent Civil War experience of military surgery. Massive popular support was also forthcoming, and the collecting branches of the National Society which were established throughout the country raised £300,000 over the course of the war.[25]

Female nurses, despite the welcome extended to them in Burgess's letter to *The Times*, played only a small part in the National Society's plans. The Society preferred its female supporters to be confined to a non-executive, caretaking role: within their separate ladies' committee they worked hard at raising funds, despatching stores, and preparing bandages and dressings. This certainly kept them very busy, as Mrs Loyd-Lindsay wrote to her mother:[26]

I sit at my counter amid mountains of unopened bales, boxes, and packages of vast dimensions. They keep coming and coming till the place overflows, and they have to be left on the pavement outside. We have increased our staff; we have six packers hard at work all day, besides several men who unpack and three or four women who sort and arrange. We have also got a third house and made an opening through the walls so as to throw the three ground-floors together, which is a great improvement, as we can now have a separate packing-up room and two rooms where we unpack – my chemist-shop and another, where Lady Agnes Grosvenor and Miss Verney sit, and upstairs half-a-dozen ladies, with Princess Christian at their head, writing all day; but even with all this there is more than can be got through each day, though we work from ten till nearly seven o'clock, and send off about twenty large packages daily. . . . I have a good many visitors dropping in to add to the confusion. Mrs Cardwell went all over the establishment the other day, and Mrs Gladstone and Lady Marian Alford (who is working up Hertfordshire) came in; also Lady Carnarvon, anxious about her two brothers-in-law – Alan, the doctor in Paris, and Auberon Herbert, absent on a philanthropic tour of the battlefields. . . .

Every letter that comes from abroad begs for more things, more instruments, more chloroform, more morphia; the want of these things conveys an awful idea of the extent of pain and suffering. Dr Sandwith says that if it had not been for the volunteer help given in this campaign by the two nations engaged and by foreign countries, the amount of suffering would have been beyond words appalling.

The National Society sent only fourteen female nurses to France: eight members of the All Saints' sisterhood from University College Hospital, engaged at the insistence of Princess Christian and Mrs Loyd-Lindsay, and six other ladies with varying degrees of nursing experience.[27] After the war, Loyd-Lindsay explained that

the National Society has sent out comparatively few nurses, not from any doubt as to their zeal and efficiency, but from the fact that the supply of trained native nurses, belonging chiefly to religious communities, both in France and Germany, have been so great as to render foreign aid in this respect in most cases unnecessary.

It seems possible, however, that the Society's male organisers were rather consulting their own prejudices in this matter. Their commissioner at Pont-à-Mousson wrote flatly on 21 August 1870: 'Do not send any more ladies; the work is too heavy for any but strong men.'[28] However, some of the Society's projects turned out to be seriously understaffed, and the wives of commissioners found themselves thrown in at the deep end of hospital work. In October 1870 Mrs Capel, wife of the Superintendent of Depots at Arlon and Château-Thierry, wrote to Loyd-Lindsay from Bazeilles: 'two All Saints' Sisters are here now, . . . which is a great comfort . . . the work would have failed from my want of experience, and I should soon have knocked up.' She added that when the caretaker-cum-cook took Sunday off, 'it is a great blow to me as it then falls on my shoulders, and as my notions of cooking are very vague, I feel rather lost and fall back upon all the Compounds sent out from England.' After the war, some National Society officers criticised 'inexperienced lady volunteers' and the 'humbug' of 'amateur female attendance', which in the circumstances was less than fair. [29]

We know tantalisingly little about those British women who did nurse in the Franco-Prussian War, or about their motives for going. Undoubtedly the 'Crimean factor' was important: Florence Nightingale and her cohort had kindled a flame of enthusiasm for war nursing which the Army Medical Department had done as little as possible to encourage; now the National Society was providing an opportunity to follow in her footsteps. Kate Neligan, for example, was the daughter of a hero of the Peninsular War, with no previous hospital experience. 'She had wished to go out with Miss Nightingale to the Crimea, but was then too young.' Captain Burgess gave her a letter of introduction to Dr Julius Pollock at Charing Cross Hospital, who after no more than six weeks 'considered that she might be allowed to go to the front as a hospital nurse'. Her stamina and devotion to duty were later reported on in glowing terms by the surgeon of the Anglo-American Ambulance. [30] Anne Thacker, moved by 'the early bereavement, through death in the battlefield, of her lover, who perished from lack of proper nursing in the terrible winter of the Crimean War', qualified herself as a nurse and left 'a luxurious English home' for the 'garrison hospitals of Cologne'. She also worked in a tented hospital, and was said to have carried out minor surgical operations. Sadly, nothing is known of her later career. [31]

Two women who went out as secular war nurses, Florence Lees and Zepherina Veitch, were, by the standards of the day, highly qualified; they may well have been in search of adventure, but they also derived considerable practical benefit from their wartime experiences: the war certainly consolidated their professional reputations, and furthered careers which were to be of considerable

importance to the development of civilian nursing. Zepherina
Veitch was the daughter of a Scottish clergyman; she had trained at
University College Hospital and worked in the surgical wards at
King's College Hospital before joining the All Saints' sisters at
Sedan in September 1870. She later joined the Anglo-American
Ambulance at the Château de Bazeilles. Her letters home showed a
sympathy for the sufferings of French civilians which was mingled
with a rather ghoulish taste in mementoes:

> I went yesterday over another part of the battlefield . . . the
> slaughter must have been awful . . . when you think that every
> grave contains a number of bodies, it is horrible to think of. I
> have got several relics, if I can manage to bring them home with me.

She regretted that she had been unable to get a good photograph of
Sedan, but she had 'a very nice large one of the burnt village of
Bazeille, so I shall have something to show you'. From Balon she
wrote that she had to be 'nurse, dresser, surgeon, and everything
else', as she was the only nurse for sixteen patients:

> There is one great advantage in any work here, *viz.*, that I
> should not have seen such cases in ten years' work in London
> hospitals . . . and being thrown so much on my own
> responsibility will make me *au fait* at anything I may have to do
> at home thereafter.

On reflection, however, she felt that the doctor in charge, 'having
heard I was as good as a surgeon, . . . left me to my own devices
rather more than was fair, seeing I am not qualified in any way.'
After the war, she qualified as a midwife; in 1876 she married
Professor Henry Smith, and subsequently helped to found the
Matrons' Aid Society; this became the Midwives' Institute, an
organisation committed to making midwifery a state-registered
profession for educated women.[32]

Florence Lees was not a National Society nurse, but was sent out
to work in Germany in response to a personal request from the
Crown Princess of Prussia to Florence Nightingale. She was one of
the earliest Nightingale disciples: the sister of a naval lieutenant
who had died in a naval hospital in Shanghai, her original
ambition is said to have been to establish a naval nursing service.
She trained at St Thomas's, and by 1870 had worked in Paris,
Berlin, Dresden, Kaiserswerth, and King's College Hospital,
London. Her war service was testing and sometimes dangerous: she

worked with very limited equipment and assistance, first in a typhus station with the 10th Army Corps before Metz, and later with an ambulance corps near Homburg. She was the first woman ever to receive the Prussian Order of the Iron Cross. After the war, she was a pioneer in the field of district nursing: in 1875 she became the first Superintendent of the Metropolitan and National Association for Providing Trained Nurses for the Sick Poor. She later married a clergyman, was a member of the Council of the Queen Victoria Jubilee Institute for Nurses, lectured for the Ladies' Sanitary Association, and was briefly Honorary Secretary of the Royal British Nurses' Association. It is pleasing to learn that it was after hearing a course of her lectures that Sidney Browne, who was to become first Matron-in-Chief of Queen Alexandra's Imperial Military Nursing Service in 1902, was inspired to take up nursing as a career.[33]

Two National Society nurses, Louise McLaughlin and Emma Pearson, distinguished themselves in the early annals of war relief by getting dismissed for inefficiency and insubordination. Louise was the daughter of a clergyman, and the granddaughter of an earl; her seven brothers included clergymen, army officers, and a magistrate in India. She trained as a nurse under 'Sister Dora' of Walsall – Dorothy Pattison – and was said to have been her favourite pupil. Emma was the daughter of a naval captain, and may also have been related to the Pearsons who were associated with the revival of the Order of St John. She too had received nursing training before volunteering for France. These two were a strong-minded pair, pro-French to begin with, and confirmed in their opinions by the harsh treatment they saw meted out to the French peasantry by their Prussian conquerors. They accused senior National Society officials of pro-Prussian leanings; they argued with their male colleagues over the distribution of aid; they took it upon themselves to transport supplies independently (unfortunately getting lost in the process). In 1870 they were sent home from France, and were unable to raise sufficient funds to return on an independent mission. By the end of 1871 they had jointly published their exceedingly acerbic memoirs of the war, and had each received the French Red Cross Society's bronze cross and diploma, 'together with a request that in any future war they will serve again with the French ambulances'. In 1876, their feud with the National Society apparently healed, they went on another British Red Cross relief mission to Serbia. Between these expeditions, they joined Dr Elizabeth Blackwell's National Health Society, and gave lectures on health education to the London poor, in addition to undertaking relief work among them. After 1876, they returned to London and opened a nursing home which catered for, amongst others, the patients of Lister.[34]

WOMEN AND WAR RELIEF

Voluntary aid nursing in the 1870s offered British women very different experiences from those of the 'Crimean generation'. They were not working under the authority of their own government, or indeed under any form of government control. It would be hard to exaggerate the incoherence of the international war relief effort in 1870–1. The plethora of organisations – Austrian, Belgian, Dutch, Italian, Russian, Swedish, Swiss, Luxembourgeois, American, British, Irish, Spanish and Portuguese – which converged over a short period on the scene of war with contributions in money, equipment and personnel, could not be integrated with the belligerent armies' own medical services in any systematic way.[35] Moreover, so motley a crew inevitably provided cover for dubious individuals, and for alternative interpretations of the notion of aid: an English lady was said to have acted as a French spy; the staff of the Irish ambulance attempted to enlist combatant aid for France, and were 'forcibly re-embarked at Calais in so wildly inebriate a condition that it was necessary to batten them down under hatches guarded by armed sentries during their homeward passage'.[36] In situations such as these, women nurses were thrown back onto their own resources and left free to improvise. Such opportunities favoured strong, and even argumentative and attention-seeking individuals: with Louise McLaughlin and Emma Pearson we are a long way from the self-effacing ladies of Mary Stanley's party, who penned their Crimean memoirs under pseudonyms; and we are also in a different world from the uniformed anonymity of the regular army nursing service.

The many Victorian women who were inveterate and intrepid travellers, as passionately involved with foreign causes and cultures as with domestic concerns, are not easy to place within the conventional canon of nursing history. They do not fit into the expected mould of career professionalism, or of nun-like dedication to service. But their 'untidy' lives, moving between many different spheres of activity, nevertheless made a vital contribution to public perceptions of women as competent workers, and as political agents in the broadest sense of the term. One such life which exemplified this process, and which in many ways did as much as Florence Nightingale's to legitimate the position of British women nurses in wartime, was that of Emily Anne Beaufort Smythe, Viscountess Strangford. She was the youngest daughter of an admiral; in 1857, when he died, she began to travel with her sister in the Middle East, and to discover a talent for writing. The publication of her *Egyptian Sepulchres and Syrian Shrines* in 1860 brought about her meeting with the orientalist Percy, Viscount Strangford, whom she married two years later. His death in 1869 left her childless and very much alone in the world; it was undoubtedly the cause of her suddenly taking up hospital work.[37]

One suspects that Florence Nightingale would have disapproved of Emily's turning to nursing for emotional solace. She had written somewhat acidly in her *Notes on Nursing* of the 'commonly received idea among men, and even among women themselves, that it requires nothing but a disappointment in love, the want of an object, a general disgust, or incapacity for other things, to turn a woman into a good nurse.'[38] But Lady Strangford put the case for the opposition most feelingly in a pamphlet, *Hospital Training for Ladies*, which she published in 1874. She described

> the poverty of love, of family ties, of close interests, of duties, of all the obligations of a woman's home life for which she was created and for which she is best fitted. We lonely women want more and more means of helping ourselves.

Her panacea for personal sorrow, from which, she insisted, the community at large would also benefit, was a year's study of nursing. For many women, acquiring the skills needed for helping others

> would be simply salvation. . . . Had they had at any previous time a year, or even a few months' training, they would turn back to it as a haven, the happiness of which none but those who have tried it under some such circumstances can imagine.

She therefore argued strongly against existing forms of nursing training, which demanded hospital residence and very long hours of work, and instead advocated part-time hospital training for women who, without cherishing professional ambitions, wanted to learn more about health care.[39]

By the time this was written, Emily had spent several years observing nursing practice and working as an unpaid volunteer, most probably in University College Hospital, London. She had also become a 'Dame Chevalière' of the Order of St John of Jerusalem, to which she appears to have been drawn by her twin interests in nursing and the Middle East: her first wish on joining was to help establish a branch of the English Order in Palestine. She became closely involved, with Florence Lees, in the work of a sub-committee of the Order set up to inquire into suitable forms of training for home nurses for the poor; the project was a milestone in the development of district nursing, and eventually resulted in the establishment of the Metropolitan and National Association of which Florence Lees became first Superintendent.[40] However, membership of the Order also introduced Emily to the concept of war relief and voluntary medical aid. She had concluded *Hospital Training for Ladies* with the words:[41]

> The usefulness of the Hospital Training which we venture to advocate, may also be very significantly quoted in the formation of such an Association as the 'Frauen-Verein' of Germany, an institution which we hope to see very soon copied in England. In case of a war, the Ladies who volunteer for service will be easily sifted into those who know how to serve and those who are willing to serve; a very great advantage where prompt measures are necessary, and many claims, perhaps, come into conflict.

In 1876 the British voluntary aid movement was galvanised into action by news from the Balkans. The reports in May of the atrocities committed by the Turks against their Bulgarian Christian subjects, and the outbreak of war between Turkey and Serbia the following July, aroused the conscience and opened the purses of the philanthropic public. The Order of St John established an Eastern War Sick and Wounded Fund, with money contributed by two women, Paulina Irby and Priscilla Johnston, who had already spent some years travelling in the area and working for and with the impoverished Christian population of Bosnia.[42] Lady Strangford was passionately involved with the cause. She sat on the committees of the Fund, but lost her place when it was absorbed by a new Turco-Servian Relief Committee established by Loyd-Lindsay's National Society. She responded by launching her own Bulgarian Peasant Relief Fund, and set off for the Balkans in September 1876 'determined to undertake not only the clothing but the healing of the country'; her fund had raised over £5000, which she intended to devote to rebuilding villages, restoring agriculture, and distributing food, clothing and medical aid. By April 1877, when she wound up her operations, she had subsidised, amongst other projects, six village hospitals.[43]

Two years previously she had written blithely that 'Cottage hospitals and temporary hospitals would be easy work to the wives and sisters of our "landed gentry" who had served a brief apprenticeship in a good country or metropolitan hospital.'[44] She had, perhaps, been over-sanguine as to her own organisational abilities. Although her village hospitals seem to have been mostly places of refuge and shelter rather than cure, she was unable to prevent them descending into chaos, as she disarmingly described:[45]

Perushtitza was very sick: typhus reigned everywhere: one doctor, a Greek, sent there by the Government, had died of it, and the man who replaced him was very ill of the same fever. Dr STOKER and Mr KENNET arranged the hospital between them, and I placed in it a sixth nurse, a Bohemian who had lately come out from England. Shortly afterwards, a Servian lady, Mdlle.PETROVICH, came down from Belgrade, to take charge of the hospital. The German nurse, however, did not get on with the people, and they became unwilling to enter the huts; and she, poor thing, took the typhus and died soon after, and then Mdlle. PETROVICH fell ill of it also. The people got drunk, quarrelled, and stole the things; they tried our patience beyond everything. I had put the place in charge of a Turk – a Bechtikbashi – a protestant reformed Turk – who I was assured was as honest and steady and high-minded as an Englishman. So he might have been, – but, unlike the unreformed Turks, he drank all day, and was never sober. Everything seemed to go wrong and fail at Perushtitza until just the end of my stay, when an English lady, Miss BARCLAY, came out to me, and undertook the charge of the unfortunate place. There were then scarcely any cases, except three or four of the worst sort – poor frostbitten creatures, whose feet had already dropped off. Happily, most of them died. One only, a woman, thanks to Miss BARCLAY's skill, recovered.

Nothing daunted, Emily accepted another assignment in 1877: that of superintending hospitals for Turkish war casualties on behalf of a new, Turcophile, 'British Hospital and Ambulance Fund for the Sick and Wounded in War'. She worked in Adrianople, Sofia, and finally in Scutari; she coped with illness, exhaustion, and frostbite; with the spectacle of local lynch mobs; and with a state of virtual imprisonment on the Russian invasion of Sofia. She also survived a dire financial crisis when the plethora of charitable appeals in Britain – including one launched by the millionaire philanthropist Angela Burdett-Coutts – began to dry up her own source of support.[46] Her achievements were celebrated by several newspapers and periodicals at home, including the liberal feminist *Victoria Magazine*, which declared in February 1879:[47]

Lady Strangford has enrolled her name among that 'noble army' of women of whom Florence Nightingale was the pioneer, and we may add that, without detracting from Miss Nightingale's merit, Lady Strangford had far greater obstacles to contend with.

In the long run, this encomium was far less important than the opinion formed of her hospital work by another Turcophile organisation, the Stafford House Committee for the Relief of Sick and Wounded Soldiers. In 1879 its own team of doctors reported at considerable length on Lady Strangford and her system of female nursing. A Dr Pinkerton claimed that:[48]

Lady Strangford, in her private hospitals, assisted by her staff of female nurses, succeeded in showing a result, in the comfort of her patients and their chances of recovery, that was utterly unapproachable in the best and most carefully conducted hospitals, where there was only the usual male nursing, . . . Women are incomparably better adapted, both physically and morally, for the duties of nursing the sick than men, and trained female nurses are simply invaluable to the surgeon. Their aid cannot well be rendered available on the battlefield, but there is no reason why it should not be ready to hand immediately in the rear of the fighting, or after the battle.

Clearly, Emily had learned much from her catastrophic experiences in Bulgaria. The Stafford House Committee remained in existence after the Turco-Russian war ended, and, as will be seen, became

11 Lady Strangford's Hospital at Carlovo, 1877, on outpatients' day.
'Besides affording medical aid and alimentary relief, the hospitals
serve as depots for the warm clothing which is being freely
distributed under Lady Strangford's directions, and also as refuges for
orphan or destitute children until homes can be found for them.'
(Bodleian Library)

12 (*Over page*) 'The military hospital at Abassieh, Egypt under the
Direction of English Sisters', 1885. (Bodleian Library)

13 (*Over page*) The Working Committee of the Princess of Wales's Branch
of the National Aid Society. All figures can be named from left to
right (Red Cross) Miss Lucy Cohen, the Countess of Rosebery, the
Marchioness of Salisbury, the Princess of Wales, Countess Brownlow,
Lady Louisa Egerton, the Hon. Lady Loyd-Lindsay, the Countess of
Morley, Miss Morck, the Duchess of Buccleuch, Miss Higgins, Mrs
W. Wilton Phipps, the Duchess of Marlborough (British Red Cross
Society).

147

staunchly committed to lobbying for the employment of female nurses in British wars.

WAR, PEACE AND FEMINISM

What significance should be attached to Victorian women's involvement in the international war relief movement? Was it anything more than a simple extension of the philanthropic activities they were already carrying out in Britain? As Lady Strangford wrote in 1876:[49]

> Heaven knows I feel for the privations of my own countrymen at home, and have seen something of suffering in England; but . . . I am ashamed of the clothes I wear, of the blankets I sleep under, and the food I eat chokes me when I think of what I have seen around me.

Among those women who already visited the poor, sick or whole, in workhouses, prisons, hospitals, or their own homes, it needed no great enlargement of the sympathies to add the sick soldier and his dependants to the list of deserving causes. The travelling and greater physical risk incurred in relief work brought novelty and excitement to a task that was not in itself unfamiliar. Certainly there seems to have been little sense of war as a unique form of human calamity among the female supporters of the voluntary aid movement. The wars of 1859–71 were in many cases seen almost as natural disasters, on a moral level with earthquakes and plagues, and almost equally unavoidable. The determined bellicosity displayed by Bismarck in his quarrels with Denmark and Austria did not brand him as a criminal aggressor in Britain. If Louis Napoleon attracted a hostile press, it was because his arrogance and adventurism recalled the period of French dominance at the turn of the century. Women war nurses and relief workers did not condemn war as an instrument of policy; and in this they could perhaps be compared to women philanthropists who did not interest themselves in the fiscal system and the distribution of wealth. Their mission was to relieve misery, rather than to inquire into its possible causes.[50]

Nevertheless, there were new political sentiments at work in the international relief movement. Many women identified strongly with the objects of their compassion; and their aid was, whether directly stated or not, a critique of their own government's foreign policy, or lack of one. For British women to succour British soldiers in 1854–6 might seem natural enough; for them to wish to help Frenchmen, Germans, Austrians, Italians, Bulgarians or Turks in the same way was a deliberate political choice, and a declaration of interest in what would previously have been considered a masculine sphere. Aid was, after all, a form of direct intervention in war: as Thomas Longmore pointed out in 1873[51]

> If the sick and wounded are very numerous, the mobility of the army is for a time paralyzed. . . . But if a system of international aid be legally established and thoroughly system-atised . . . the Commander of the Forces will be at once ready to march onward, and, should occasion occur, to fight another battle. Thus the very object for which such societies would be established – that of mitigating suffering – would be defeated.

Thus, although the women involved in the voluntary aid movement might be thought to be exercising no more than a conventionally feminine, caring function, they were also crossing social and political frontiers. They were not a wholly different breed from the 'Crimean generation': an earlier ethic of service was still strong, and religious feeling continued to underpin their enterprises. But they were conscious of working for secular causes of their own choosing; there was self-assertion as well as dedication in the undertaking. Emily Strangford's published attitude to her work can only be described as self-advertising:[52]

> no one in the village . . . would be denied the privilege of touching or kissing my hand, – or at least my dress. . . . The schoolchildren sang songs composed for the occasion. These songs – often of many verses, with a *refrain* of my name again and again repeated – will perhaps be sung in the country villages long after the subject of them is forgotten.

This individualism makes it impossible for us to characterise the women of the voluntary aid movement as 'militarised', even if we look in vain for expressions of pacifism in their writings. They did not submerge their identities within a larger organisation, or justify their work solely with reference to it. They did not see themselves as servants of one particular national state. Their careers moved freely between civilian and military, domestic and international spheres of philanthropy.

Nevertheless, the ideal of service to the state was becoming discernible on the horizon of women's ambitions. At the beginning of the war, the British press had printed an appeal for aid from German women to their British sisters:[53]

> The privilege of taking up arms for the defence of the honour and independence of their country has been denied to women, but another and even more sacred duty is theirs. . . . Tears will flow, widows and orphans will call for help, the wounded soldier for assistance. It is woman's noble mission to alleviate these sufferings.

This was different in tone from the letters appearing in British newspapers in 1854. War had not then created a specific mission for all women. Now women were assuming a duty, and indeed a right, to intervene in this most public sphere of public life. Although the number of women giving aid near the battlefield was still very small, voluntary war nurses were a growing band who bore witness that Florence Nightingale's expedition to the Crimea was not an exceptional or unrepeatable adventure. The free agents of battlefield philanthropy were, in fact, helping to normalise the idea of women's war service. This development was to be of the utmost importance in the expansion of the regular British army nursing corps; but it also carried wider political implications for women in general.

As we have seen, the equation between war service and citizenship was beginning to gain currency in Britain in this period. The Volunteer Force, however amateurish, nevertheless embodied a sense that wars were now to be won or lost by citizen armies. Contemporary foreign wars indicated that membership of society involved a personal, and physical, obligation to defend it against aggression. This same period saw the small beginnings of a movement for the legal emancipation and political enfranchisement of women in Britain. Some of the new suffragists espoused the cause of Italian liberation, and helped to provide medical aid for Garibaldi; many were closely in touch with their sister movement in the United States. They were not slow to draw political morals for women from the new era of national wars and mass mobilisation. They noted that during the Civil War, the massive military drain on manpower not only required the nursing and fundraising activities of American women, but also created vacancies in Federal and State administrations which they were admitted to fill. Concepts of female emancipation were assimilated to a male, arms-bearing model of citizenship. The nation state at war supplied a working definition of civic need and responsibility. Thus the *Victoria Magazine* was able to comment on the death through illness of a French war nurse, as no one had written of the deaths of nurses in the Crimea:[54]

> We are of opinion that if her blood was not literally spilt in the battlefield (which is what in some people's minds constitutes the right to the Suffrage) her life was just as fairly lost by the means of the battlefield. Therefore her compeers have a right to be heard for her sake and for the sake of all those noble women who have nursed the sick and wounded in war and at home.

By the 1870s, war had begun to provide public status and political validation for all manner of women, whether suffragist or not in their persuasions. Military nursing and medical aid were legitimated as a principal route to the public arena. The link between war, war nursing and equal citizenship had been established, with results as significant for feminism as for the ultimate peace of Europe.

CHAPTER 6

======================

'COMFORT AFTER COMFORT': NURSING LOBBIES AND THE WAR OFFICE, 1879–85

======================

Whatever British women and British nurses may have thought in the 1870s about their rightful role in time of war, military-medical authorities remained highly resistant to the notion of change. A long civilian campaign of attrition was needed to legitimate the employment of female war nurses. Army medical officers, still smarting from the memory of Crimean brickbats, had every reason to be suspicious of civilian offers of help; and even though the stormy Jane Shaw Stewart had been succeeded by the peacemaking Jane Deeble, proposals for the further feminisation of military hospitals were bound to provoke frissons of alarm. The nursing lobbyists subjected the Army Medical Department to an almost ceaseless barrage of such proposals, occasionally varying their tactics to include subversion from within, or at least from the combatant wing of the army. With such supporters as Florence Nightingale, Emily Strangford, the Order of St John of Jerusalem, and the National Society for Aid to the Sick and Wounded in War, 'the increasing demand for adding comfort after comfort to the hospitals into which sick and wounded soldiers are to be received in time of war' was almost certain of victory.[1] Military writers might consider that replacing male orderlies with female nurses was merely 'gratifying a philanthropic craze',[2] but by the 1880s such emotional factors had to be taken into account in the planning of wars. Nevertheless, the Army Medical Department did strike back where it could; and the reforms which gave female

154

military nursing greater importance in the new decade were framed in such a way as to check the further progress of this 'civilianising' and feminising movement.

MANŒUVRES FOR REFORM

British voluntary aid agencies, having cut their teeth in France and the Balkans, were eager for new challenges. They wished to prove their importance to the armed forces of their own nation; and they found their earliest opportunity during the Zulu uprising of 1879. In June, as General Sir Garnet Wolseley was preparing to avenge the humiliating defeat of British troops at Isandhlwana, the Duke of Sutherland re-convened the Stafford House Committee. The Committee had significantly changed in character since the Russo-Turkish War which had called it into existence. Then, its relief operations had been organised by an all-male committee for an all-male medical and administrative staff: its report had acknowledged the help of ladies only in the collection of bandages, blankets, clothing and funds, and, of course, in paying generous tribute to Emily Strangford's separately organised hospitals. In 1879, however, the male committee was strengthened by the addition of Angela Burdett-Coutts; she also presided over a new ladies' committee whose members included Lady Wolseley, a strategically important choice. The ladies selected and despatched a corps of seven nurses to Natal, accompanied by two surgeons acting as the Committee's Chief and Assistant Commissioners.[3]

The nurses went 'with the warm and hearty approbation of Sir Garnet Wolseley',[4] but the General's views were not necessarily those of his Medical Department. William Muir, the Director-General, resented having his hand forced by civilians. Although he had admitted to the confidential Army Mobilisation Committee that there was a serious shortage of male orderlies in South Africa, the fact was not released for public consumption.[5] To Thomas Longmore he wrote:[6]

> I hope the exodus of Mrs Deeble & Co. won't much dislocate your hospl. arrangements. The ladies in the West End have gone mad as to nursing and other aid for our poor fellows at the Cape, and the Govt. felt bound to be a match for them. . . . As to the wisdom of the step we have our own doubts and misgivings.

A month later Mrs Deeble and six Netley nurses were permitted to follow the Stafford House contingent.

The Stafford House Committee saw their female nursing expedition as a triumph of civilian intervention in an imperial military cause, and one which proved beyond doubt the worth of women as war nurses. Their report made much of the 'pluck and endurance' shown by their female staff, who had coped with long journeys over rough country, and taken in their stride such hardships as upset mail carts, and 'sore backs for the horses, broken girths, and consequent falls for the riders'; implicitly this challenged the establishment assumption that female nurses were useless in wartime unless they could be safely assigned to a fixed base hospital. The Netley nurses seem to have yearned for similar trials of strength. Emma Durham, a Stafford House nurse, recollected preparing rooms for them at Ladysmith: 'However, Mrs Deeble had quite made up her mind for a life under canvas, so with thanks declined our roof.' Unfortunately, a heavy rainstorm that same night flushed the Deeble team straight back into lodgings.[7]

The points which Stafford House had stressed in their report on female nursing in Turkey and Serbia were now reiterated in a more combative tone:[8]

> the committee trust that the work which has been recorded in this Report may finally remove any prejudice that may still exist with regard to the employment of trained female nurses in military hospitals during war-time; and they venture to hope that, should England again be unfortunately called to arms, no time will be lost in organising committees similar to the one which has now closed its work, and that no intimation given on the part of Governing officials that such assistance is not required will be listened to by the public, or any effort relaxed to mitigate by the aid of private efforts the sufferings of our soldiers during the war.

On the army medical side, this conclusion was received in an almost deafening silence. The Principal Medical Officer in Natal, reporting in January 1880 on the medical services of the war, rather pointedly singled out the Netley nurses and the nursing sisters of Anglican communities in the Cape for praise, and made no special reference to the Stafford House contingent.[9]

The flood of civilian interest in the female nursing service could not, however, be easily checked. At the same time that Stafford House took its decision to send nurses to South Africa, Emily Strangford put forward her own long-term scheme for expanding the Army Nursing Service by special training programmes for army wives. In *Hospital Training for Ladies* she had argued that long-term residential training was not essential for women wishing to qualify as nurses; now she proposed that army wives should be trained by regimental surgeons on the basis of the short courses devised by the Order of St John's new Ambulance Association.[10] Lady Strangford was undoubtedly inspired by existing training schemes for army midwives, whose originator, Sir Edward Sinclair, encouraged her initiative; but in her published introduction to her proposal, *The Soldier's Wife as his Nurse*, she wrote that it 'was first suggested by Miss Stanley, whose valuable work among soldiers' wives had given her a large experience of the needs and capabilities of these women', and that its details had been worked out since Mary Stanley's death in November 1879.[11] By the end of 1880 both the Commander in Chief and Major-General Sir Frederick Roberts were supporters of the scheme, and the following April the first batch of students were ready to be examined on their course work.[12]

Winning golden opinions in the War Office, however, did not guarantee a warm reception either in the Army Medical Department or among the women already involved with the military nursing establishment. Muir wrote in fairly measured terms that 'As a *rule* Soldiers' Wives belong to a class of Society which is but imperfectly educated, and very few of such women would benefit by attending a course of lectures as proposed.'[13] The utterances of Surgeon Evatt, a keen advocate both of civilian aid and of an expanded female military nursing corps, were less temperate, his comments being recorded (by Florence Nightingale) as:[14]

> Soldiers' wives. Not the pick but the reverse of domestic servants. Married quarters always the focus of epidemics – always the dirtiest part of the Cantonment – don't know how to nurse their own babies. How can they be Nurses? And greatest difficulty to get a Midwive-Matron among them.

Two years after this conversation, Evatt added for good measure that, 'In the Army he found that the ignorance of the officers' wives was only equalled by the ignorance of the soldiers' wives.'

An officer's wife, Amy Hawthorn, who did not share Evatt's opinion of her own kind, wrote with some anxiety to Florence Nightingale concerning the scheme:[15]

> I have had 20 years' experience of Soldiers' wives . . . there is not one in a hundred who is fitted for it. A Hospital in charge of Orderlies and Soldiers' wives would indeed be a Pandemonium – especially in wartime.

Behind these arguments, however, there was a strong hint of 'jobs for the girls' – or rather 'jobs for the ladies'. 'Surely', Mrs Hawthorn remonstrated, 'when so many educated and refined women are needing employment we need not go to the class of Soldiers' Wives to supply Nurses?'[16] Florence Nightingale needed little encouragement to shoot down a scheme conceived by a woman who was a friend of Mary Stanley's, and who had been lauded in the press as having achieved in some ways more than Florence Nightingale herself. She assured Mrs Hawthorn that an order had already been issued forbidding the Strangford trainees to bear 'their self-assumed title of "Military" . . . Sir Frederick Roberts, it is true, made a speech in their favour: but I saw him before he went to Madras and he was enthusiastic about our highly trained Mrs Fellowes . . .'[17] After the 1883 Commission on the Army Hospital services, nothing seems to have been heard of Lady Strangford's scheme: Sinclair, potentially a powerful supporter, died in April 1882 after several years of failing health.

There were better auguries for the National Society's scheme, conceived while its president, Loyd-Lindsay, was serving as Financial Secretary at the War Office. Like that of Lady Strangford, it received official approval in 1880. A group of 'lady probationers' was to be selected for three years' full-time training at Netley, rather than at a civilian hospital. Their tuition and other expenses were to be paid in full by the National Society. The first eight ladies commenced training in May 1881, on a syllabus prepared by Surgeon-General Longmore. By 1885 twelve had been trained, of whom two had transferred to government service and two, on leaving Netley, undertook to come forward whenever the government might require their services.[18] At least two of them, Miss Stewart and Mrs Fellowes, had previous experience of civilian hospital work. Several were officers' daughters; Mrs Fellowes was a general's widow.[19] Mrs Deeble, who had helped Longmore prepare supplies for the National Society in 1870, and who had been the

National Society's agent in Natal in 1879, threw herself energetically into the new scheme, and passed up an opportunity to nurse British soldiers in the Transvaal in order to work out the training course for the National Society probationers.[20]

By the time the National Society scheme was implemented, its only serious opponent was, perhaps surprisingly, Florence Nightingale. Loyd-Lindsay was too valuable a contact in War Office, Volunteer and parliamentary circles for her to risk an open display of opposition to the scheme, or of pique at seeing it launched independently of her. But she objected to the Netley training on the grounds that the nurses would deal with a very limited range of cases there; civilian hospitals, paradoxically, prepared nurses better for war nursing than did military general hospitals in peacetime, because the former cared for many victims of violent industrial accidents. Without a broadly based training, military nurses could not take on the task of instructing male orderlies. Somewhat unreasonably, having voiced these objections, she refused to admit the National Society probationers to St Thomas's for any portion of their training.[21] She had, in fact, plans of her own for the reform and expansion of the Army Nursing Service, and with these she was proceeding in a manner so discreet as to be almost conspiratorial.

In April 1880 Florence Nightingale had received a letter from General Gordon on the subject of army nursing. It was written in order to introduce her to Amy Hawthorn, who was his cousin, and who had married a colonel in his own regiment, the Royal Engineers. She had been involved for some time in army welfare work, and had recently prepared a paper on the inadequacies of the male orderly system. Gordon had not studied the army hospital question himself: but as a Christian, he believed that the prosperous had a duty to the wretched, and as an officer, he was convinced

> that the truest way to gain recruits to our army would be, by so remedying the defects, and alleviating the sufferings of soldiers, that universally should it be acknowledged that the soldier is cared for in every way. Decorations may popularize the army to the few, but proper and considerate attention to the many is needed to do so, to the public.[22]

Florence Nightingale asked Mrs Hawthorn for further information, proposing to forward it directly to the Secretary of State for War. This intervention bore no apparent fruit;[23] but the correspondence between the two women took on a new urgency early in 1881, with the renewal of hostilities in South Africa, this time between Britain and the Boer settler population. Mrs Hawthorn reported that, although Netley sisters were being sent out to army hospitals, nursing care was still scandalously deficient. She herself had been nursing soldiers at the Fort Amiel hospital in Natal, where her services 'were only accepted by the medical officers when the long delay in the arrival of the Bloomfontein (sic) nurses (owing to swollen rivers) made them fear they would not come at all.' Florence Nightingale was delighted with her '*un*official and yet experienced and able helper', and pressed her for a full paper on the orderly system. She asked if certain named medical officers were 'favourable to *trained* nurses' (if not, by implication, to the charitable wives of certain officers), and assured her that the facts would be used with discretion.[24] The memorandum was despatched by the end of 1881, and throughout the next year Mrs Hawthorn continued to transmit information on hospital care in the Transvaal where, although peace had been re-established, the troops continued to suffer losses from typhoid.

The use made of Amy Hawthorn's memorandum showed Florence Nightingale at her most circumspect. In the first place she made all her representations through (male) third parties, and in the second she by-passed the Army Medical Department altogether. She rightly surmised that within the upper ranks of the army, commanders such as Wolseley and Roberts shared Gordon's concern for making military life more attractive to potential recruits, and less remote from civilian norms and values. Her old friend Dr Henry Acland was put in touch with her brother-in-law Sir Harry Verney; Verney went to see Lieutenant-Colonel Sir Evelyn Wood, who had commanded the British troops in South Africa; third parties, unnamed in her correspondence, contacted both the Secretary of State for War and Loyd-Lindsay, who was now an opposition MP. On 12 May 1882 Loyd-Lindsay rose in the Commons with an unsigned copy of Amy Hawthorn's notes in his hand, raised the question of Army Hospital Corps abuses in Natal, and obtained the promise of a War Office investigation. As president of the National Society, he knew that his request would command widespread popular support; he appears to have been unaware that he had been manœuvred into this action by two women.[25]

There was little delay in setting up a Court of Inquiry, of which, at Wolseley's insistence, Wood was appointed president. The Court reported in June that there was not enough hard evidence against named individuals to justify disciplinary measures: the orderlies had, indeed, been hotly defended by the medical officers who had been responsible for them in South Africa. But Wolseley and Wood submitted separate memoranda which demonstrated their strong inclination to believe the allegations of abuse. Wolseley recollected that

> When, as a General, I have inspected hospitals, I always felt I could not really "get at" the patients; few men would dare to speak against the orderlies of a hospital, no matter how you may question them, . . .

and Wood reflected

> I have been many months in a hospital myself, and, speaking from that experience, and some knowledge of soldiers, I believe that most patients, when very ill, are afraid to complain of paid nurses, whether male or female.

Their judgment was corroborated by the blunt statement of a former trumpet-major that

> I did not complain of these things to the visiting officers, because when Gunner Lester reported George, the orderly, he threatened to 'jump on his stomach and stamp his lights out'.[26]

The medical officers had been willing to admit that the orderly system was not perfect, and that Army Hospital Corps training still left much to be desired. The combatant officers went further, urging the more widespread employment of lady nurses: a further 'intermediate and quasi-independent supervision' was required between doctor and patient, in addition to the orderly staff.[27]

The Court of Inquiry's conclusion that reform was overdue would, in a time of quiet, almost certainly have gone unnoticed. But its recommendations were made on the eve of the British invasion of Egypt, a major military initiative taken to defend a client ruler, the Khedive, who was threatened by religious and nationalist uprisings. There seems to have been no hesitation over the decision that female nurses should accompany the troops to the Near East in July and August 1882; and in October the War Office decided to prolong the existence of Wood's committee. Its remit was now extended to include medical provision in the field and sea transport of sick and wounded; and it was to discuss any lessons drawn from the experience of the Egyptian campaign. Delightedly, Florence Nightingale wrote to Amy Hawthorn, 'We are coming in on the wave.'[28] The committee's report, submitted on 25 April 1883, committed the Army Medical Department to the immediate and permanent expansion of the Army Nursing Service.

FEMALE NURSES IN THE EGYPTIAN CAMPAIGN

For the Army Medical Department, the experience of employing female nurses on war service in Egypt was distinctly mixed. In 1882 a team of nurses from Netley was reinforced by a party of six sponsored by the National Society: five more nurses were despatched in 1885, in the wake of Wolseley's Sudan expedition, and the failed attempt to relieve Gordon at Khartoum. The second group, who went under the superintendence of Rachel Williams, a Nightingale protegée now matron of St Mary's Hospital, Paddington, were sent by 'The Princess of Wales's Branch of the National Aid Society'. This had been formed by a group of National Society ladies wishing to take a relief initiative independently of the (still all-male) executive.[29] Other reinforcements were periodically drafted in, and between 1882 and 1885 approximately thirty-five women served as official military nurses in Egypt and the Sudan.[30] They worked at Alexandria, Cairo, Suez, Ismailia, 'Suakin, Wady Halfa and on Nile hospital transports and hospital ships conveying the sick and wounded home to military hospitals in Britain. They were a hastily assembled collection of women, recruited from many different hospitals, mostly non-military. No one female superintendent was appointed for them, and Director-General Crawford chose to keep overall control in his own hands.

This was, predictably, a source of great annoyance to Florence Nightingale. The issue of a female chain of command was still, it seemed, as far from being resolved as it was in her days in the Crimea and Jane Shaw Stewart's time at Netley. Several of the nurses sent to Egypt came directly from the training institute at St Thomas's of which she was head, and she was also a committee member of the 'Princess of Wales's Branch'. This, she felt, justified her taking every opportunity to intervene and comment on the nursing arrangements of the campaign. She had persuaded Crawford, like his predecessor, Muir, to take a place on the Council of the Nightingale Fund; he was thus subject to cross-pressures where the well-being of the Fund's trainees was concerned.[31] The intensity of her concern with the Egyptian expedition, though in some ways counter-productive, was understandable. It was some years since she had been closely involved with the workings of the Army Nursing Service: Mrs Deeble had not accepted a position of tutelage, and had gone very much her own way after 1870. The colonial wars of the 1880s had, indeed, given Florence Nightingale her very last opportunity to impose her ideas on the army hospitals. Her training school was now producing 'graduates' of a high calibre, and she was determined that they should make their mark on the system.

She was particularly ambitious for one of her protegées, Mrs Fellowes, the general's widow who had trained both at St Thomas's and at Netley. She saw her as the army nursing reformer of the decade – a cause which was promoted with more passion than tact. In 1881 Mrs Fellowes had gone out to South Africa, and on arrival in Pietermaritzburg reported having

> impressed upon the P.M.O. that I was one of '*Miss Nightingale's Nurses*' and trained *at her School*!!! I hope I may have plenty of opportunity of showing them how thorough the training is and do credit to dear St Thomas's.

Four days later she wrote that only two Netley nurses had been chosen for Fort Amiel, and that she was not one of them:[32]

> I fear I must go without ever *seeing* a wounded Soldier!! . . . I see how sorely the military wants *good* nursing, and still I see the 'obstructionists' in force!

When Mrs Fellowes was sent out to Egypt a year later, the story was the same: her services were still not, to Florence Nightingale's mind, being properly used or appreciated. In private correspondence, her patroness fumed:

> Mrs Fellowes was born to be a Military Hosp.l reformer. And I had purposely *insensed* (sic) her with what she would have to guard against and prevent in the Orderlies when she came to be 'Sister in charge' if a war broke out.[33]

Such pretensions to command cannot have escaped the notice of the army medical officers; it is hard to believe that the thwarting of these ambitions was purely coincidental.

Most of Florence Nightingale's complaints and manœuvres were made through the Loyd-Lindsays and the National Society. She tried to arrange through them for Mrs Fellowes to be assigned to one specific hospital where she could superintend staff supplied by St Thomas's. She was disgusted to learn, that once Mrs Fellowes and her colleagues arrived in Egypt, they would be placed 'under some very inferior women' – though she did at least counsel her disciples to obey War Office orders and not to make their discontents public.[34] Both in 1882 and 1885 she objected to the way in which the nurses were deployed, and insisted that the talents of her best pupils were under-used on hospital ships: they should be transferred to the larger fixed hospitals where their skills as surgical nurses would be at a premium. Soon after they were transferred, she complained that they were being overworked.[35]

One of her nurses, Sybil Airy, found the leisure to report to her at considerable length on her experiences; the information she provided found its way into Florence Nightingale's discussions with the Army Hospital Services Committee. The failings of the orderly system seemed to have changed in very few particulars since the Crimea: the men were constantly being withdrawn from ward service at short notice; most of them were weak in such elementary skills as washing patients' backs and making and applying poultices. Their drunkenness was such that Sybil was 'thankful that Christmas is over' though 'one quite dreads "Pay-day" for them'. There were, nevertheless, some 'really *good workers* among them'; Florence Nightingale herself thought that 'the Orderlies who were picked men would have done pretty well if they had not had "hours" on duty which would have killed a camel.'[36]

It was clear that all the nurses, whether overworked or underemployed, were thrilled to bits to be nursing the nation's heroes. 'How very nice the soldiers are to the nurses!' Sybil Airy cooed, conceding 'the one exception of their nasty habit of spitting on the floor which we *cannot* break them of!' Some categories of patient were, of course, deemed more heroic than others. There was, indeed a certain amount of competition for them. Sybil was somewhat piqued that two colleagues, Sisters Yardley and Cannel, had bagged all the surgical cases:[37]

Although I have not the great privilege of having many
wounded, – I prize several of my cases as having been at the
Front, – . . . Poor, brave fellows! I have had several interesting
battle talks with them, even with some of the wounded, though
I am *not* nursing them! Never mind!

Sybil was convinced that the female nurses' presence had gone a
long way towards converting the medical officers to the cause of
women's war nursing in general. But in many cases the conversion
was less than wholehearted. The reforms in the army hospital
system which were on their way by the end of 1883 were accepted
in the spirit of weary resignation betrayed by the comment of
Director-General Crawford: 'Nothing short of this will meet the
requirements of an Army which is rapidly becoming as luxurious
in its habits as the civilian population of the country.'[38] The
Middle Eastern campaign had set in motion a massive extension of
British colonial commitments; without popular support, the
movement could not be sustained. Accommodation to some of the
values of the civilian elector and taxpayer was becoming a practical
military necessity. And where wounds and sickness were concerned, female nursing was the civilian norm. Gordon had written
to Florence Nightingale that civilian standards of care – 'proper
and considerate attention' – were necessary to keep up recruitment
levels. A year after his martyrdom, an anonymous military writer
echoed his sentiments: 'Whatever our country may be, it is at least
"respectable", and the army must be placed in harmony with
respectability, so that decent men may not dread association with
it.'[39] One man's luxury was another man's respectability: Crawford
would have to bow to the inevitable.

All that the Army Medical Department could do was limit the
potential damage to its long-established structures. The experience
of the Middle Eastern campaigns confirmed the Director-General's
already strong disposition to free the army nursing service as far as
possible from overpowering – and predominantly female – external
influences. The Army Hospital Services committee of 1883
recommended a considerable expansion of the female nursing corps;
the new regulations for military hospitals issued in 1885
implemented these recommendations, but in such a way as to
eliminate the last vestiges of the old 'parallel power'. The female
nursing service was to be extended to all hospitals containing over
100 beds; female nurses were to help to train male orderlies; in any

military engagement, a lady Superintendent was to be appointed under the Principal Medical Officer. However, all female nursing staff were now to be selected by the Director-General alone, who would 'nominate Superintendents and Nurses from a list in his office', and no dismissal was to take place without his sanction. At the same time the National Society training scheme was abruptly terminated.[40]

The construction of a female nursing reserve for the emergency of war seems not to have been contemplated at this stage. The primary responsibility of a wartime medical service was still seen as the emergency succour of the wounded, rather than the lengthy nursing of the sick. The former was men's work, undertaken on or near the battlefield. Women's work, notwithstanding the typhoid outbreak among the troops in South Africa in 1881, and the cholera outbreak in Egypt in 1883, was assigned a secondary importance. The fact that Britain was deepening its military commitments in climates where debilitating intestinal illness was an ever-present hazard had not yet forced a reconsideration of such judgments. Nearly twenty years were to elapse before the experience of the Anglo-Boer War finally altered military-medical priorities.

CIVILIAN AID AND THE ORDER OF ST JOHN

For Thomas Crawford, virtually every change in the army nursing system signalled a victory of civilians over soldiers. The events of the 1880s appeared to register the triumph of a process which had been discernible even before the Crimean War, and which had been strongly in evidence after it: the re-fashioning of the soldier in the image of middle-class society. But it would be equally true to say that the contrary process was at work. The voluntary agencies despatching female nurses to the seat of war were identifying closely with the army as an institution. They were scrupulous to avoid imputations of amateur heroics or indiscipline: none of the auxiliary nurses gave grounds for criticism, scandal or dismissal. Florence Nightingale's complaints notwithstanding, the organisers were making strenuous efforts to adapt to official requirements. It could be said that the civilians themselves were becoming militarised.

A closer insight into this development can be gained by

examining the work of the Order of St John of Jerusalem in this period. In the early 1870s, the movement's strategy for placing a British branch of the Red Cross in close and permanent relationship to the War Office was blocked by official indifference. But the long-term goal of creating civilian auxiliaries for the military was not jettisoned. In February 1877 a leading figure in the Order, Henry Brackenbury, published a programme of action to which the Order adhered for the rest of the century. In an article entitled 'Philanthropy in War', Brackenbury outlined a scheme for involving civilians in war preparations. He pointed out that Britain's military-medical services were less ready for mobilisation than those of any other European nation. A constant state of preparation in time of peace could only be financed by voluntary civilian contributions; but how – if Britain did not appear to be in imminent danger of invasion, and remained remote from the military alarms of the Continent – could civilian enthusiasm be harnessed to such aims? Brackenbury's answer was that military-medical facilities must be made to serve humanitarian functions in peace time. If a voluntary ambulance service were created which was available for all national disasters, it would[41]

> become the great centre for aid in all national disasters, it would gain a new life, and grow as that in Russia has done. Think what a hold it might gain on the hearts of the people, were its railway waggons for relieving wounded despatched to the scene of every accident, its ambulances at hand to bring succour to the pit's mouth in cases of colliery disasters, or to seek out in villages and bring to town hospitals the victims of accidents far from surgical aid! Every farthing so spent would bring in a hundredfold; while every railway carriage and ambulance waggon would be available in time of war.'

Brackenbury was writing at a time when few observers thought that the wars in the Balkans between Serbia, Turkey and Russia would lead to British military intervention. Nevertheless, by September 1877 members of the Order had guaranteed the sum of £1000 for the immediate expenses which an ambulance team might incur on the outbreak of hostilities, and the War Office had begun to make discreetly encouraging noises. The Secretary of State sanctioned the Order's purchase of army ambulance wagons; and, in a move which had great significance for the future, an Army Medical Department Surgeon-Major was detailed to give members of the Order instruction in first aid and ambulance work. The first of many local ambulance committees was set up in Woolwich, the home of several regular army personnel who were also members of the Order. A ladies' committee set to work preparing bandages to be used in ambulance classes, and by the new year classes for men and women were spreading further afield.[42]

In February 1878, Russia appeared to be about to trample on British interests in Constantinople, and the British public was in its fullest flowering of 'Jingoism'. The Order took advantage of the moment to launch the St John's Ambulance Association as an organisation separate from the parent Order, from the National Society, and from a rival organisation, the Volunteer Sick Bearers' Association, which Loyd-Lindsay had inaugurated in an apparent attempt – largely unsuccessful – to steal St John's thunder.[43] By June 1878, public enthusiasm had attracted 1100 men and women to St John's first aid classes; had pushed the guarantee fund up to £2330; and had brought the names of 192 qualified surgeons and nurses on to the register which the SJAA had opened for medical volunteers in case of war. Medical staff at St Thomas's and Bart's hospitals were promising full co-operation; the Army Medical Department was assuring the SJAA the free supply of all necessary equipment in wartime if the latter would supply and pay for medical personnel.[44] A year later, SJAA branches were still sprouting rapidly, particularly in the south of England. It was reported that in London alone, 1580 women and roughly the same number of men had attended first aid classes. The culmination of all the Order's original hopes seemed near at hand, and Major Duncan concluded triumphantly, 'The work has spread as only a movement will spread which is hungered for.'[45]

What was the hunger that the SJAA classes satisfied? Men and women who were seeking medical knowledge, who wanted the opportunity to help their workmates and their families as well as the citizenry at large, could use the first aid instruction for their own purposes, regardless of any military ambitions entertained by those offering it. Every ambulance centre formed undertook to enrol in the register kept at headquarters 'the names of certificated pupils who would consent in war time to assist the Order of St John in certain capacities', but not all the SJAA branches formed ambulance centres. In 1879, for example, the Association reported a flurry of letters from Bath, Clifton, Wimbledon and

Cheltenham on the question of forming, in the first place, ladies'
classes, and at a later stage, ambulance centres. 'The Central
Committee would infinitely prefer reversing the process, but it is
unwilling to check the zeal of the ladies concerned.'

It is indeed possible that the women involved in the SJAA saw
themselves as budding war heroines, who might emulate the
exploits of Florence Nightingale or Emily Strangford. It is equally
likely that they were bearing out the latter's thesis in *Hospital
Training for Ladies* that the country was full of women with both
the desire for, and the capacity to profit from, part-time nursing
instruction. Duncan reported that the first ladies' class 'so much
enjoyed the instruction that when they were threatened with a
conclusion of the course, and examination, there was almost a
mutiny amongst them, and they wanted more lectures first.
(Laughter).'[47] During the 1880s the energetic women of the SJAA
went on to establish a training system for district nursing, and to
form their own nursing corps for the sick poor.[48] But they also
continued to support the Association's war relief schemes. At the
commencement of the Egyptian campaign, reports of distress
among the civilian population of Alexandria found an immediate
response among them. In August 1882 a circular was sent

> to all the Ambulance centres in the United Kingdom appealing
> for volunteers from the ladies holding certificates, who would
> act as district visitors among the poor, and it is proposed also to
> send a staff of trained nurses. The Arab customs make it
> necessary that female visitors should be employed in searching
> out sickness and starvation among the native families. . . .
> Viscountess Strangford has kindly consented to go out in charge
> of the nurses and visitors. . . . In the event of any unforeseen
> emergency the scheme now submitted to the public will be
> found useful by the military authorities, and in the meantime it
> is proposed to organise and ration the nurses and visitors sent
> out with Lady Strangford on a system which would prove
> suitable for military as well as civil hospital duties.

The appeal for volunteers was answered by over 1000 ladies with
SJAA certificates. In the end, however, Lady Strangford went to
Cairo with Dr Herbert Sieveking and a staff of only five English
nurses. By the time they arrived, the war was over, but the
hospital which they established to serve both the sick and wounded
soldiers of the Khedive and the sick and wounded officers of the

British expeditionary force, was warmly welcomed by the military authorities.[49]

A great variety of motives went into the founding of the St John Ambulance Association. The desire for self-education, and for practical service in the neighbourhood or workplace were undoubtedly as important factors as nationalism or 'scarlet fever'. In the 1890s, indeed, many members of the Association were openly rebelling against the military style of their uniform and drill and the somewhat authoritarian constitution imposed upon them by the leadership.[50] Nevertheless, the Association had taken an important step in making explicit its members' potential relationship with the army, and had given a new direction to the voluntary aid movement. Hitherto, sympathisers with foreign armies had, for the most part, to content themselves with fundraising; and the National Society and the 'Princess of Wales's Branch' placed the burden of welfare work for British troops on committee men and women, and on trained nurses. The SJAA changed the emphasis of humanitarianism and partisanship by asking individuals in their hundreds to register for personal service. The cry was, 'Here I am: send me.'

In the first twenty years of the SJAA's existence, there were many women who went to classes, took their examinations, formed little district nursing corps, and lived in hopes of coming forward in their country's hour of need. The expansion and greater publicity given to the regular Army Nursing Service, as well as the gradual development of a male military-medical reserve, helped to keep these hopes of national service alive. The influence of the Association was revealed in many of the applications to nurse which were processed during the Anglo-Boer War; and the apotheosis of the original vision of the Order was reached on the eve of the First World War, when, as will be seen, the educational structure devised in the 1870s was made the basis for the training of thousands of VADs. In the last two decades of the nineteenth century, the work of St John, which remained purely voluntary, was as much a symptom as a cause of the process by which civilians became 'war-minded'; and many other such symptoms could be cited. It was, however, one of the more important means by which the concepts of nursing, war and empire became interlinked. In the final section of this book, we shall look more closely at the ways in which the prospect of helping the imperial state at war shaped the ambitions of British women and girls. The Lady Bountifuls, disinterested humanitarians, and army reformers who promoted the 'philanthropy of the battlefield' did not disappear from the stage in the 1890s; but the uniformed war nurse was increasingly the role model for female aspirations.

PART III

THE BIG SHOW

CHAPTER 7

++++++++++++++++++++++

HEROINES FOR THE EMPIRE
1883–1902

++++++++++++++++++++++

The army nurses who went to Egypt in 1882 wanted more than the chance to serve. After spending over a decade 'in but not of' the army, they wanted a more clearly defined position, better integrated within the system. They wanted combatant status, and the normalisation of their right to war service. They wanted commissioned rank, and the salutes of the male orderlies. Above all, they wanted medals. So at least thought Colonel Sir Owen Langton, who on 22 November informed the Royal Commission on army hospital services:

> I think there is a further cause of bitterness amongst them, and that is that they are not put in the same category as soldiers in the way of receiving a medal. I think there is nothing they would like more.

The matter was, in fact, already in hand. On 12 September Queen Victoria had informed the War Office of her desire to establish a decoration in connection with war service, and on 23 April 1883 a Royal Warrant created the Royal Red Cross. The award was for women only. It was for 'Nursing Sisters . . . for special devotion and competency which they may have displayed in their nursing duties with Our Army in the Field, or in Our Naval and Military Hospitals': it could also be conferred upon 'any ladies . . . for special exertions in providing for the nursing, or for attending to, sick and wounded soldiers and sailors', and upon 'any of the

14 Eleanor Laurence, whose ambition to become a nurse dated from
1883, when the Royal Red Cross was instituted. She won it during
the Boer War. (Bodleian Library)

Princesses of the Royal Family of Great Britain and Ireland'.[1]

The immediate origins of this initiative are obscure. After the Zulu War, Director-General Muir had written to Sir Henry Ponsoby on behalf of Mrs Deeble and the Army Sisters that 'a word of recognition of their services from the Queen, if I may make bold to suggest this to you, would make her and them happy and proud for the rest of their lives'.[2] One can only speculate as to the other factors which had influenced the Queen. She had already shown her interest in nurses in 1880 when she founded the Order of St Katherine 'for Hospital Nurses, who have particularly distinguished themselves by their good behaviour and attention to duties, and by their aptitude for teaching others';[3] and her female relatives had shown considerable interest in the first aid movement, particularly the Princess of Wales, who joined the Order of St John as early as 1877, and Princess Christian, who translated Esmarch's *First Aid to the Injured* from the German in 1882.[4] The women of the British royal family were deeply impressed by the example of their German counterparts in co-ordinating aid to sick and wounded soldiers during the unification wars in the 1860s. They must have seen that Prussian queens and princesses mobilised civilian support for the wars by their example: and they might also have realised that the relationship worked both ways. By identifying themselves with what was defined as a popular cause, the royal sponsors of relief work established themselves as part of a popular and national institution rather than an aloof, dynastic one.[5] In an age of political turbulence and change, all monarchies were under pressure to achieve the delicate balance between mystique and accessibility. It is arguable that Queen Victoria achieved this balance from an early date; nevertheless, she and her family were willing to learn from German models. At the time that the Royal Red Cross was being established, Princess Christian was hard at work on a biographical sketch of Princess Alice of Hesse, and editing letters which dealt extensively with her work for German soldiers between 1866 and 1870.[6] The fact that Bismarck's wars had produced a crop of national distinctions for women, among them several British volunteer nurses, may well have provided food for thought.[7]

In 1883 a schoolgirl named Eleanor Laurence

> was grieving over the fact that none of the professions in which my brothers were distinguishing themselves would be open to

me, as I was 'only a girl'; so I at once decided that I would try
to win the Royal Red Cross.

She had much in common with the members of the Army Nursing
Service. The Army Sisters, working alongside men in the same
public institution, their separate powers of appointment and
discipline eroded by successive changes in the official regulations,
had begun to compare themselves directly with their male
colleagues. In consequence, they demanded parity of recognition
and esteem with them. Eleanor was part of the generation which
filled the new schools established for middle-class English girls
in the 1870s and 1880s: schools which modelled their games
and curricula on those already devised for boys, and encouraged
their pupils to compete for distinctions with each other, as
their brothers did. Perhaps it is not insignificant that, looking
back, she thought she would never have survived her initiation
into the hard grind of hospital work had not one of her brothers
bet her that she would give it up in a fortnight. She did, indeed,
succeed in all her ambitions, achieving distinction as a civillian
nurse, and earning the Royal Red Cross and the South African War
Medal in 1901.[8]

The idea that women might not only distinguish themselves in
the public sphere, but might even do so in much the same way as
men, was growing: the Royal Red Cross was not to be awarded for
staying at home and keeping the house tidy, but for involvement
in that archetypally masculine activity, war. The recipients of the
award had in many cases been through the most thrilling
adventures. In 1891, the Royal Red Cross was awarded to
Mrs Damant and Mrs Cawley, who nursed the wounded under fire,
and cooked for civilians and soldiers – until the food and water ran
out – during the siege of the hill fort in Kohima; to
Mrs Grimwood, who also attended the wounded under heavy fire
during the siege of the Residency at Manipur, and after its
evacuation 'acted as a guide, her knowledge of the country
proving invaluable'; and to Catherine Grace Loch and Elizabeth
Lickfold of the Indian Army Nursing Service, who received
revolver practice before accompanying the Black Mountain
expedition of 1888. The *Woman's Herald* thought that 'a little story of
[Mrs Grimwood's] bravery should be in every young girl's reading
book with numerous other examples, for only in that way can we
train the young feminine mind to higher ideals of conduct in times

of panic and disaster'. *The Queen* declared that 'deeds of heroism, deeds of valour, deeds of true nobility are, the world is beginning to discover, as frequent among women as amongst men.' The *Nursing Record* thought that Mrs Grimwood should have been given, not the Royal Red Cross, but the VC.[9]

Of course, women's incorporation into this new public sphere was not on exactly the same terms as men. The exemplary female lives anthologised for schoolgirls in the 1880s for the most part presented the Christian philanthropists of the previous three decades as role models. Indeed, under the clauses of the 1883 warrant, the Royal Red Cross could be, and was awarded for activities no more hair-raising than committee work, fundraising, and the weekly visiting of hospitals: all traditional pursuits amongst middle- and upper-class mothers, wives and daughters. The quality of 'womanliness' was still placed at a premium in women's literature and in girls' schools where, alongside more masculine innovations, domestic subjects continued to be taught.[10]

And, of course, even the most courageous war nurse and dedicated career sister in the Army Nursing Service remained in a subordinate position to the male medical officer, and of uncertain status in the male army. Nevertheless, the supporting roles played by British women on the frontiers of the empire, even if only on rare occasions, required far from conventionally feminine qualifications. The courage and independence demonstrated by a relatively small number of exceptional women in the 1850s, 60s and 70s – volunteer war nurses, eccentric and intrepid travellers, enthusiasts for the cause of new nations – were now given wider and more continuous scope. Women were going out to the empire in increasing numbers, as wives, nurses, governesses and missionaries. They had to learn to cope with difficult, inconvenient and even dangerous living conditions. They needed to be cool, self-disciplined, 'plucky' and, as the Royal Red Cross awards indicated, able to wield a firearm in an emergency. Such women would not be embarrassed when their portraits appeared in the newspapers. Their achievements were publicly recognised, not just by newspaper readers, but by the head of state; the Royal Red Cross was even shared with her.

The new perceptions of female heroism affected nurses more directly than any other group of women. The creation of the Royal Red Cross sent frissons through the nursing community: why were only military nurses to have the privilege of being members of the same order as the Sovereign? Might it not be possible to create a civilian division of the RRC? Why was so much glamour attached to war, when ordinary civilian nurses accepted an equal risk of death from infection, and fostered the health and strength on which the whole nation's future depended?[11] To argue, however, that all nursing was heroic, and of benefit to the state, was to accept the premises of those who held out medals and distinctions as an inducement to service. It did not go to the core of the tensions which were growing between different generations of nurses.

The lady-nurses of the Crimean War undertook their work in a spirit of religious dedication: if they sought public prestige, it was for their sect or sisterhood; their ambition was to widen the field for the philanthropic mission of their own kind. The era of nursing reform which followed the Crimean War, although marked by the foreign exploits of such as Florence Lees, and producing the occasional near-beatification, such as that of Agnes Jones by Florence Nightingale, and that of Dorothy Pattison (Sister Dora) by the people of Walsall,[12] continued to require a high degree of self-abnegation from its acolytes. Their labour was immensely rigorous; their seclusion was almost conventual; their uniform cloaked them with anonymity. As if this were not enough, sisters in large hospitals were known not by their own names, but by those of the wards or departments they supervised, as in 'Sister Leopold' or 'Sister Casualty'. The individual had to be subsumed in the whole. In 1888 the Rev. W.F. Hobson, writing a memoir of his late wife, who had nursed with Mary Stanley at Koulali, declared:

> She had an absolute indifference to all record of the past, for her own sake. She *could* not, I feel sure, have grieved at being 'unacknowledged and almost unknown', or forgotten wholly. She was incapable of the faintest desire for any recognition.

This was written in response to Arthur Stanley's obituary comment on his sister Mary:

> The feeling that her public labours were for the most part unacknowledged and almost unknown – a circumstance due to various causes – cast something of a shade over her life.

But it could have stood equally well as a rebuke to a discontented and restless new generation of women.[13]

Despite all the continuing practical and hierarchical restrictions of the nurse's working life, individualism and self-assertion were becoming important elements in her sense of vocation. Virtue no longer had to be its own reward. Patriotism offered a secular standard and validation of worth. The RRC promised women of all classes incorporation in an order with the queen and the ladies of the court at its apex. The widening empire held out the prospect of earthly adventure in place of the spiritual pilgrimage. Military nursing was only one of the possibilities: the growing population of expatriate Britons created a demand for the importation of home products and services, including trained nursing, and opened up many opportunities for British nurses to travel. They could work for the Up-Country Nurses' Association in India, for the Colonial Nursing Association in other colonies, as private nurses anywhere.[14] A British nurse wrote from South Africa in a matter-of-fact way of 'an English nurse who seeks her fortunes in South African hospitals, as her brother seeks it in the mines of Kimberley or in far-off Rhodesia.'[15] These developments provoked expressions of alarm amongst the more senior nurses: fame and excitement were not proper motives for taking up nursing work, and the reputation of all could suffer at the hands of a few adventuresses; Catherine Loch's fears for the Indian Army Nursing Service found many echoes at home. Young heads, it seemed, were too easily turned, and good nurses were abandoning their home hospitals – and their obligations to their matrons – to answer the call of the wild. 'The spirit of the age is restless,' noted the *Hospital 'Nursing Mirror'*, 'and our nurses have not escaped being possessed by it. Let a call come for them for Klondyke, for war, for plague, for South Africa, and hundreds respond with an eager "send me"; and when the choice falls upon another a crowd of disappointed women surge through every door that seems to open to them some new experience.' 'BE LOYAL,' urged 'A Hospital Matron'. 'We hear of women hastily relinquishing their work, and flinging themselves into alluring schemes, eager for self-advertisement, dazzled with visions of possible aggrandisement, and blind to the fact that by their impetuous action they may be doing an injustice to their employers and neglecting their immediate duty.' Battling against the tide, writers in the nursing press urged the care of the poor at home, the improvement of workhouse infirmary nursing, and 'hourly disregard of self' on their readers.[16]

MILITARY SERVICE AND STATE REGISTRATION FOR NURSES

The bulk of British nurses, of course, continued to work in the United Kingdom. The organisation which was heir to all their discontents and aspirations was the British Nurses' Association. This was formed in 1888 to campaign for a national register of nurses, whose professional qualification should be a certificate of three years of training in a general hospital. Its founder was Ethel Gordon Bedford Fenwick, née Manson, the former Matron of Bart's; Princess Christian became its president, and helped to ensure its incorporation by Royal Charter in 1893. The *Nursing Record*, a pro-registration weekly of which Ethel Bedford Fenwick eventually became proprietor as well as editor, was founded in the same year as the BNA. The Association was strongly opposed by Florence Nightingale and most of the large metropolitan training hospitals, who 'disapprove of an innovation, which they honestly believe would in a manner dissociate the nurse from her parent school'. The pro-registration nurses wanted to cut precisely this tie: to make their qualification uniform and transferable, and to free themselves to work where they wished.[17]

From the first, the BNA tried to associate itself with the military service of the state. Jane Deeble, Lady Superintendent at Netley, and Louisa Hogg, Superintendent of the naval hospital at Haslar, were elected to the Association's first executive committee; and in 1889 Ethel Bedford Fenwick 'sent a carefully drafted scheme for a Corps of Volunteer Nurses to the then Director-General of the Army Medical Department at the War Office, which was politely acknowledged, and, no doubt, at once pigeon-holed.' In 1894 the executive returned to the subject, and established a sub-committee to discuss the formation of an army nursing reserve.[18]

This was a natural progression of events: if the BNA wanted the state to recognise nursing as a profession, it was necessary to establish the usefulness of professional nursing to the state. Ethel Bedford Fenwick's concern to make her Association indispensable to the War Office was an extension of the feminist argument, voiced at the time of the Civil War in the United States, and the Franco-Prussian War, that women's necessary services in war demonstrated their *de facto* equality of citizenship with men, and their right to the franchise. Ethel Bedford Fenwick was herself a staunch suffragist, and did indeed see war service as the ultimate qualification for membership of the commonwealth. Of a nurse who died of enteric during the Boer War, she declaimed: 'The obligations of Empire are incumbent upon women as well as men, and they claim their right to face danger and death in the discharge of their duty.'[19]

It is also most likely that in linking the question of state registration for nurses with that of women's nursing service in time of war, Ethel Bedford Fenwick was strongly influenced by a pamphlet published in 1885 by Surgeon-Major Evatt of the Army Medical Department, and distributed by him among 'many hundred' of 'the Nursing profession'. This was entitled *A Proposal to form a Corps of Volunteer Female Nurses for Service in the Army Hospitals in the Field, with Suggestions as to the Incorporation of the Nursing Profession*. Evatt proposed a volunteer arm of the Army Nursing Service on the lines of the combatant Volunteer Force, to be composed of trained and serving civilian nurses, who would serve with the Regular Army alongside the Army Nursing Service in a foreign war, or with the Volunteer Force in the event of an invasion. The creation of the corps would require the appointment of a Superintendent of Volunteer Female Nurses; and a uniform training curriculum and diploma, a pension fund, and powers of self-government and expulsion, would all flow from these military requirements. Thus 'the formation of such a Corps . . . is, I think, the first definite attempt to Incorporate the Nursing Profession.' After a period on foreign service, Evatt returned to his theme at the end of March 1894, in a letter to the *Nursing Record*. The achievement of the Royal charter of incorporation by the RBNA, he argued, at last made it possible to set up a centralised organisation which could prepare in peacetime for the emergency of war, co-ordinating the nursing corps to be drawn from different civilian hospitals, and integrating them with their military colleagues. Candidates for the nursing reserve would have to be classified and graded; and the 'real Nurses' would be able 'to guard us from an invasion of sham Nurses, without training or knowledge, who would rush in upon us in the hurry and confusion of a campaign.'[20]

George Joseph Hamilton Evatt had joined the Army Medical Service in 1865. His service in India and Afghanistan had made him very critical of the organisation of military hospitals; and he was in general convinced that 'good nursing has become essential, and we see more and more how useless without that aid is all the work of the physician or the surgeon.' Unusually, he believed that doctors as a body were extremely ignorant of good nursing practice, and should themselves undergo instruction in nursing and sick cookery. By 1883 he had already published, in his *Army Medical Organisation*, the view that the Volunteer Force needed a medical branch, and that this should include 'a regular body of female volunteer army nurses who, after undergoing a certain training and passing a defined examination, would have their names inscribed in readiness.'[21] Evatt's experience with the Suakin expedition in the Middle East in 1885 confirmed his belief that the Army Medical Service needed a larger reserve force, and that this should include female nurses. Since 1882 he had supported the work of the St John's Ambulance Association by acting as an examiner for first aid classes; when the Volunteer Force began to follow the St John example and to create stretcher corps, he worked enthusiastically with James Cantlie, Assistant Surgeon at Charing Cross Hospital, to set up a national Volunteer Medical Staff Corps. It was through this organisation, which had achieved full War Office recognition by 1885, that Evatt hoped to co-ordinate the response to his appeal for a volunteer female nursing reserve.[22]

By the time of Evatt's second appeal, opinion was stirring on defence questions in Britain. There had been an invasion scare in April 1888; and from 1891 onwards – after a gap of nearly twenty years – the army resumed large-scale summer and autumn manœuvres. Service literature discussed the shape of wars to come, and in particular the likely effects of the new small-bore rifles. It was thought that these would wound combatants at a far greater distance than previous weapons, producing very great numbers of casualties over a wide area. The increase in ambulance provision, and subsequent hospital care, would have to be correspondingly enormous.[23] These military and military-medical concerns were not translated overnight into practical measures. However, in 1895, when Lord Wolseley was promoted to Field-Marshal and Commander-in-Chief, and a new Conservative government secured the largest establishment and the greatest increase of the army ever known in peacetime, rumours and anticipations of war spread to unofficial and unlikely quarters.

In mid-March 1894 a meeting was convened in London by a Miss

Ethel Stokes and a Mrs K. Hetherley for the purpose of establishing a Women's Volunteer Medical Staff Corps. It was to be formed on the same lines as its male counterpart, which had now been in existence for a decade. Its members were to undergo medical training based on the manual of the Medical Staff Corps of the regular army; they would also be trained in musketry exercises, and do company and squad drill. They would learn how to camp, and to take care of all cooking and transport arrangements, down to mending carriages, harness, and tents, and shoeing horses.[24] At present, little or nothing is known of the originators of this enterprise. Ethel Stokes may have been related to the Surgeon-Major H.F. Stokes who was appointed Senior Medical Officer Instructor of the Volunteer Ambulance School of Instruction in 1890.[25] Several VMSC men were present at the women's inaugural meeting, which was addressed by Evatt. None of the men were encouraging: Evatt insisted that women's sphere of wartime work lay in base hospitals only. One press report stated that 'at the conclusion of the lecture most of the audience felt that woman's sphere lay nearer home than on the eastern battlefields' – an allusion to the renewal of British concern over the Eastern Question at the time of the Armenian massacres.[26] It was, however, a mistaken inference, for Ethel Stokes's movement continued its controversial career for at least another twelve months.

The idea of a women's VMSC outraged public opinion – at least as expressed in the metropolitan, nursing and volunteer force weeklies – on a number of grounds, not least because of the uniform proposed for its members. The subject was discussed at a meeting at the end of March, where 'a divided skirt, removable in case of necessity, only found one or two timorous supporters' and there was near unanimous approval for 'knickerbockers . . . to be adorned with stripes and braid'.[27] Mrs Hetherley, now chair of the Executive Committee, declared that

> old as she was, she intended to adopt that which should be devised, and at any risk of ridicule, so that younger women might be induced to follow her example. She was decidedly against the use of the present heavy skirts, and would like to know what men would think if they had to run up and down stairs with such a cumbersome garment clinging to their legs.

One timid lady 'inquired if it would be legal to dispense with the

DONNA QUIXOTE.

["A world of disorderly notions *picked out of books*, crowded into his (her) imagination."—*Don Quixote*.]

15 'Donna Quixote', *Punch* cartoon 1894 Bespectacled 'New Woman'
dreams of donning breeches (see figure, top left) and joining the
Volunteer Force. Abetted by Ibsen, Mona Caird and Tolstoi, she
takes on 'Tyrant Man', the marriage laws, Mamma and Decorum.
Generally taken to be an allusion to Ethel Stokes's ill-fated attempt to
form a women's ambulance corps. (Bodleian Library)

skirt?' but her qualms were not shared by the rest of the meeting. The proposed costume was satirised in *Punch* at the end of April, and described in scathing terms by the *Nursing Record*:[28]

> from the perky straw hat perched on the side of the head down to the casing of the lower limbs, the *tout ensemble* is eminently peculiar and decidedly ugly.

Another controversial issue raised by the WVMSC was that of women's physical strength. At the inaugural meeting, Evatt had 'insisted on the necessity for the employment of only the very strongest of men in field Nursing'[29] but his audience was unwilling to accept this as the final verdict on their enterprise. Some members believed that women's powers of endurance had always been as great as men's: Mrs Hetherley wondered how men 'would like to spend their time as women had to do, with a heavy squalling baby cutting its teeth. That would decidedly show the amount of endurance which they could put up with.' Ethel Stokes thought that what might once have been true had now changed, and that 'as women's physical education has been greatly improved of recent years, they are rendered capable of performing more arduous duties than they have hitherto been able to fulfil'.[30] Others argued that physical strength and endurance were largely a matter of habit, training and adaptation:

> the physical labour involved in military campaigns in tending the sick might, after all, become a matter of practice and habit, as was instanced by the many cases abroad and even at home where women had to do work which required the expenditure of great manual strength.

A Dr Alice Vickery declared that it was precisely in order to strengthen themselves that women ought to take up the work:[31]

> Any means which would develope (sic) the strength and physical powers of women must be a useful one, for they would be as anxious as men to assist in any warlike struggle that might be going on.

All this was too much for the *Nursing Record*, which exploded:[32]

> Strongly as we shall always uphold the equality of men and women before the civil law, we bow to the great and indisputable laws of nature, and recognise the *physical* inferiority of the female sex.

187

The nursing community's opposition to the WVMSC was based on more than theories of difference between the sexes. The Royal British Nurses' Association had ambitions of its own where aid to the sick and wounded was concerned. It wished to convince the public that its members were uniquely qualified to render state service; the value of their potential contribution would be debased if the proposals of the WVMSC were accepted. The profession as a whole could suffer, both from official recognition of low standards of training, and from this further demonstration of the equation between nursing work and thrilling adventure. 'Nursing is not a military art, nor will musket practice and drill help a woman to heal the sick', wrote Henrietta Kenealy,' . . . and it would be a grievous thing if the public, dazzled by the glamour that attaches to all military manœuvres, were to regard as trained and qualified Nurses such Lady Volunteers as it is proposed to institute.'[33] The St John Ambulance Brigade was another body which stood to gain by the WVMSC's failure. The Brigade had been established in 1887 as a permanent body of male ambulance volunteers trained by the SJAA, and it had also kept alive the Order of St John's original ambition to provide an auxiliary military ambulance service in time of war or invasion. In 1890 General Wolseley had encouraged the Brigade to see itself as a potential reserve for the Army Medical Service, and had included the women of the Brigade Nursing Divisions in his remarks. In February 1895 the magazine *First Aid* urged the claims of male Brigade members to be incorporated in the ambulance corps of the Volunteer Force, and suggested that the women who formed the SJAB Nursing Divisions should be recruited as assistants to the Army Nursing Service in times of emergency.[34]

Ethel Stokes's initiative thus threatened corporate ambitions and corporate *amour-propre* to a considerable degree; but it threatened accepted ideas, even relatively progressive ideas, as to the relations and distinctions between the sexes, even more. The *Nursing Record* felt that the WVMSC was going beyond the bounds of a sensible, suffragist feminism in arguing with biological facts. What was perhaps worse, its members were making a ludicrous spectacle of themselves: this was 'a movement which only tends to bring ridicule upon the whole sex'. The WVMSC was denounced with even more vehemence by Sister Janet King, who had nursing experience of the Russo-Turkish campaign of 1878, and of the Zulu War of 1879–80:[35]

Soldiers in war look upon the Red Cross Sister as an angel of mercy, ready to succour friend and foe alike; but how would the woman be regarded who unsexes herself, as it were, and, dressed in masculine attire, with arms in her hands, essays to share the combat? . . . [men return from battle] a motley crowd, maddened with battle, clothes tattered and torn, faces blackened with powder, and stained with blood, eyes glaring forth with the fury of wild beasts. How would your lady volunteer fare then? Will she look for any distinction in the treatment of sexes? And what would be her fate as a prisoner of war to savage Cossack, or brutal Bashi Bazook, to fierce Zulu, or cruel and crafty Afghan?

These responses marked in the clearest possible manner the boundaries of the new conception of female heroism which had been developing in England over the previous two decades. Men's superior physical strength and aptitudes were to remain uncontested; firearms training and rough living in camp were to remain largely male preserves. Above all, the battlefield itself was to stay out of bounds. It was for woman to maintain her philanthropic persona: to support her nation at war at a discreet distance, carrying out the work of healing which was to be regarded as war's antithesis, rather than as one of its maintenance services. To look war full in the face would be 'a degradation to woman's nature, which should revolt at the idea of taking the lives of others'.[36] The logic of such propositions was not debated, any more than was the premise that women should be subordinate because men were beasts. As will be seen, some of these boundaries to female activity were breached between 1909 and 1914, when official planning sanctioned the creation of the Voluntary Aid Detachments.

Under pressure, the WVMSC attempted to placate its critics. They insisted that they were not in competition with qualified hospital nurses. They wanted to train only to the level of ward orderlies. The civilian nurses who could expect to serve in time of war would rank with the Army Nursing Service sisters, and would, therefore, supervise the work of the less qualified WVMSC. They did not contemplate actually going onto the field of battle, but nevertheless thought it worth while learning stretcher drill. It was true that there was unlikely to be any lack of civilian nurse volunteers in time of war, but there might well be a shortage of orderlies and stretcher bearers. None of these arguments was enough to keep the movement afloat. Its founders thought it would need a membership subscription of ten shillings a year, a government grant, and public contributions in order to secure its existence, none of which appear to have been forthcoming.[37] The collapse of the WVMSC was reported in April 1895. A friendly Major W.E. Eldon Sergeant (possibly of the Volunteer Force) had urged its members to join the St John Ambulance Association. It is tempting to detect their influence, and perhaps even their presence, in the London SJAA in 1897, when Deputy-Commissioner Bowdler, after inspecting the Wembley and Harlesden divisions,[38]

> repaired to the drawing-room where he said a few words to the nurses. Speaking of the stretcher work he said he did not believe in ladies doing it. The ladies in the Crystal Palace Division did carry patients, but he did not think it was right. He spoke from a medical point of view.

The one positive result of Ethel Stokes's initiative seems to have been to goad others into the formation of an army nursing reserve. Evatt addressed the WVMSC on only one occasion; immediately afterwards he wrote to the *Nursing Record*, and approached the executive committee of the Royal British Nurses' Association, on the subject of forming a body which would 'not attempt the impossible by competing with the Medical Staff Corps'. His suggestions were accepted with particular enthusiasm by the Association's president, Princess Christian. At the end of April 1894 she published a circular letter to the governing bodies of all metropolitan hospitals with established nurse training schools, inviting them to participate in the formation of a military nursing reserve corps.[39] On the same day she wrote to Florence Nightingale that 'far from rivalling the already existing Corps of Army sisters, it would become the subordinate auxiliary of those admirable public servants' and invited her suggestions on the project. Predictably, Florence Nightingale and other opponents of the Association's policy on a professional register of qualified nurses refused to co-operate with this new scheme, which might, so to speak, establish the principle of registration by the back door.[40] The Association nevertheless felt sufficiently confident of support within the nursing community to go ahead, but in order to avoid a public débâcle à la Stokes – and perhaps on Evatt's advice – no immediate attempt was made to gain official approval for the scheme.[41]

In July 1894 the RBNA published regulations for the proposed reserve corps and invited applications for enlistment. It was proposed to form in the first instance a nucleus of one metropolitan corps of sixty nurses, all of whom should have a minimum of three years' hospital 'training or experience'. Enrolment was to be for three years, and by permission of the matron and chief executive officer of the hospital to which the candidate was attached. Her employers would be asked to agree that the nurse should not forfeit either her employment, or her prospects of promotion, through absence on military service. The nurse undertook 'to attend any special Lectures and Classes of Instruction to which I may be summoned in the name of the Executive Committee of the Royal British Nurses' Association'. The corps, if it were sufficiently expanded, would have at its head a Superintendent General, Princess Christian; three Deputy Superintendent Generals; a Lady Superintendent for each corps of sixty nurses; Ward Sisters; and Staff Nurses.[42] These organisational details bristled with potential points of conflict with the regular Army Nursing Service, which was most unlikely to agree to separate, civilian, positions of authority; and the proposal to include a grade of Staff Nurse showed profound ignorance of the structure of the regular service. (Mrs Deeble's successor, Miss Norman, had not followed her into the BNA in 1889.) Over the next two years, the corps existed less in fact than in discussion, little of which seems to have been recorded, but which involved Isla Stewart, President of the newly-formed Matrons' Council, Sidney Browne, Superintendent Sister at the military general hospital at Woolwich, Princess Christian, and officials of the War Office.[43]

In 1896 the War Office finally took action, and decided that no existing civilian nursing bodies could be recognised as officially responsible for an army nursing reserve. A new scheme was to be devised by a committee consisting of three War Office officials, Colonel N.G. Lyttleton, Major-General Taylor and Surgeon-Colonel Gubbins, and Princess Christian; enrolment was to be on an individual basis only, and on conditions 'as nearly as possible identical' with those laid down for the Army Nursing Service.[44] The formation of the Army Nursing Reserve was announced in

March 1897, and the first sixty-five members were presented with their badges and certificates in May. A corps of around a hundred members was anticipated, which was to be under the direction of Princess Christian's committee in peacetime. Only in time of war would the reserve come under the direct control of the War Office. Lord Lansdowne thanked the Princess 'for undertaking a duty which primarily was a duty that devolved upon the authorities, but which he had no doubt her Royal Highness would be able to carry out far more effectually than they'.[45] This would appear to have been a tactful way of shrugging off financial responsibility for an initiative which had not originated within the Army Medical Department. The small numbers envisaged, and the absence of any provision for in-service training in military hospitals, suggest that the Army Nursing Reserve, despite its royal patronage, was not yet taken very seriously in official circles.

The question of military-medical reserves was, however, re-opened when the War Office decided to be represented at the sixth International Conference of Red Cross Societies at Vienna in September 1897. A lengthy report was commissioned from the delegate, Surgeon-Major W.G. MacPherson, and published as an appendix to the Army Medical Department's official report for that year. The conference impressed on MacPherson the enormous differences between Britain and the Continental powers in the matter of medical preparations for war, and relations between voluntary agencies and the state. He was convinced that, if Britain were involved in anything more than a limited colonial skirmish, 'voluntary aid . . . would come upon the military authorities in the form of a mass of unorganised and untrained elements . . . for a time at any rate, the working and administration of the regular Army Medical Services would be considerably hampered and embarrassed.' What was needed was a clear division of labour between voluntary and state agencies, laid down well in advance of the outbreak of war.[46]

The War Office responded to this report by initiating discussions in 1898 with the Army Nursing Reserve, the National Aid Society and the Order of St John, 'to consider the best means of bringing all voluntary aid societies under one controlling head in time of peace so that they may be able to work in the uniform manner necessary for efficient auxiliaries of the Army Medical Service in time of war.'[47] Representatives of all the voluntary societies agreed to establish a Central British Red Cross Committee as sole channel for wartime offers of medical help. The rules and regulations devised for this committee in July 1899 proposed District Committees at the headquarters of certain military districts, where the work of the voluntary societies would be co-ordinated with that of the local military, and military-medical authorities. In time of peace the Army Nursing Reserve would maintain a list of 'ladies willing to act as nurses'; the Order of St John would enrol male medical personnel and collect lists of hospital and transportation equipment; and the National Aid Society would collect funds. In time of war the National Aid Society would undertake the formation of field depots, and the Order of St John the reception and forwarding of material.[48] Within less than a year, these arrangements were to be put to the test.

THE SOUTH AFRICAN OPPORTUNITY

In the last years of the nineteenth century, British nurses' appetites for service abroad, and in aid of the sick and wounded, were whetted by a plethora of minor conflicts: the war between Turkey and Greece, Kitchener's expedition in the Sudan, Lugard's expedition in West Africa, the Afridi war in India, even the war between the United States and Spain in Cuba, all produced their large crop of would-be volunteer nurses, of whom only a minute proportion were accepted.[49] It was indeed a kind of war-fever, and, of course, it extended to many women who were not working nurses. One did not have to be devotee of the divided skirt, or of improving the strength and stamina of the female physique, to have caught the infection. Dosia Bagot wrote in 1900:

> In going out to a war, however, I have fulfilled a dream of twenty years' standing, and in preparing for it I have seized every available opportunity of acquiring practical nursing experience and getting surgical and medical training.

She had also acquired a 'nursing dress' which she wore when applying – successfully – for work at Naauwpoort General Hospital.[50] A Miss Phipps in 1898 begged a friend to ask Lord Wantage, as head of the National Aid Society,

how I, an amateur nurse, can get into the Red Cross
Society – tell him I have done good work under St John's
Ambulance for which I got a Jubilee Medal and have worked as
a nurse in a surgery in Rome – and all my life practised on our
farm people – how brutal that sounds! . . . I *would* like to have
the chance of being a R.C. (sic) nurse in case of war.[51]

Clearly, if a major conflict were to break out, the rush of female
nursing volunteers, with training ranging from a three-year general
hospital certificate to the first aid and home nursing qualifications
of the SJAA, to nothing at all, would be overwhelming.

The Central British Red Cross Committee, formed so shortly
before the Boer War, had foreseen this particular difficulty. In
September 1899 it agreed that all offers of assistance as nursing
sisters were to be referred to the Army Nursing Reserve, and 'the
Committee should not in any way use their influence to obtain the
employment of nurses whose qualifications did not entitle them to
enrolment in the Reserve'. However, these good intentions were
soon under siege, and during the Boer War 'in order to permit of a
desirable amount of elasticity, the Committee of the Army
Nursing Service Reserve invariably took into consideration
applications made for the special enrolment on their books of
nursing sisters belonging to other recognised Nursing Associations
and Hospitals, or selected by Committees or donors of the private
hospitals that were sent out.'[52] This rather large loophole was to be
the cause of much heartburn and division within the nursing
community between 1899 and 1902.

Even before the outbreak of the Boer War, the issue of campaign
service had threatened to exacerbate divisions between nurses. The
Army Nursing Service had worried lest the Army Nursing Reserve
be given first option to serve in the Sudan in 1898; both bodies
fretted when wholly civilian nurses were sent out by the National
Aid Society. It was not just a question of the lack of official regard
for seniority. The regular army sisters 'failed to reap such honours
and awards, as would naturally have fallen to the Army Nursing
Service, if they had been sent on active duty'. Several members of
the ANS wrote to their Lady Superintendent to ask her to
intervene in this matter with the War Office, but she did not,
apparently, respond.[53] The flood of female volunteers in 1899 and
1900, however, produced a new element of discord: the contest
was now seen as one between professional nurses and rank

amateurs. There was an explosion of bitterness, fuelled in the first instance largely by social resentments:[54]

> We observe that already the society women's papers are throwing out feelers as to the ultimate honours to be awarded to society women for their 'devotion to the sick and wounded'. In this age of frauds we have little doubt that social pressure will be brought to bear upon the 'fount of all honour', . . . no doubt the Royal Red Cross will make an effective addition to the toilet in the coming bye and bye. It already reclines on the august bosoms of various women who have never done a week's consecutive nursing in their lives; and it is deeply to be regretted that some other distinction has not been selected in return for their social services.

The grievance articulated was not new, but of long standing, if hitherto repressed. The RRC was an order which honoured the nursing profession – but it diluted that honour by embracing other sorts of women. While it was possible to feel flattered by the knowledge that the RRC was shared with Queen Victoria and her female relatives, a nurse might reflect somewhat cynically on how much harder than them she had had to work for it. Much had been made of the fact that the decoration was open to women of any class,[55] but its bestowal hardly obliterated class distinctions. After the first presentation of medals, for example, 'lunch was served to those nurses who had been decorated, in a special apartment of the Castle, while Lady Strangford and Lady Loyd-Lindsay lunched with the ladies of the Court.'[56] Even more brutal distinctions were made after the Boer War:[57]

> A number of nurses who came home from the war something like a year or more ago, having served only a comparatively short time, were presented with their medals by Royalty, whereas those who have worked to the bitter end have received theirs through the post like a housemaid's wages. Again, why should a distinction have been made between the nurses who worked in the ordinary hospitals and those who served in the Imperial Yeomanry Hospital? The latter received their medals at the hands of the Queen, the former by post.

One may speculate that such injuries to personal, social and professional pride may have stiffened the resolve of many nurses to fight for state registration after the war.

With the outbreak of the Boer War, 'the Lady', who had been kept waiting several years in the wings, returned in triumph to the centre stage of military nursing organisation. The world of female philanthropy, of voluntary committees and fundraising, could be dispensed with only while the Army Medical Department could depend on its own resources. This very rapidly ceased to be the case. In early October 1899, the Department was employing 12 female nurses, 1000 subordinate hospital staff, and 50 medical officers in South Africa; by the end of March 1900, these figures were 800, 6000 and 800 respectively.[58] The extra personnel had not only to be selected, but paid for. Selection of female personnel for such voluntary hospitals as the Portland, Langman, Imperial Yeomanry, and the Princess of Wales's hospital ship, was rarely in the hands of professional nurses; and it was hard for the authorities to turn down volunteers who offered to go out at their own expense, or to refuse offers of sponsorship for a particular group of nurses. However, all nurses whose applications to serve were approved were obliged to become members of the Army Nursing Reserve, so that some controls were applied.

The *Nursing Record* was convinced that many volunteer nurses were accepted without a three-year certificate of training, but at least in the early stages of the war the Central British Red Cross Committee maintained strict standards: even when the Princess of Wales insisted on personally selecting twelve nurses of her own, Lady Wantage, on behalf of the Red Cross, politely but firmly insisted on the three-year qualification being met. At the end of the war, the Central Committee reported that 27 per cent of all nursing applications had had to be rejected.[59] Certainly the services of the SJAB Nursing Division were turned down – a bitter disappointment after the hopes expressed for them in the 1890s.[60] It was not, then, the case, as the *Nursing Record* asserted, that the voluntary bodies had no respect for the new standards in hospital nursing; but it rankled that nurses were still very much objects of patronage, and in the gift of society ladies, and that the latter kept the positions of leadership and control for themselves:[61]

We know that Lady Chesham has been doing kind and womanly work with the Yeomanry Hospital, but to assume, because she happens to be the wealthy daughter of a Duke, that she is capable of 'supervising' a great military hospital without any knowledge of medicine or nursing, is carrying British snobbery too far.

The serious competition between nurses and amateurs took place not in Britain, but in South Africa. John Furley, the Chief Commissioner of the British Red Cross in South Africa, complained to Lord Wantage towards the end of 1900 that the Central Committee's position at home had not been respected there: the War Office had not instructed the South African military authorities that the Red Cross was the sole body through which offers of aid were to be co-ordinated. Any woman who could afford it could take herself off to South Africa and offer her nursing services there, and, 'Nurses with excellent qualifications were mingled with others who could show no testimonials.' Earlier in the year, the Central Committee had sent a stiff letter to its counterpart in the Cape, pointing out that some of the nurses recruited locally 'have been commented upon, in a manner that tends to bring discredit generally upon the conduct and qualifications of all nursing sisters employed to supplement the regular army nursing service.' At the same time, Lord Wantage wrote to *The Times* disclaiming Red Cross responsibility for locally recruited nurses.[62]

In all the welter of criticism of the 'monstrous regiment of women' invading the war hospitals, only one of the society amateurs, Lady Jessica Sykes, went to the lengths of a public counter-offensive. In 1900 Jessica Sykes published her *Side Lights on the War in South Africa*, in which she claimed that professional nurses were weaklings, requiring 'almost as much care as their patients, and must have their food, exercise, and rest at stated times, and with every possible attention to their comfort. Notwithstanding this, they are perpetually breaking down, becoming really ill, and seem extraordinarily susceptible to all complaints, such as typhoid, dysentry, etc.' They were also, as obvious failures in the marriage market, incapable of understanding the finer points of caring for male invalids: 'few female nurses realise what a terrible and agonising craving their male patients feel for that pipe which has been taken from them. From the fact that the greater portion of our hospital nurses are drawn from the class of women who have little companionship except with persons of their own sex, it is easy to understand that such intimate details of male feeling hardly appeal to their imagination or intelligence.' She therefore had nothing but praise for the Portland Ambulance, where 'the plan of placing two educated and *married* women in control of the army and hospital nurses is admirable, and protects the patients from all those forms of annoyance and petty tyranny which are so rampant in the purely military hospitals.'[63]

Objections to the pushy behaviour of well-connected ladies in South Africa were by no means confined to the Red Cross, or to nurses suffering from professional pique. In April 1900 Furley wrote to Lord Wantage:

> it is understood here that the Queen has expressed her strong disapproval of the way in which ladies are pushing their way to the front. At any rate, two ladies of unimpeachable position have been sent back from Bloemfontein.

And Sir Alfred Milner, the government's High Commissioner for South Africa, went to the lengths of sending a telegram to Joseph Chamberlain, the Colonial Secretary, deprecating the increasing number of lady visitors, who put a strain on limited accommodation, pushed up prices, and interfered with military and civilian administration. Roberts himself sent a telegram insisting that a prohibition on ladies visiting hospitals without the medical officers' sanction should be maintained in force. Society ladies were accused of frivolity and flirtation as well as of 'bossing' medical officers and trained nurses: the 'notorious wife of a notorious peer' was reported to have 'exchanged the nurse's costume in which she had masqueraded for the uniform of a complacent admirer', thus offending all the canons of decency, morality and patriotism before 'finally, Lord Kitchener sent her home.'[64]

Such escapades furnished the daily and weekly press with excellent copy on the theme of female folly, but it is not easy at this distance to distinguish fact from rumour.[65] The convergence of women on South Africa may have been a mindless stampede on the part of the feather-brained or the vicious; but the women's motives may not have been essentially different from those of thousands of male volunteers who surged to the colours. For decades, war had been held up to women, as to men, as the most thrilling spectacle of the century, one which offered the most honourable prospects of public service. Small wonder that the women flocked to the scene, especially when it was set in a colony extensively settled by whites and enjoying a relatively benign and fever-free climate. Moreover, even the most obnoxious society adventuress could end up making a valuable contribution to the war effort: Lady Sarah Wilson was wounded during the siege of Mafeking where she managed a convalescent hospital;

Mrs Richard Chamberlain brought serious defects in military hospital provision to the public notice.[66]

By no means all trained nurses went out to South Africa in a spirit of patriotic self-sacrifice: a large number of nurses from a London training school were observed in Harrods buying 'evening gowns and shoes to take to the front: and evidently they meant to have a "real good time!"' Eleanor Laurence, who superintended Princess Christian's Hospital at Pinetown, Natal, found that 'there are just a few sisters who don't care what they do – one of them was seen at a hotel at the next station smoking cigarettes with a most undesirable companion!' and others behaved 'in a way which no lady would care to emulate'.[67] The key word, as ever, was 'lady'. This was the title which an army nursing sister had always claimed: she did not identify with ordinary working women, or with the male orderly staff. Indeed, qualified and unqualified nurses in South Africa seemed united only in their condemnation of the poor orderlies; these were the true heirs of the Crimean paid nurses, widely assumed to have no fine motives for their work, although, as we have seen, they actually put in far longer hours than the sisters.[68] Amateurs were criticised by professional nurses if their pretensions exceeded their qualifications: but they were much more heavily criticised for letting down ladylike standards of behaviour.

This reaction arose from the long-standing anxieties of the nineteenth-century nursing reformers. Intimate services had to be performed by the nurse in a context utterly divorced from personal familiarity, or she would lose her authority over her patient and her professional standing with the public, to say nothing of her reputation at large. But this preoccupation took on added force during the war. Nurses who wished to improve the status of the military sisters were determined that they should be seen on a level of equality with the heroes of the empire. Women who were transparently after husbands, or the vicarious excitement of battle, would only enjoy secondary status in this most public of arenas. They would be camp followers, not heroines. Camp followers did not win medals: but every nurse who served officially in the Boer War was rewarded with the South African War Service Medal. This, the first British military decoration to be awarded in large numbers on the same terms to both women and men,[69] was the definitive recognition of equal service, and it presaged a new role for the female military nurse of the new century.

NURSING, WAR AND EMPIRE

What evidence is there that nurses in this period criticised or condemned war as an instrument of policy? Towards the end of the century, and before the Czar of Russia's proposal to hold an International Peace Conference at the Hague had stimulated public debate on the subject, the *Nursing Record* had voiced its reservations. With reference to the controversy over dum-dum bullets, it declared:

> We think that most women hold that war is brutalizing and degrading, and a blot on our nineteenth century civilization; but, if war still continues, the methods employed should certainly be less, not more, degrading than those of previous centuries.

It greeted the news of Kitchener's successes in the Sudan by asking 'is there no way of settling national differences but by cold steel?' Even at the height of the Boer War, the funds spent on the exercise were deplored, and better uses – for example, in the education of women and girls – were suggested for them.[70]

These dissenting opinions, however, seem not to have been representative of the majority of nurses. None appear to have seen the retention and expansion of the British empire as anything but desirable in itself. More than this, nurses accepted the definition of the empire as the public arena in which they themselves should seek distinction. They not only supported every measure promoted to strengthen and protect the empire, but demanded equal rights with men to participate in these measures. A few months before the outbreak of the Boer War, Ethel Bedford Fenwick declared:

> we feel sure that the Nursing Profession is with us in our belief that wherever the British Flag goes, and British people need the attendance of skilled nurses, there it is their duty to follow and they claim the right, in the exercise of their profession, to perform this duty, and, side by side with men, to encounter the risks involved.

She greeted the declaration of war with editorial disapproval of this means of solving disputes; however, since she fully supported Britain's imperial role, she could ultimately do no other than endorse the war as being in the national cause – and demand parity

16 Boer War memorial plaque, St Helens, Lancs. The first war memorial to carry a woman's name, that of an Army Nursing Reserve sister. (Author's collection)

17 Stained glass window, the parish church of St John, Great Clacton,
Essex, depicting Red Cross nurse, Zulu chief, Jack Tar, and soldier
in Khaki and bushwhack hat. (Author's collection)

of recognition for British military nurses with British soldiers.[71]

No nurse appears to have been troubled by the thought, expressed succinctly by Elizabeth Haldane after the First World War, 'that she who binds up the wounds that war has made has also helped that war to be carried on'.[72] Nor did the thought occur that her work, even where it consisted in soothing the terminally ill rather than in actually restoring cannon fodder to the front line, was nevertheless assisting the progress of the war by making imperial and militarist policies more palatable to combatants, their relatives, and the British public at large. The early critics of the Red Cross movement had pointed out that in many ways the voluntary provision of ambulances made it easier for governments to launch and wage wars,[73] but at the turn of the century the double-edged nature of humanitarianism in war escaped comment: and the fact that so many more British soldiers died of disease than of wounds in the Boer War may also have helped to obscure the connection between the military hospital and success in the battlefield. The British war nurses saw their work as a simple good, the one bright spot on a dark horizon. They felt this to be particularly true in regard to the care they bestowed on the Boer sick and wounded; however, those British nurses who were sent to work among the Boer women and children in the concentration camps were for the most part seen by their patients as the accomplices of an oppressive and brutal colonial regime; and very little publicity was given to this aspect of the nursing contribution to the war effort.[74]

For most of the nurses, the war was (as they thought) a once-in-a-lifetime experience, of which every exotic detail was to be relished. There was no revulsion from the trappings of war. Nurses did their share of collecting shrapnel for souvenirs, and indulged in the 'khaki craze'. A marriage took place between a doctor and nurse in Pietermaritzburg in 1900 where 'not only the bride, but also many of the guests, were arrayed in khaki, enlivened by scarlet trimmings'. Rosamund Rolleston 'created no little sensation' in returning to Bart's 'in the Yeomanry uniform, wearing a khaki colonial hat turned up at one side, with a black feather'.[75] Boer War nurses who were townees very often were taught to ride. Many had to be accommodated in tents, and wondered how they would 'ever again be able to live inside the four walls of a ward'.[76] Hundreds of nurses had been transformed from domestic servants, or cloistered anchoresses, into dashing New Women; many of them decided against coming home. It was hardly to be expected that these experiences would turn them into critics of militarism.

British women were involved in the Boer War as daughters, sisters, wives and widows, as orphans and philanthropists and adventuresses, as well as nurses. But the military nurse was, beyond all these, the personification of women's desire to participate in great events upon the world stage; to serve in a grand secular cause; and to stand alongside the 'real' actors and 'real' citizens, who were men, rather than to wait passively in the background, victims of the action, or largely irrelevant to it. The image of the Red Cross nurse helped women to channel new aspirations towards service, citizenship, equality, and agency, in a military direction. The military mystique, in its turn, coloured older ideas of woman's purifying mission in society, and her unique spiritual qualities. This tendency was, if anything, confirmed and sanctified by the deaths of twenty-four army nurses in South Africa.[77] Dosia Bagot wrote of a nurse who died from the enteric fever of her patients:[78]

> what would the reader have felt had he passed one, wrapped like a soldier in the nation's colours, borne by soldiers to a soldier's grave, who was receiving the only earthly honour that could be done to a noble woman – a soldier's funeral!

A Reserve nurse, Clara Evans, earned the melancholy distinction of being the first woman to have her name engraved alongside those of combatant soldiers on a memorial to the war dead.[79] As the war drew to a close, a parish church commissioned a stained glass window in which an idealised representation of a Red Cross nurse figured prominently.[80] Perhaps it is not surprising that, a decade later, many spokeswomen of the Women's Social and Political Union seemed almost incapable of describing the sacredness of their struggle except in military metaphors.[81] By the turn of the century, it was as if femininity itself, and with it much of feminism, had been militarised, and provided with a new uniform: a nurse's dress, the Red Cross emblem, and a war service medal for the live model; a union jack and a war memorial for the dead one.

CHAPTER 8

DISASTERS AND REFORM: THE ANGLO-BOER WAR AND AFTER, 1899–1906

The British government and War Office embarked upon the South African War as upon yet another colonial skirmish, in which the integrity of the empire could be maintained by a thin red line of professional troops. It lasted from October 1899 until May 1902. In order to crush the Boer republics, Britain was obliged to commit – in addition to more than 250,000 regular troops – over 100,000 men enlisted through the British Militia, Yeomanry and Volunteer Force, a further 50,000 troops raised in South Africa itself, and 30,000 volunteers from the white self-governing colonies. The military establishment was totally unprepared for a conflict of this magnitude, and the military medical services were correspondingly unprepared to deal with its casualties. Of the 22,000 recorded deaths, less than a third took place on the field of battle.[1] It is hard to approach the medical history of the Anglo-Boer War without a strong sense of *déjà vu*. As in the Crimean War, overcrowded hospitals and neglected patients led to more soldiers dying from preventable disease than from the weapons of the enemy; newspaper coverage of the scandal provoked a civilian demand for more female nurses, and several royal commissions of inquiry; subsequent committees on reorganisation devised reforms for the army medical services. Here the historical parallels end. The post-Crimean reforms produced a tiny, marginal female nursing service. Those inaugurated in 1902 represented a major and irreversible policy shift on the employment of female nurses in wartime. The prolonged and bitter struggle against the Boers effected crucial changes in the way Britain's relations with other powers were perceived, and foreshadowed the shape of wars to come. Viewed through this prism of state interests, the involvement of women in war nursing could no longer be dismissed as a 'philanthropic craze'.

THE SICKNESSES OF WAR

The early months of the war saw the British army trapped into the three sieges of Kimberley, Mafeking and Ladysmith, as well as defeated outright by the Boers at Magersfontein, Stormberg, Colenso, Spion Kop and Vaal Krantz. With the arrival of Field-Marshal Lord Roberts in the Cape in January 1900, the Boers' successes began to be reversed. By February, Kimberley and Ladysmith had been relieved, and General Cronje had surrendered at Paardeberg; Bloemfontein was captured in March; in May and June Mafeking was relieved, Johannesburg and Pretoria captured, and the Orange Free State annexed. However, as Britain's fortunes in war advanced, the health of her soldiers deteriorated. By March over 8,000 men were in hospital – a percentage of sick to strength of more than 5; by May the figures were over 14,000 and nearly 7 per cent respectively. Each of the sieges had of course had a debilitating effect on the troops, subjecting them to cramped accommodation and shortages of food and medical supplies. Inadequate sanitation was the most important cause of invalidism: at Ladysmith, for example, out of a total of 13,500 troops, 10,688 were admitted to hospital between November 1899 and February 1900, and 551 died of (chiefly gastro-enteric) disease. But the subsequent capture of a Boer city was to prove even more disastrous to the health of the British forces than the siege of a British one. The population of Bloemfontein shot from 4,000 to 40,000 in the space of a month, and an impossible strain was imposed on every form of provision for the occupying troops, who rapidly succumbed to a violent epidemic of typhoid.[2]

The RAMC responded to these trials by accepting the contributions of voluntary agencies, and by heavy recruitment of additional staff: around 500 civilian surgeons, nearly 3,000 male orderlies, and around 900 nurses. Male medical personnel were chiefly recruited in Britain, from the RAMC Reserve, and from

Table 8.1 Female military nurses in South Africa, other than those locally recruited, September 1899–July 1900

		A	B	C
September			5	
October	30th	14	28	28
November			24	26
December	4th	51	31	10
January	1st	63		
	29th	92	11	9
February	26th	103	58	9
March	26th	220	110	100
April			21	17
May	7th	353	15	19
June	4th	377	127	96
July	2nd	477		
	16th	547	1	85

Key A = *Report of the Royal Commission on the War in South Africa*, PP XLII, 1904, Appendix no. 39, p. 267, 'Statement of the Strength of Medical Corps and other Arms in South Africa, including Colonials and Voluntary Hospitals, on certain dates from 2nd October 1899 to 16th July 1900'. The final figure includes 48 nurses from overseas Colonies.

B = *Appendix to the Report of the Royal Commission on the Care and Treatment of the Sick and Wounded during the South African Campaign*, PP XXX 1901, Jameson I, p. 261, 'Embarkation of Army Medical Services'.

C = W.O. 108/88 'Embarkations in connection with the South African Campaign, 1899–1901'.

veterans, from the Medical Staff Corps of the Militia and the Volunteer Force, and by direct enlistment; around 1400 men were obtained through the St John's Ambulance Brigade.[3] As for the nurses, exact figures are impossible to come by. Roughly a third of them were said to have been taken on in South Africa, but no record was kept of these local recruits;[4] and there are wide discrepancies between official statements of female nursing strength (see Table 8.1). Various reasons can be suggested for these discrepancies: figures may have been inflated by the inclusion of wardmaids and female servants; nurses who were already on the establishment may have been counted again when they returned from leave. Certainly as the public outcry over medical misman-agement grew, the army medical authorities were under pressure to exaggerate the size of the female nursing staff.

The shortage of skilled female nurses in South Africa became one of the main themes of public discontent. Professional civilian nurses played an important role here: they criticised Army Nursing Service methods of working; they also accused many volunteer nurses of frivolousness. Worse charges were levelled at the orderlies: they were callous and neglectful, and they stole the patients' rations; those who were not deliberately unkind were almost criminally incompetent. *The Times*, perhaps self-consciously repeating its scoop of 1854, despatched a special observer to report on the condition of the sick and wounded. This was William Burdett-Coutts, Unionist MP and husband of the millionaire philanthropist Angela Burdett-Coutts. His accounts of filth and neglect in hospital and in transit from the front, and of shortages of food, medicine, equipment and personnel, fuelled the demand for a Royal Commission, which took evidence in Britain and South Africa in July and August 1900. Among its recommendations, published in January 1901, were a larger and more easily expandable RAMC; improved professional standards among military medical officers; the appointment of sanitary officers; and the more widespread employment of female nurses.[5]

Whether better nursing in itself would have mitigated the medical disasters of the war is doubtful. As in the Crimean War, many other factors contributed to the high rates of sickness and mortality. Above all, it seems clear that prevention of disease was given too low a priority. Less than 4 per cent of the troops were inoculated against typhoid, although Almroth Wright, the Professor of Pathology at Netley, had conducted pioneering and successful trials of typhoid vaccine from 1895 onwards.[6] Nor did the RAMC make any very strenuous efforts to create a pure water supply. The 1904 Commission on the war criticised the Corps for having no general system for testing and purifying water supplies in the field, such as existed in the German army. Medical officers claimed that 'filters have not formed a part of the normal equipment of a regimental unit on field service, mainly on account of the difficulty of obtaining a good pattern'; nor was fuel always available for boiling the water instead. They also argued that equipment was only as good as the men who used it:

> The soldier will take absolutely no trouble, if left to himself, because he neither knows nor believes in the danger of using bad water, rather than go 100 yards to fill his water bottle with filtered water he will resort to the nearest Railway tap which provides water of the filthiest description.

A large intake of untried civilians could only aggravate sanitary problems:

> One of the disadvantages of civilisation is that the individual is relieved of all responsibility for the disposal of his excreta – a condition which does not exist under the barbaric regime of war.

The RAMC as a whole had not yet grasped the need to educate soldiers in sanitary skills; it was thought that regiments with recent Indian experience had a better record in this respect than those coming straight from Britain.[7]

If prevention was certainly better than a cure, there was more to the cure than provision of female nurses. Medical and dietary supplies were needed, in quantities which the Army Medical Services had failed to anticipate. These supplies in turn required a dependable transport system. The Boers' success in sabotaging the railway network reduced Bloemfontein and Pretoria to the use of one single-track railway line on which troops, animals, weapons and equipment of all kinds had to travel. Since 'the object of war is not the care of the sick and wounded, but the winning of battles', medical supplies could not take priority over ordnance.[8] However, when all the factors contributing to misery in the hospitals were taken into account, it remained true that, the damage done, a large and experienced nursing staff was essential to the care of gastro-enteric sufferers. Patients needed food and medicine; to be kept clean; to be kept in bed; to be kept from getting dehydrated; to be kept apart. In short, they needed constant attention and supervision; and in the end, successful nursing was largely a matter of numbers. RAMC wards and hospital tents were almost inevitably overcrowded. The much-praised voluntary hospitals had a lower death rate, because they had the right to say they were full; thus staff-patient ratios remained manageable, wards and tents were cleaner and airier, and one distinguished volunteer surgeon,

Conan Doyle, even had the leisure to write a history of the war.[9]

Why, once disaster had struck, did the Army Medical Services persist with a policy of recruiting nearly ten male orderlies for every female nurse? It would seem that even the South African catastrophe was not enough to change the *idées fixes* of the military-medical establishment. The regular Army Nursing Service was so small and scattered that many military medical officers were still unused to working with the Sisters. 'I never thought', Col. W. Macnamara told the Royal Commissioners in 1900, 'you could get one lady to manage forty ladies coming and going; but we have not had the slightest trouble. . . . The great difficulty in a hospital is you have to house them and treat them as ladies should be treated – differently, of course, from men. . . . I was surprised; we never had the slightest difficulty with the nursing sisters. It was simply wonderful.'[10] One implication of 'treating the nurses as ladies' was universally understood as the requirement to provide them with servants. In some hospitals, one servant was found for every four nurses; in others the ratio was one to seven. One nurse reported that 'so many English maids have broken down out here' that the Sisters were obliged to employ native servants, which some of them experienced as a great strain; Eleanor Laurence was unusual in preferring African to English domestics. In some cases, male orderlies were told off to act as servants to the nurses.[11] The fact that male orderlies did not require any of these adjuncts was a strong argument for employing them, rather than female nurses.

A more positive argument in the male orderlies' favour was that they could be employed in a great variety of capacities. Female nurses did none of the fetching, carrying and cleaning work of the hospitals; they could not put up or pull down a tent, or act as officers' servants; and they did not even undertake very much personal nursing of patients. Male orderlies were Jacks-of-all-trades, 'running about unendingly', 'terribly overworked', and, in one sense, very good value for money. They could be employed in field as well as base hospitals, as stretcher-bearers as well as ward-maids. Specialists appeared to be a luxury item in the emergency of war. However, as pre-war critics of the army hospital system had already pointed out, this policy might be one of false economy. The system was producing good general servants and handymen and very poor nurses. When the immediate scandal surrounding the condition of the sick and wounded in South Africa had died down, thoughtful voices were raised to urge that more male orderlies should be allowed to specialise in nursing work; and that, to justify their employment, female nurses should no longer be restricted to the supervisory role of the ward sister.[12]

WOMEN, WHITES AND 'CIVILISED' WAR

Before the war, the received wisdom on female military nurses had been that their role, if any, was in base hospitals. They were not to be employed in field hospitals, or anywhere near the front. This was reiterated in the Commissioners' report of 1901. But the experience of the war threw the terms 'base' and 'front' into question.[13] Was a city under siege 'base' or 'front'? A nurse at Mafeking recalled that 'one man who was in hospital with a wound was wounded a second time by a bullet from outside; we had put him in a safe place, as we thought, but a shot struck him. . . . We had often to pick the bullets out of the walls over the beds. . . . Once a shell burst in the ward, but only one person was killed, a native boy.' The nurses at Ladysmith were shelled for a week before the hospitals were moved two and a half miles out to Intombi Spruit, which was still directly under the flight path of the Boer guns. 'Being just under the Boer camp we were virtually prisoners of war, and had to absolutely observe all the conditions laid down by General Joubert, one of which was that we were to hand over cameras and field-glasses.' Guerrilla warfare, moreover, turned any area into a potential battleground. Trains were frequently shot at, and tracks were mined. Sisters Rose-Innes and de Montmorency, who accompanied a hospital train from Graspan to Cape Town, were described by an RAMC officer as 'two of the pluckiest women alive. They do not mind the bullets one bit, and attend the wounded as though they were in the ward.' The first two nurses to reach Waterval Onder, in the Transvaal, were told that 'it was not very fair to send us, as the Boers were all around, and that, only the night before, a train had been attacked, five Coldstream Guards killed and twenty-one wounded. We saw the graves as we passed.'[14]

These nurses were breaking the unwritten rules in admittedly ambiguous situations. Four others contravened them more directly by travelling with a field hospital. This was organised on a voluntary basis, and led by Frederick Treves, of the London

211

Hospital. It accompanied General Buller's column over a period of three months, from Frere to Ladysmith. Treves had his own transport facilities, as well as some given him by the War Office, and he had Buller's special permission for his experiment on the understanding 'that if anything occurred these nurses could retreat at a moment's notice'. At one point it was, indeed, 'thought desirable that the women should be at once got out of danger, and so they were bundled down to Frere with little ceremony in a mule wagon.' Sisters McCaul and Tarr, who worked at a London nursing home used by Treves's patients, and Sisters Sammut and Martin, from Netley, were employed 'on the condition that it should not be used as any kind of precedent'; but it was inevitable that their adventures should have been widely publicised, and that they should have been held up by the female nursing lobby as an example of how women's role in war could be extended.[15]

Throughout the war, the nursing press printed hundreds of letters from nurses in South Africa, which were full of graphic detail on their living and working conditions. Their accounts gave substance to pre-war arguments, especially those of the pro-registration, pro-suffrage *Nursing Record*, that women had the right and the capacity to participate with men in the defence and expansion of the empire. Here were nurses living under canvas, and loving it, even when their tents collapsed, pinning them to the ground, or forcing them to dine on the bare veldt; here were nurses belying the medical officers' expectations by doing without servants:

> We do our own washing, and you would laugh to see us with our sleeves rolled up and washing away with limited water. We pin our clothes on to the tents to dry as we finish them, and the result is quite ornamental.[16]

The Assistant-Director of Army Medical Services insisted that female nurses would always be out of place in field hospitals, because 'they want beds, and there are no such things', but the readers of the nursing press knew otherwise: female nurses at Ladysmith 'found that there was nowhere for us to go except the Cricket Pavilion, where other Sisters were already sleeping on the bar, or counter'. Frederick Treves wrote to the Duchess of Bedford that at Chievely his female nurses 'did not have their clothes off for two nights and were at work night and day. Miss McCaul gave away all her handkerchiefs, gave up her water-bottle and her

18 Nurses with a Hospital Train in South Africa. (Bodleian Library)

19 Nurses with Sir Frederick Treves's Field Hospital in South Africa, 1900. No other nurses had official permission to work in mobile field hospitals during the war. Note the bushwhack hats. (Bodleian Library)

mattress.' Afterwards 'the four of them slept on the floor of a looted and empty room' in a hotel in Frere. 'This was their only "night in" in three days.'[17]

The female nurses of the Boer War demonstrated that even a service 'composed of ladies' could live and work and display great stamina in fairly rough conditions. Adventures which before the war had been confined to a few individuals in exceptional circumstances were now the experience of hundreds of British women volunteers. However, women's evident ability to 'rough it' – which had, after all, been demonstrated on previous occasions – was not in itself enough to dispel official prejudices against employing them in the field. Rarely stated before the war, but undoubtedly important in official thinking, was the objection to exposing women to sexual danger. In 1894 Sister Janet King, excoriating the ambitions of Ethel Stoke's WVMSC, had given a fairly strong hint as to why women should stay well away from the battlefield – 'what would be their fate as a prisoner of war to savage Cossack, or brutal Bashi Bazook, to fierce Zulu, or cruel and crafty Afghan?' These objections now had to be qualified. 'What harm came to Mr Treves's four nurses at Colenso?' asked Burdett-Coutts. None, because they were nursing 'in a distant, but civilised country, a country in which none can say the sanctity of womanhood is not recognised.'[18]

The conflict with the Boers differed from all others in which Britain had been involved since the Crimea in being primarily one between white men. Other races, it was thought, might indulge in rapine, and the slaughter of prisoners; Europeans, whether or not formally bound by the Geneva convention, could be expected to abide by its terms. The Principal Medical Officer for Natal declared that 'a nurse can never go into a Soudan campaign, where we are liable to attack, and most of our campaigns are like that. If we are camping in civilised country I think nurses can go, and I think they are extremely useful.' An Army sister at Maritzburg echoed his views:

One thing we have all decided; and this is, that in future white wars both hospitals and women nurses must be carried nearer the front. . . . The women would not be murdered or ill-treated – in a white man's land, at any rate – any more than the sick and wounded are.[19]

As a 'white man's war', the Boer War had a very ambiguous

character. Non-whites fought and suffered alongside whites. The appalling episode of the concentration camps exposed a racist contempt for Boer women and children among many of the British officials (male and female) responsible for them. The settlement of the war reduced the Boer republics to colonial status, and imposed upon them a culturally humiliating regime. Nevertheless, the Boers *were* Europeans. Britain's European rivals, France and Germany, actively sympathised and identified with their cause – a boon which had not been extended, for example, to the inhabitants of the Sudan. The British victory had been far harder to achieve than in previous conflicts with native races of the empire, and it conjured up prospects of future military trials in which a Continental power might intervene on the side of the enemy, or even sieze the opportunity to invade the British Isles. If the future of war did indeed lie among competing 'civilised' nations, then women need not be prevented from participating. (In this context, the devastating impact of the German execution of a female nurse, Edith Cavell, in 1915, should not be underestimated. In shooting, rather than interning, a white woman for espionage, the Germans placed themselves in the imagined world of non-European races; this in turn lent enormous force to racist propaganda against them on the Allied side.)

The perceived courage and powers of endurance of British women, and the assumed chivalry of European males, while among the necessary pre-conditions for admitting female nurses to war service, were not in themselves factors which would impel the army medical system towards reform and a change in the ratio of female to male military nurses. From the Crimean War onwards, a female nursing service had been something forced on the Army Medical Department by civilian pressure groups; it had been dispensed with, or marginalised, whenever the influence of these groups could be blocked, or when they voluntarily dissolved. Permanent and large-scale institutional change could only take place when public opinion became intrinsic to military recruit-ment, mobilisation and medical care. Here the voluntary surgeons and nurses recruited in such large numbers into the RAMC and Army Nursing Reserve turned out to be a mixed blessing for their hosts. Many of them came fresh from the most distinguished metropolitan teaching hospitals: they were shocked to find old-fashioned and cumbersome equipment, and medicines which they suspected were twenty years old. They found the organisation of nursing irrational, and standards of hygiene disquietingly low. The surgeons made their views known to the Royal Commissioners, and published them in the *Lancet* and the *British Medical Journal*. They wrote moderately, constructively, even supportively: but the cumulative effect of their comments was damning.[20] The Army Reserve sisters gave interviews to the nursing press, or wrote letters home which were printed there, anonymously; a few gave evidence to the Royal Commissioners. Without explicitly criticising the army medical authorities, the sisters expressed a lively astonishment at the division of labour they found in the military wards, and a profound perplexity in the face of bureaucratic supply procedures. They could not give even the most neutral account of their own work without graphically conveying the acute over-crowding and under-manning – or under-womanning – of the military hospitals. Ethel McCaul, one of Treves's field hospital nurses, condemned the equipment of field hospitals, and the dirt and neglect at base hospitals, in a series of articles in the *Daily Chronicle* from which Treves dissociated himself, and which the newspaper cut short owing to 'pressure of space'. However, in April 1901 her more temperate 'Some Suggestions for Army Reform: Army Nursing' was published in the *Nineteenth Century*, with an approving foreword by Treves.[21]

It was impossible for the RAMC to shrug off as merely opinionated and uninformed such an overwhelmingly negative verdict on its wartime performance. The critique was based on experience in the field, and came from the heights of the medical profession. Moreover, and more significantly, it articulated and gave substance to a mounting disquiet amongst the non-medical public. Despite distance and censorship, the families of soldiers knew that things were going badly in the military hospitals.[22] They knew that husbands, fathers, sons and brothers were dying in large numbers, not of wounds received on the battlefield, but, in Kipling's words, of[23]

> Dysentery that milks the heart out of a man and shames him before his kind; rheumatism, which is the seven devils of a toothache, in the marrow of your bones; typhoid of the loaded breath and the silly eye, incontinent and consuming; pneumonia that stabs in the back and drives the poor soul, suffocating and bewildered, through all the hells of delirium.

It was one thing to be killed by the enemies of one's country and its empire; it was quite another to die in a hot, crowded, fly-ridden tent, for lack of clean drinking water, sanitation, and medical attention. This was not what eager young men of the Yeomanry and Volunteer Force had enlisted in their thousands for.[24]

In previous colonial campaigns, criticism of the care of sick and wounded British soldiers had been a protest mounted on behalf of a relatively mute and isolated military caste, by self-consciously philanthropic bodies or individuals. But the medical scandals of the Boer War affected 'ordinary' people: the distress of the relatives of 100,000 civilian volunteers had less to do with humanitarianism than with a very human self-interest. The army and its medical system also responded in terms of self-interest, rather than philanthropy. It was clear that 'the standard of hospital comfort has been raised, and that public opinion will demand its maintenance in future wars'. Conscription remained alien to the British military system: and Burdett-Coutts was not alone in thinking that the military hospital scandals could 'injure the popularity of the military service, and that would be a fatal thing in a country which depends and must depend on the voluntary spirit for even its regular army.'[25] As official thinking in the new century drew closer to the concept of 'the nation in arms' and 'the citizen army', the army medical services at last allowed a civilian panacea – a female nursing corps – a permanent place in its planning for war.

But the reform was more than a public relations exercise. The experience of the war had convinced several army medical officers that good nursing was now crucial to military efficiency. The most important of these was Alfred Keogh, who on becoming Director-General in 1905, drew up a programme based on lessons learned in South Africa, which was to influence all medical planning for the First World War. Keogh believed, along with many of his predecessors, that the Army Medical Services existed to prevent the onset and spread of disease through sanitary precautions, and to recover non-effectives from the fighting zone through efficient lines of communication and ambulance services. He went further than them, however, when he committed the Services to restoring men to the front. For this to be possible, expert nursing personnel were essential. Given their 'knowledge of the soldier and his duties', they would be able to single out from among the invalids those men who could, with appropriate treatment, be restored to fighting fitness.[26]

Keogh was convinced that a quite unnecessary number of men

had been lost to the army in South Africa through the RAMC's policy on invaliding. General Buller explained to the Royal Commission on the South African War that 'I should have been smothered in Natal had I not at my own instance provided five hospital ships . . . consequently I kept my hospitals always fairly free . . . it is far better for a sick man, no matter what the journey is, to get him put on board ship, and sent home than to have him at a convalescent depot pining his heart out and doing nothing.' At the Cape Town base, it was reported that the MO's work 'was increased by the necessity of sending off an average of eight hundred invalids weekly to their homes overseas, to make room for the new comers from up country'. Lt-Col. Simpson reflected in 1911 that 'The opportunities for sending men home were so frequent that invaliding was carried out largely as a means of dealing with temporary inefficiency, and preventing an undue accumulation of sick in the hospitals.'[27] The large numbers of sick in South Africa had thus been seen chiefly as an administrative problem to be cleared out of the way whenever possible. Keogh thought this was due not only to the lack of hospital accommodation, but also to the shortage of suitably trained hospital staff, and to a general attitude of defeatism with regard to the wastage of military manpower. The army could no longer afford to tolerate this attitude, and a modern military medical corps ought to possess the means 'of gathering up and returning to the ranks those who have fallen out and are fit to return. They number thousands in every campaign. The hospitals are filled with them . . . they gravitate to "billets", to the homeward bound Troopships, pass to their homes in England, and are not gathered up again.'[28]

Underlying all Keogh's reasoning was the conviction that, in the twentieth century, numbers were the key to military victory. Extensive losses of sick and wounded were not only medically unnecessary and politically unacceptable – in any subsequent war they might be strategically catastrophic. Britain's previous wars against indigenous colonial populations had been won on the basis of superior organisation and technology. These advantages had not told in Britain's favour in South Africa. If the marksmanship and firepower of Boer farmers had stretched the British military establishment to the limits, what was to be expected of a conflict with a major European power? All Continental belligerents now possessed long-range artillery weapons of considerable accuracy which could inflict very heavy casualties. Although those who forecast a defensive stalemate in the trenches as the inescapable pattern of wars to come were hotly opposed and derided, influential writers, such as the German General von der Goltz, author of *The Nation in Arms*, depicted the coming power struggle more as a huge slugging match between heavyweights than as a duel of skill.[29] In this context, 'repairing the losses' ceased to be a figure of speech: nothing must be allowed to diminish the fighting strength of the nation. The balance of military-medical thinking was thus shifting from battlefield rescue to nursing care; from field to base hospitals; from orderly fatigues to skilled nursing – and therefore, given the structure of the nineteenth- and twentieth-century nursing profession, from male to female personnel. On the combatant side, moreover, it was becoming increasingly difficult to justify setting aside thousands of able-bodied males to serve as hospital nurses and domestics at a time of national crisis. The same pressures which in 1903 drove Lord Roberts to form the National Service League to campaign for military conscription, and which set off a multi-faceted quest for 'national efficiency',[30] were also to confirm the gender of the military nurse as female.

LEGITIMATION AT LAST? THE CREATION OF THE QUEEN ALEXANDRA'S IMPERIAL MILITARY NURSING SERVICE

Well before the outbreak of the Boer War, pro-registration, pro-suffrage nurses had argued for their own profession's involvement in official planning for war. Their call was echoed within the wider feminist community by women such as Mrs Fawcett, who advocated a larger role for women in the management of the machinery of the state. 'Women in the War Office! I think I hear my readers exclaim in horror,' she wrote in 1899. 'Yes, it may be rejoined, women looking after, or helping to look after, the feeding, clothing, and sanitation of the army, just as they always have been responsible for similar duties in household affairs.'[31] Mrs Fawcett's desire to serve the state was rewarded in 1901 when she was appointed to head an all-female committee to investigate conditions in the concentration camps where Boer women and children had been interned.[32] The nursing lobby was rewarded by reforms which increased the number of army sisters, and placed them on the war establishment of the military medical services. If these were blows struck in the cause of sexual equality, an even more momentous advance was discerned in the post-war reorganisation of the army medical services. The War Office set up an Advisory Board and a Nursing Board to supervise army medical matters: two matrons of civil hospitals were to sit on the latter 'appointed by the Crown, on the advice of the Secretary of State'.[33] Women were, it seemed, at last ensconced at the War Office, and the new Queen Alexandra's Imperial Military Nursing Service, which by royal warrant replaced the Army Nursing Service in March 1902, seemed in many ways designed to meet the civil nurses' criticisms of the pre-war service. The nursing lobby was, however, to find that these advances were neither unambiguous nor uncontested.

The War Office committee on the reorganisation of the army medical and army nursing services, appointed in June 1901, consisted of civil surgeons, combatant officers, and representatives of the RAMC and Indian Medical Service, and it was chaired by the Secretary of State, St John Brodrick, himself.[34] No nurses, and no other women were appointed to the committee, which sat in private and did not take evidence. The 'nursing offensive' had to be mounted from outside the gates, by personages no less than Queen Alexandra, who was to be president of the new nursing service, and her friend Lady Roberts, wife of the Commander-in-Chief. But the nursing interest faced formidable opposition. For the medical members of the committee, both military and civilian, the supreme objective was – as it had been for forty years past – to head off any challenge to the authority of military medical officers. For all the admiration which they had publicly expressed for the female nurses' contribution to the war effort, their private voices told a different story. Resentment of nurses' ambitions, and even hostility to women in general, spill out from the record of the committee's proceedings, which were, unusually, minuted verbatim.

One of the thorniest issues dealt with by the committee concerned the right of matrons to make completely confidential reports on their nurses to the Matron-in-Chief. Since this required that they act without reference to their medical officers, the proposal provoked the most vituperative outburst from Keogh:

> I do not believe you could trust a lot of women with the power you are going to give them here. I believe a man is much more

221

honourable. I believe in petty spites. Look at what goes on in a garrison. These ladies are going out into society, going to tea and to dances. They are taken up by certain people in the garrison. If the matron is not taken up – if a pretty girl, or a taking girl, goes out into society more than she does, and people will not have anything to say to her – she will give it that girl very hot in her confidential report. Women have not the same feeling about these things.

Sir Gerald Morton objected mildly: 'That has not been my experience, and I have seen a great deal of the Indian Nursing Service.' Treves, however, weighed in on Keogh's side against the professional claims of nurses:[35]

I think if you take cases in private practice, you certainly would not go to this lady or that to know whether so-and-so is a good nurse. She may be ill-mannered, or what not, but the question is, is she a good nurse? and the only person capable of giving an opinion on that point is the Surgeon or Physician in charge of that individual patient. I think that is a thing that admits of no controversy. . . . I do not know what sort of insubordination you will not have in that hospital. The nurse does not care *that* for the Surgeon.

It was in vain for Brodrick to urge that 'Lord Roberts, to whom I referred this, is strongly in favour of the complete autonomy of the Matrons in this respect', for his audience almost certainly suspected that the Commander-in-Chief was merely his wife's mouthpiece in nursing questions. It was equally vain for him to say that 'those who represent the nurses will take this as the death-blow to their hopes if we do put it "in conjunction with the Senior Medical Officer",' since the medical members of the committee were only too happy to inflict such a blow. The regulations finally stipulated that a matron's reports be submitted to her medical officer before being forwarded to the Matron-in-Chief.[36] With this question settled, the problem of confidential reports on the matron herself provided only a minor hiccup. It was at first decided that the Principal Medical Officer should report on the matrons in his district via the General Officer Commanding to the Matron-in-Chief. But this was too much for Cooper Perry: 'I speak with all submission, but I did not know that it was according to Military custom for the Principal Medical Officer to report to a woman.'

His colleagues took the point, and amended the proposal to read that the report should be made to the Nursing Board.[37]

In one area alone was women's control seen by all members of the committee as wholly uncontentious: this was the responsibility for linen and laundry, hitherto assigned to the MO and the quartermaster or steward. Here the committee seemed to be echoing Mrs Fawcett's views on the suitability of women to take on the domestic responsibilities of departments of state. This was a safe outlet for the nurses' ambitions; and one in which, it must be noted, they had shown no previous interest whatever. 'I should think', Howard Tooth, of Bart's, opined, 'that the Medical Officer would be very glad to have that duty shifted on to someone who knows more about it. I think the Matron would do it a good deal better.' Keogh agreed: 'I should like to see a woman in charge of it all.' Ward, the Vice-Chairman, Permanent Under-Secretary at the War Office, was with them: 'Everyone knows that a woman would do it better.'[38]

If the military nurses faced the most serious challenge to their professional ambitions from the medical men, they faced another threat from the vestiges of lay control and philanthropy enshrined in the new administrative structures. The royal patronage of the new service was a doubtful advantage. Although Queen Alexandra argued hard for higher wages for the army sisters, and for increasing their authority over male personnel, her chief recorded concern was to attract candidates 'from a *better class and more* cultivated and educated than is generally the case'. She complained that the thirty-six nurses she had 'most carefully selected' for South Africa had been placed 'under *Superintendents* of a *lower* grade and inferior class to themselves'. She referred to the Nursing Board as 'my Board', and its first meeting took place at Buckingham Palace.[39] She did not wish the Matron-in-Chief to have a seat on it, and Brodrick had to rally the members of the committee to insist that the Matron-in-Chief was not excluded.[40] The two members whom the Queen nominated to the board were Viscountess Downe, a figure not previously associated with the nursing interest, and Sydney Holland, chairman of the managers of the London Hospital, one of the fiercest opponents of the registration of nurses, who was also strongly opposed to the raising of a military nursing reserve from civilian hospitals during a time of peace.[41] Thus the body on which the nursing lobby had pinned such great hopes, which was officially empowered to lay down the precise duties of army nurses, to select candidates for admission and make recommendations for their promotion, distribution, and dismissal, and to advise on the formation of a reserve in case of war or epidemic, was largely dominated by the male medical profession, the world of aristocratic female philanthropy, and individuals hostile to demands for greater professional autonomy for nurses.

The major innovation promulgated with the regulations for the QAIMNS in October 1902 was an extended hierarchy: where once had been only Lady Superintendent, Superintendent, Acting Superintendent and Sister were now Matron-in-Chief, Principal Matron, Matron, Sister and Staff Nurse. Together with the expansion of the service to more than twice its pre-war numbers, this reform offered opportunities for promotion which had hitherto been lacking in army nursing. For the grades of matron upwards, salaries were considerably higher than pre-war levels. In 1904 all salaries were again raised: army staff nurses and sisters were actually paid more than sisters in the Metropolitan voluntary hospitals; but army matrons' salaries remained uncompetitive (see Table 8.2).

Another reform of 1904 which enhanced army nursing as a career was the provision made for in-service training. Sisters and matrons were now obliged to spend special leave on full pay at large civil hospitals, observing advances in medical and surgical treatment, and changes in nursing techniques.[42]

While most of these changes were welcomed by army nurses and the wider nursing community, the introduction of the non-supervisory grade of staff nurse was greeted with something approaching dismay. One former army sister wrote that[43]

> In the Army there is so much in status and name that women who would gladly join as Junior Sisters will not do so as Staff Nurses – the term 'nurse' usually means one Tommy's wife who acts as Gamp to another. A Nursing Sister has acquired quite another grade of prestige.'

A more significant grievance was the fact that a nurse, after gaining the certificate of three years' training and service which was now the qualification for entry, would be employed at a lower level than she might have expected from her next civilian post. She would have to wait at least two years in a military hospital before getting the chance of promotion to sister grade, during which time

Table 8.2 Starting salaries for army nurses, 1897–1904 (£ per annum)

	Army Nursing Service 1897	ANS Reserve 1899– 1902	QAIM NS 1902	QAIM NS 1904	Metropolitan voluntary hospitals 1905
Matron-in-Chief/ Lady Superintendent	200		250	300	
Principal Matron			150	175	240–300
Matron/Superintendent Acting Superintendent	50	60	70	75	
Sister	30	40	37.10	50	30–40
Staff Nurse			30	40	

Sources: Regulations for the Army Nursing Service and QAIMNS; *Nursing Record*; H.C. Burdett, *How to become a Nurse* (London 1905); IOR, L/MIL/7/11316 f. 11.

the regulations did not regard her as competent to take charge of a case where anaesthetics were given, or to measure poisonous drugs for hypodermic injections.[44]

How staff nurses and ward orderlies were to work together under the new regime was a vexed question. The first regulations for QAIMNS suggested, rather than stated that the matrons and sisters exercised authority over RAMC non-commissioned officers and men: they had some responsibility for training the latter in nursing duties, and matrons were now responsible for the cleanliness and good order of the wards, instead of, as before the war, for the cleanliness of the patients only. In the absence of a sister from a ward, the staff nurse, and not one of the orderlies, took change. But the regulations for staff nurses also stipulated that 'they must scrupulously refrain from relegating an unfair share of routine ward work to the orderlies' and 'must take a full share in duties which are necessary, however unpleasant, and must set an example of cheerful alacrity in attending to the patients' wants. . . .' The implication here was that the actual duties of staff nurses and ward orderlies were equivalent.[45] The hospital hierarchy was clarified in subsequent regulations for QAIMNS and

Standing Orders for the RAMC. These stated that ward orderlies 'will in hospitals when working under sisters and staff nurses, give prompt obedience to all instructions given to them'; and that 'as regards medical and sanitary matters and work in connection with the sick, the matrons, sisters and staff nurses are to be regarded as having authority in and about military hospitals next after the officers of the Royal Army Medical Corps, and are at all times to be obeyed accordingly, and to receive the respect due to their position.'[46] This differential ranking of men and women doing essentially similar work was to be the source of continuing resentment between staff nurses and male orderlies.

The fact that, after decades of official equivocation on the subject, female military nurses were now empowered to exact obedience, rather than hope for courtesy from male ward orderlies, reflected the major shift in army medical policy by which female nurses had become central to planning for war. An assured position within a military hierarchy could only be derived from combatant status. Although members of the QAIMNS were still not entitled to commissioned rank and male salutes, and although they were – Queen Alexandra's protests notwithstanding – still designated a 'Service' rather than a 'Corps',[47] they were unarguably destined for active service. In 1904 the Matron-in-Chief was asked to prepare estimates of a female nursing establishment for wartime stationary hospitals partially manned by male nursing staff; and the Advisory Board supplemented her work with revised estimates for general and stationary hospitals nursed by women only. It was laid down that members of QAIMNS ordered on active service would be 'supplied with a field kit as supplied to an officer on joining', which would include a portable camp bedstead, a folding chair, and a waterproof bucket; and they would be instructed further to equip themselves with oil stoves, candle lanterns, mackintoshes, gumboots and other necessities of life under canvas.[48] The argument that women required too much baggage, and too many comforts, to be mobilisable for any service outside base hospitals no longer had any official currency.

The original projection for the female military nursing establishment was 228 women, and a commitment to maintain and increase this establishment was sustained despite the evidence that it was more expensive to employ female nurses than male orderlies. By 1905 it was estimated that the cost per annum of a sister and a staff nurse was £196 and £186 respectively, as compared with the cost of a non-commissioned officer at £90 and a nursing orderly at £80.[49] The extra expense went into quarters, messing and servants, and did not take into account a heavy initial outlay on renovating and refurbishing military hospitals, which took place after the reform of the nursing service in 1902. A major programme of hospital inspections was undertaken by the civilian members of the Advisory Board in November and December 1902, largely to check that suitable quarters could be prepared for the expanded female service: the inspectors were appalled to find 'that the sick pauper in our principal cities has better hospital accommodation than has the sick soldier', and that 'of two or three of the hospitals it is not too much to say that they are a disgrace to any civilised country'.[50]

The decision to create a much more expensive army hospital nursing service dictated important changes in the entire provision of military medicine in peacetime. Overall military hospital accommodation was reduced, and the time-honoured practice of incarcerating every non-effective soldier was abandoned. It was decided that convalescent homes should be established in each military district 'with the view of reducing the number of slight cases of illness in hospital', and medical officers were given permission to detain trivial cases in barracks as out-patients. Some of the smaller hospitals were closed, or converted to convalescent homes; more use was henceforward to be made of local civil hospitals, and of a special staff of female nurses whom the Matron-in-Chief would detail for service with isolated severe cases. Female nurses were assigned additional areas of responsibility for which they had not previously clamoured: matrons and sisters in effect took over a large part of the duties of the old wardmaster, becoming responsible for diet sheets to the steward, as well as for patients' property and ward equipment to the quartermaster; and matrons were now to assume responsibility for station hospitals for soldiers' wives and children.[51]

In 1904 the female nursing establishment was raised to 342, and in 1905 to 420. These were projected rather than actual figures: in 1906 there were in fact only 271 female nurses, of whom 70 were in South Africa. But numbers rose steadily, and by the middle of 1914, 466 applications had been accepted by the QAIMNS.[52] The committee on reorganisation had in 1901 accepted as a '*lex non scripta*' the recommendation 'that preference is always given to the relatives of Military Officers'; but the admission records provide no evidence of an unstated bias against civilians. What the regulations did specify was that a candidate 'must satisfy the Nursing Board that, as regards education, character, and social status, she is a fit person to be admitted to Queen Alexandra's Imperial Military Nursing Service'.[53] In practice this rubric covered quite a broad range of social backgrounds. The largest social category of the 466 candidates for admission between 1902 and 1914 comprised the 54 daughters of clerics, both Anglican and nonconformist; the next largest group was the 41 daughters of military officers; 35 candidates had fathers who were civilian medical practitioners. Nine women had fathers in whose occupations these categories overlapped: they were army medical officers, or naval surgeons, or army chaplains. Five women had fathers in the Indian Civil Service, four in the Mercantile Marine. Among the many other fathers' professions listed in the records were landowners, solicitors, War Office clerks, and officers of the police, customs and inland revenue.[54] (Professions of grandfathers, uncles and family friends, which might be equally influential, are not, of course, obtainable from these records.) Of the four Matrons-in-Chief who held office between 1902 and 1914, the first, Sidney Browne, was the daughter of a civilian doctor;[55] the second, C.H. Keer, was described as the daughter of 'an English officer in the Indian service';[56] the third, Ethel Hope Beecher, was the daughter of a Colonel of the Bengal Staff Corps; and the fourth, Emma Maud McCarthy, was the daughter of a lawyer. The latter two Matrons-in-Chief had both entered the QAIMNS after joining the Army Nursing Reserve for the duration of the South African War, and 51 other recruits entered the service by the same route.[57]

The expansion of the female nursing service was accompanied by radical changes in the orderly section of the RAMC. The 1902 reorganisation created two categories of orderly, nursing orderlies and general duty privates. The former were primarily nurses, doing no heavier domestic work than dusting, washing-up, fetching and distributing meals, and cleaning items such as splints and mackintoshes. A link was established between the male and female services, whereby selected members of the RAMC became eligible to join the QAIMNS. This change was made possible by a new system of training devised for ward orderlies. All would receive a preliminary two months' training at Aldershot, and a year's subsequent elementary course at the hospital to which they were

20 Sidney Browne, first Matron-in-Chief of Queen Alexandra's Imperial Military Nursing Service, 1902–6, and of the Territorial Force Nursing Service, 1908–19. (QARANC)

posted. Some would then train for a second and third year, qualifying as Second Class and then as First Class orderlies. The latter might apply to join QAIMNS after a further examination, after which they would rank below a staff nurse, while being placed at the upper end of her salary scale.[58] By 1907 matrons and sisters conducted lectures and ward demonstrations for all three years of the orderlies' training; the 1904 regulations required the matron to receive quarterly confidential reports from the sisters on the male trainees, which were signed and commented on by the medical officers, and to keep a register of the orderlies' progress in her office. In 1906 promotion to the grade of matron was dependent on passing an examination, which *inter alia* required the candidate 'to deliver, before the examiners, a lecture adapted to the training of orderlies, Royal Army Medical Corps', and to devise a set of written questions on the lecture.[59] (see 1907 syllabus, appendix, p. 232).

It was only to be expected that these new arrangements would prove unpopular. The orderlies complained that their training role gave matrons the opportunity to hamper their careers. The matrons' and sisters' lectures were criticised as being too theoretical, or too repetitive of preliminary topics; apart from somewhat frequent references to bedmaking and the use of the clinical thermometer, these complaints seem not to have been justified by the published evidence of the syllabus. The fundamental objection to the new system lay in the changing balance of power in the wards. *Broad Arrow* claimed that 'many most desirable men in the corps will not join the nursing section, being unwilling to be commanded by women'. There were calls for a return to the old regime, based on the argument that only men would be deployed in wartime. The general duty privates would be useless in an emergency, because they had no nursing training; female nurses would be useless because they were women, and could not be sent into the field. The reorganisation was an expensive mistake.[60]

These complaints did not move the military medical authorities, for they were by now beside the point. The decision had been taken to employ female nurses in wartime and steadily to increase their establishment, and was not to be reversed. Moreover, the Advisory Board was committed to looking ahead to the formation of an adequate female nursing reserve; part of its remit was to prepare schemes for the expansion of the army medical service in time of war or epidemic, for the utilisation of voluntary effort, and the employment of civilian surgeons, orderlies and female nurses.[61] In March 1904 the Board estimated that the shortfall of female nursing personnel required for a mere three army corps and three cavalry brigades was between 934 and 2,854.[62] At the height of the Boer War, the number of female nurses employed in military hospitals had been roughly 1,000. Disputes over ward discipline, over superfluous or inappropriate training, or over expense were, after forty years, being dismissed as irrelevant. Both civilian and military female nurses were now to be integrated in planning for war on a scale hitherto unimaginable. In Keogh's words, 'Their work is not purely humanitarian. Their importance to efficiency is greater than they themselves know.'[63]

Appendix: from 'Standing Orders, . . . RAMC and QAIMNS (1907)

No of lecture	Lectures by Officers	No. of lecture	Lectures and Demonstrations by Matrons Sisters QAIMNS
	Elementary Anatomy		General Nursing and ward management
13	The abdomen. Its boundaries, contents and position of organs, &c.	13	Padding of splints; plaster of Paris splints; improvised splints; starched bandages.
14	The thorax. Boundaries. Contents and position of viscera. Brief description of mouth, pharynx and oesophagus, &c.	14	Care of simple fractures, sprains and dislocation.
		15	Care of burns, scalds, &c., shock.
15	The nervous system. Brief description of the brain and its membranes. Spinal cord. Nerves, &c.		
	Elementary Physiology		
16	The nervous system. General description of the brain and its functions in general. Spinal cord and its functions. Nerves and their functions.	16	Surgical dressings. The necessity for absolute cleanliness. The surgical toilet.
17	The excretory systems. General description and functions of the kidneys. Ureters. Bladder and urethra. The urine, &c.	17	Lotions; varieties and strengths. Application of wet and dry dressings.
18	The spleen, general description and functions. Lymphatic vessels and glands. Other glands, &c.	18	Prevention and care of bedsores. General outlines of nursing in acute rheumatism.
19	General description of the special senses, with special reference to the eye and ear. The throat.	19	Observation of patient — secretions, expectorations, pulse, skin, appetite, delirium, breathing, sleep. The taking of notes of cases.

Elementary Surgery

20	Germs in their relation to wounds. Asepsis, antisepsis, &c.	20	Observation continued – effects of diet, medicine, and stimulants; modes of reporting accurately obser-vations taken. Signs of approaching death.
21	Diseases of urinary and generative organs – kid-neys, bladder, calculus, stricture, retention of urine. Special operations and instruments. Catheter-ization, &c.	21	General outlines in the nursing of enteric cases.
		22	General outlines in the nursing of pneumonia, pleurisy and bronchitis.
22	Diseases of rectum. Fis-sure, fistula, stricture, haemorrhoids. Operations.	23	Ward management. Method of cleaning and polishing floors, corridors, utensils, brasses, tins, mackintoshes, bedsteads, &c.
23	Venereal cases.		
24	Surgical and other emer-gencies. Spinal injuries. Artificial respiration. Restoration of apparently drowned.	24	Ward management. Heat-ing and ventilation. Clean-ing annexes and sculleries, ice boxes, and filters. The disposal of refuse and the preservation of food.

SYLLABUS FOR 2nd YEAR OF TRAINING
AUTUMN SESSION

No. of lecture	Lectures by Officers	No. of lecture	Lectures and Demonstrations by Matrons
	Anatomy		Surgical Nursing
1	The skeleton, individual bones. Arrangement. Structure. Those more commonly fractured. Liability to injury of adja-cent structures, &c.	1	The qualifications of a good surgical nurse and how these may be obtained
2	Joints. Variety and uses. Movements. Dislocations, &c.	2	Bandaging.

3   The muscular system. Diaphragm. Action of groups of muscles – flexors, extensors, &c. Mode of action, &c.

4   The thorax. General anatomy. Position and structure of organs. Brief description of larynx and trachea.

Physiology

5   General view of the structure of the animal organism. Protoplasm. Cells. Fibres. Protoplasmic movements. Reproduction. Bacteria. Amoebae. Chemical basis of body, &c

6   The circulatory system. The blood – composition. Corpuscles and their uses. Coagulation. The cardiac cycle. Structure of vessels, &c.

7   The respiratory system. The air and its composition. Changes on respiration. Mechanism of respiration, circulation of blood in the lungs. Asphyxia.

8   The digestive system. Mechanism of deglutition. General description of salivary glands and their secretion. Gastric juice. Bile. Intestinal secretions. Peristalsis. Digestion. Absorption, &c.

Surgery

9   Wounds and their complications. Pathogenic germs. Aseptic and antiseptic treatment of wounds.

3   Cleansing and sterilization of instruments and dressings.

4   Nursing of sequelae of wounds. Erysipelas, pyaemia, &c.

5   The nursing of fractures, joint cases and dislocations. Splints. Fracture beds.

6   Nursing of chest injuries and tracheotomy cases.

Medical Nursing

7   Food and the principles of diet, as applied to special cases. The hospital diet scale.

8   Nursing in heart cases and aneurism. Signs and care of cases of internal haemorrage.

9   Nursing of lung diseases generally. Nursing of tubercle of lung. Expectoration. Blood spitting.

10	Operation-room techniques	10	Nursing of pneumonia, bronchitis and pleurisy.
11	Fractures and dislocations.		
12	Hygienic principles as applied to hospitals in the field.	11	Infection and disinfectants. Disinfection generally.
		12	Nursing of patients suffering from paralysis, apoplexy, epilepsy, fainting, delirium, or coma

---

SPRING SESSION

No. of lecture	Lectures by Officers	No. of lecture	Lectures and Demonstrations by Matrons
	Anatomy and Field Surgical Apparatus		Surgical Nursing
13	The abdomen. General anatomy and position of organs. The peritoneum, &c.	13	The nursing of burns and scalds; their degrees and complications.
14	Arteries. Veins. Lymphatics. Arrest of haemorrhage. Contents of surgical haversack.	14	Bleeding, its varieties, causes, symptoms; the temporary arrest of haemorrhage.
15	The eye and its surroundings. The orbital cavity. The eyelids. The optic nerve. Blood vessels and nerves of the orbit. The lachrymal apparatus. Contents of Pannier No. 1.	15	The nursing of cases of head injuries and operations. Injuries of the spine.
		16	Nursing of abdominal cases.
16	Contents of surgical haversack, field fracture box, antiseptic case.		
	Physiology, etc.		
17	Eye, ear, and throat. Eye as optical instrument. Media. Retina. Optic nerve. General description of the larynx. Vocal cords	17	Preparation of patients for operation, and points to be observed in their after-care.

and auditory apparatus. Contents of Pannier No. 2

18 The nervous system. The brain. Its structure. Cerebellum. Medulla. The cranial nerves, special senses.

19 The excretory systems. General structure of kidneys. Excretions. The urine and its composition. The skin, its structure and uses

20 Glands. Duct glands. Lachrymal; mucous, submucous, mammary, prostate, sudoriferous; ductless glands; spleen, thyroid, &c. Lymphatic glands.

Ward Hygiene, etc.

21 Cubic space, ventilation. Lighting. Warming. Protection of food and drinks. Removal of soiled articles of bedding and clothing.

22 Ward hygiene, continued. Annexes, lavatory, bathroom, w.c., and slop sink fitments. General cleanliness. Disposal of discharges and excreta; the incinerator and its uses.

23 Ward hygiene, continued. Infectious diseases. Isolation of cases. General preventive measures, disposal of infectious discharges, excreta, and soiled bedding and clothing. Personal hygiene of attendants in infectious wards.

24 Contents of medical panniers companion and surgical saddle bags.

18 Names, uses and care of surgical instruments.

Medical Nursing

19 Points to be observed regarding the excretions. Nursing of kidney disease.

20 Nursing of throat, ear and eye diseases.

21 Nursing of skin diseases. Hypodermic injections.

22 Nursing of fevers, non-infectious and infectious.

23 Nursing of emergencies. Frost-bite. Cases of poisoning; antidotes, snake-bite.

24 Ward management.

CHAPTER 9

THE BIRTH OF THE VAD: NURSING RESERVE SCHEMES 1906–1914

The history of British military nursing between the Anglo-Boer War and 1914 is bound up not with war but with rumours, fears and expectations of war. It was not the regular army nursing service, but future nursing reserve forces which formed the chief preoccupation of army hospital planning. Before 1899, the War Office sponsored one small army nursing reserve corps; ten years later, there were three – the Queen Alexandra's Imperial Military Nursing Reserve, the Territorial Force Nursing Service, and the Voluntary Aid Detachments. The gallant record of all these bodies during the First World War has tended to obscure the complex, and not always heroic story of their origins. In this chapter we shall examine the evolution of the institutions which prepared more than 50,000 civilian females for a role as military nurses; and in the succeeding chapter we shall consider the climate of opinion which fostered their readiness to serve, and the ways in which their activities changed perceptions of women in the years before 'the deluge'.

CREATING A RESERVE

After the Anglo-Boer War, the construction of an official nursing reserve got off to an extremely shaky start. It was felt appropriate to create a new body in tandem with the QAIMNS, but this raised

237

delicate questions with regard to royal patronage. Princess Christian did not wish to relinquish her position as head of the pre-war Army Nursing Reserve which she had founded; and she resented any criticisms which might be made, for example, of some of its wartime appointments. As Lady Roberts wrote:[1]

> Princess Christian has always personally administered her nurses and I have been told that if any one ventured to disagree with H.R.H. she has simply said 'it is my wish that is sufficient' which always ended the discussion. The Princess Christian would never consent to be a mere figure head.

Queen Alexandra, on the other hand, was not only proud to preside over the new regular service, but was determined to be head of any reserve corps which might subsequently be established. This barrier to progress was exacerbated by the intrusion of civilian nursing politics into the business of the Army Nursing Board. Several of its members were hostile to the concept of state registration for nurses: Sydney Holland, Chairman of the London Hospital, was no more anxious to establish a national register of nurses qualified for military service than he was to see a professional register of civilian trained nurses. He insisted that war nurses could always be found when they were needed, and that a nurse had no right to volunteer for war in her individual capacity. This might inconvenience her hospital, and the power to decide who should or should not serve ought to remain with the civilian matrons.[2]

The issue was kept dangling until December 1905, when the Liberal government of Sir Henry Campbell-Bannerman entered office. The appointment of Richard Burdon Haldane as Secretary of State for War ushered in a period of major reappraisal and restructuring within the armed forces; and the military nursing service and its reserves were early beneficiaries of the new broom. Haldane's vision of a new defence system for Great Britain, as embodied in the Territorial and Reserve Forces Act of 1907, was an essentially British version of the Germanic ideal of the 'Nation in Arms'. Although conscription would not be imposed, the entire manhood of the nation was nevertheless from its schooldays to be imbued with a sense of personal obligation to military service: and the Volunteer Force of 'Saturday-night soldiers' was to be converted into a Territorial Force, organised by county associations in close conformity with War Office requirements. Ostensibly, the

TF was designed purely for defence against invasion, with foreign service being left to the regulars: awkward moral questions as to participation in aggressive or imperialist warfare were excluded from public discussion. This was to be a 'citizen army', created for an increasingly democratic age.[3] The nursing service for this new force was officially inaugurated in July 1908; however, Alfred Keogh, the Director-General of army medical services, had been elaborating plans and canvassing support for it well before this date. His scheme was for 23 military general hospitals of 520 beds each, to be established on civilian premises and staffed by pre-selected civilian personnel immediately on the outbreak of war. A roll of qualified volunteer nurses would be kept for each hospital, which would require 91 nurses, but would select 120 to keep a safety margin. Like their combatant colleagues, Territorial nurses were to come under a local administration. A committee was to be formed in each area designated a 'hospital centre', consisting of local ladies and the 'organising matron' of the proposed general hospital, together with the principal matrons and nursing superintendents of the area, who would enrol nursing staff and make recommendations for superintendent posts.[4] No male nurses were to be recruited: the RAMC and its Reserve were thought to be furnishing these in adequate numbers.

An unlooked-for result of Haldane's appointment at the War Office was the promotion of his sister Elizabeth to a position of influence in military nursing circles, and a consequent alteration in the balance of opinion on the Nursing Board, which was to be of enormous help in the implementation of Keogh's plans. Elizabeth Haldane was a remarkably talented woman, who in a later period might have had as distinguished a public career as her polymath brother. She was the unmarried daughter of the family who moved from Scotland to London to keep house for R.B. Haldane, who was also unmarried. She participated actively in charitable enterprises and Liberal party affairs. Both a linguist and a philosopher, she translated Hegel and Descartes and wrote a life of the latter; St Andrew's University awarded her an honorary LLD in 1906. The development of the nursing profession was one of her strongest interests: she was a manager of the Royal Infirmary, Edinburgh, and by early 1905 was a member of the Society for the State Registration of Trained Nurses. Her close friend Lady Henry Munro Ferguson, also a member, was the wife of the MP who in that year introduced a bill supporting registration into the House of Commons. A few months after her brother entered office, Elizabeth was introduced to Miss Sidney Browne, Matron-in-Chief of QAIMNS, who was also a registrationist, keen to find allies to counter the anti-registrationist bias of the Nursing Board.[5] She and Elizabeth Haldane formed a close friendship which lasted up to and beyond the outbreak of the First World War; they maintained a regular correspondence whenever Elizabeth was at home in Scotland, and in London they were constantly discussing military nursing issues, 'caucussing' before meetings, and successfully building links with sympathisers.

The first visible outcome of this association was the appointment of Isla Stewart, Matron of Bart's, ardent registrationist and President of the Matrons' Council, as a member of the Army Nursing Board. This ruffled Holland's feathers more than somewhat. 'We must all take Miss Stewart in hand . . . ,' Queen Alexandra wrote to him in March 1906, 'should we by any chance find that she has communicated any of our proceedings to the outside world we will on no account tolerate it – I am glad you wrote in this spirit to Mr Haldane.' Two days later, Haldane was asking his sister to write to Miss Stewart 'and say that it will be best, should she be appointed, that she should attend no meetings or work with Mrs B. Fenwick'.[6] It seems unlikely that this self-denying ordinance was ever upheld. A few months later, the Vice-Chairman of the Board, Lady Roberts, wrote to Elizabeth that 'it is very unfortunate that Miss Stewart's opinions, however reasonable, are like a red rag' to Sydney Holland.[7] By this stage Nora Roberts was an ally, having become anxious to see a nursing reserve prepared and co-ordinated with the regular service well in advance of the outbreak of war, and willing to struggle with Sydney Holland for the soul of Queen Alexandra on this question.[8] These changes of alignment in the Nursing Board were a boon to Keogh, its chairman. He was deeply committed to improving the professional standard, and increasing the military importance, of army hospitals; like Sidney Browne, he found in Elizabeth Haldane a civilian after his own heart.[9] He discussed in great detail with Elizabeth his plans for the territorial medical services;[10] when in 1908 an Advisory Council was established, under the presidency of Queen Alexandra, for the Territorial Force Nursing Service, he became Chairman, and Elizabeth was appointed Vice-Chairman. Sidney Browne, who had retired from QAIMNS in spring 1906, was appointed Matron-in-Chief of the new service, and Secretary to the Advisory Council. Interestingly, Elizabeth Haldane was able to continue 'in office' after her brother left the War Office to become Lord Chancellor; although he was replaced by Col. J.E.B. Seely, she was not supplanted by the latter's wife:[11]

> I called on Mrs S. to enlist her sympathies. However she is ladden down by an immense family (to be yet increased I fancy) and cannot do much so she wanted me to keep on as I was.

No matter how satisfactorily the boards and councils of the military nursing services were packed, they could nevertheless achieve very little without the co-operation of their royal president. It is not easy for the late twentieth-century reader to appreciate the extent of royal influence in so vital a state interest as military medicine in this period, and Haldane objected to it strongly. In the spring of 1907 he was forced to employ the good offices of Viscount Esher to 'carry out the King's desire that the old friction between the *two Royal ladies* should not be revived'; Esher had to negotiate a reform in the military nursing reserve system which did not involve the outright abolition of Princess Christian's creation, but allowed it to fall into disuse. The result of his compromise was that by 1910 the nurses of the Princess's Army Nursing Reserve ceased to be employed in military hospitals at home or abroad, but their names remained on its roll.[12] In 1908, when the Territorial Force Nursing Service was in the making, Haldane hoped to give it a quite separate existence from other reserve corps by keeping it out of the Queen's control. He wrote to his sister:[13]

> The Queen has refused to allow the P of Wales to preside and wants one organisation. This we cannot consent to. They must be separate. We had better dispense with Royalty. I have asked Lady Roberts – to whom I returned it – to send you the Queen's letter. She is about the stupidest woman in England. Can't we organise this business without a Royal Pres.t.

But with military nursing, no less than with army affairs proper, Haldane had to temper notions of progress and modernity with deference to an aristocratically-based social hierarchy; and the Queen duly became president of the territorial nurses.

The formation of the QAIMNS Reserve was announced at the same time as the Territorial Force Nursing Service was launched. Just over a year later, the former reported 'many vacancies', and by the end of 1911 had attracted so few recruits that the War Office was asking certain hospitals to guarantee the services of some of their nurses *en bloc* in time of war or national emergency.[14] The progress of the territorial service could not have been more different. Local committees quickly sprang up and began enrolling staff in the wake of Keogh's visits to the provinces; Elizabeth canvassed particularly successfully in Scotland. By early 1909 only Cardiff, Newcastle, Sheffield and Oxford had an incomplete territorial hospital organisation,[15] and in London political differences over the registration issue were still delaying its introduction: in October 1907 Keogh had considered that 'we are on very dangerous ground' in the metropolis, and in January 1909 some London matrons were said to be repeating all Sydney Holland's old objections to a military reserve scheme.[16] A month later, however, a ladies' committee of the TFNS for the City and County of London was convened, appointed an executive committee, and elected Isla Stewart as one of its 'organising matrons'. By January 1910, Sidney Browne reported that 2600 nurses had been enrolled; and by the summer of 1914 the service had a strength of 2576 and a further reserve strength of 1115.[17]

The immense enthusiasm and energy which went into the launching of the Territorial Force and its medical service is in itself enough to explain the different fates of the two new military nursing reserves. The Territorial Force was presented to the public quite differently from the regular army: not as a professional force, but almost as an instrument of national moral regeneration in the face of external danger and internal division. Territorial nurses were appealed to as a privileged group of women, who were alone qualified to join men in the great endeavour of defending the state. 'The manhood of the country are playing up splendidly,' Elizabeth Haldane told a London meeting, 'and now it was for women – for nurses – to play their part also in the scheme of defence, and she felt sure that they will not be behind the men.'[18] Elizabeth was a suffragist, and so was her brother, who saw no reason to confine patriotism to the male half of society. In August 1909 he told the International Congress of Nurses, meeting in London, that nurses were acquiring an increasingly important role in the territorial organisation, and that this would one day 'be recognised as a manifestation of the movement which would demonstrate the fallacy of the old-fashioned, ridiculous idea that women were not the equals of men in regard to citizenship, and in regard to their title to a just recognition of their rights to participate in the advance of humanity.'[19]

From an early stage, the territorial nurses were made to feel an integral part of the new organisation. Their very presence demonstrated the characteristics which Haldane wished to ascribe to his creation: this new army was neither an aristocratic preserve, nor a caste apart from the rest of society; it was to draw support from all social classes and both sexes; it was to be fully representative of civilian society, not its antithesis. Whereas the nineteenth century regular army nurse had been 'in but not of' the army, and little seen in public, by the summer of 1909 the TFNS was almost as visible as the Territorial Force itself – officially inspected, and invited to local reviews of troops, and to Windsor when the King presented colours to combatant units. The *Nursing Mirror* reported of a Lancashire territorial general hospital staff dinner: 'It is worthy of note that this is the first occasion on which hospital nurses have taken part in an official military function in Liverpool!'[20] Arrangements were made for 130 members of the TFNS to line the route of the coronation and the following day's royal procession in 1911, all wearing their 'blue-grey cape with scarlet facings and silver "T" in each corner'. It had originally been proposed to give the territorial nurses the same red cape as the regular army nurses, but Queen Alexandra drew the line at this.[21]

All official communications, all speeches made to territorial nurses, stressed that they were part of a system of defence against invasion, and were not being asked to serve outside their own country. Territorial organisation as a whole was indeed presented as defensive only; but in the year before Campbell-Bannerman and Haldane took office, the General Staff and Committee of Imperial Defence had swung round strongly to the view that invasion was not the most serious military danger facing Britain, and had authorised discussions with the French on joint resistance to a German offensive through Belgium. Towards the end of February 1907, Haldane dropped a strong enough hint to the House of Commons when he said that territorial units might wish to volunteer for service overseas.[22] In March 1907 Keogh prepared a paper which envisaged the staff of a territorial general hospital volunteering *en bloc* to accompany an expeditionary force; and in 1913 members of TFNS were given permission to volunteer for service abroad if they were not required for duty at home.[23] There was, moreover, little in the territorial medical scheme which was incompatible with planning for a campaign on the Continent. If it was assumed that a foreign campaign would be limited to Flanders and north-eastern France, and that Britain would at no stage lose control of Channel communications, then military general hospitals in Britain could easily serve the needs of wounded soldiers evacuated from the battlefield. In fact, the one eventuality which the territorial medical organisation did *not* provide for was an invasion of the British Isles during which the metropolitan government lost control over any or all of the regions.

There was thus scope for further thinking about the forms of medical aid which might be appropriate to an invasion or other national emergency; about the ways in which civilians might be affected by war; and about different forms of co-operation between government and voluntary agencies. While Haldane might be inspired by German philosophy or by Cromwellian precedents, other examples of the nation in arms were at hand. Japan's victory over Russia in the war of 1904–5 had made an enormous impression in Britain, which had formed an alliance with Japan in 1902. Britain despatched military and military-medical observers to the theatre of war; chief among the latter was Lt-Col. W.G. MacPherson, the medical officer who before the Boer War had reported with admiration from Geneva on the close working relationship between Continental Red Cross societies and their respective national armies, and who had been appointed secretary of the co-ordinating Central British Red Cross Committee on the eve of the Boer War.[24] In June 1904 MacPherson submitted a report on the medical organisation of the Japanese army to the War Office which was lengthy, enthusiastic, and destined to be highly influential. It came to the attention of a wider readership in 1906. He described the territorial system by which Japan's army was organised: Japan was divided into twelve military districts, each of which was self-sufficient in respect of combatant and auxiliary services; the army could be mobilised with as many or as few territorial units as were required. Each military district had its own reserve hospital; evacuation of sick and wounded from the field, to the field hospital, line of communication hospital, hospital ship or base hospital, was organised with great smoothness.[25]

MacPherson was, however, particularly impressed by the Japanese government's organisation of voluntary aid through the Red Cross: 'By means of centralised control independent local associations and rival societies do not, and are not, permitted to exist.' Moreover, the Red Cross's war organisation 'has been carried out on lines laid down by the Medical Departments of the Army and Navy'. The chief form of organisation was the 'Relief Detachment'. This consisted of medical and pharmaceutical officers, and either male or female nurses. Each detachment, with a staff of 28, took charge of 100 military patients in home territory, thus releasing military hospital staff for war-theatre service; if necessary, detachments could also be employed on lines of communication. Similar units, consisting of surgeons, male nurses and stretcher bearers, were being organised as transport columns, and the Red Cross also made itself responsible for refreshment, rest and medical attendance stations along the line of railway between Japan's ports and the military base hospitals. As well as undergoing appropriate training in time of peace, local Red Cross branches also obtained and stored medical and surgical material, clothing, bedding and transport equipment which would be needed on mobilisation. Here, it seemed, was the perfect model for military-civilian co-operation.[26]

At the time of MacPherson's report, the Central British Red Cross Committee was all but moribund. Its chief component parts, the Order of St John of Jerusalem and the National Society for Aid to the Sick and Wounded in War, led entirely separate existences. In November 1904 the Red Cross executive appealed for funds to set up a complete regional organisation for times of war and national emergency; but several members had strong reservations against placing themselves at the disposal of the War Office. In particular, A.K. Loyd MP (nephew of Lord Wantage, who had died in 1901) was unwilling to see the National Aid Society lose its identity in a larger association.

Early in 1905, Sir Edward Ward, Permanent Under Secretary at the War Office, and Viscount Esher, a leading member of the Committee of Imperial Defence, undertook an inquiry into a major regeneration of the Red Cross. When, in March 1905, representatives of the Red Cross and the National Society met at Buckingham Palace, Loyd objected pointedly to 'the pressure that had been brought to bear on the National Society recently to bring it, the Red Cross societies, into conformity with that of Japan, the success of which appeared to be due to its complete submission to the Japanese War Office', but his opposition was eventually ground down and a merger was agreed.[27] In July 1905 an inaugural meeting of the new British Red Cross Society was held at the Palace; Queen Alexandra was to be president of the new association, which was to be 'recruited from all classes throughout the Empire'. She launched an[28]

> appeal to all the women of the Empire to assist me in carrying out this great scheme, which is essentially a woman's work, and which is the one and only way in which we can assist our brave and gallant Army and Navy to perform their arduous duties in time of war.

All the women of the empire did not immediately respond to the call of the Red Cross, which was not initially couched in very concrete terms. However, in July 1906 the Red Cross Council 'agreed to a Committee of the ladies of the Council undertaking to assist in the formation of a number of County Branches'. This committee invited the wives of Lords-Lieutenant to take over the responsibility for the Red Cross in their respective counties. Exactly what the county branches were supposed to do remained obscure. There was some discrepancy between the War Office's aims and the Red Cross's aspirations. At the end of 1905 the Red Cross had agreed that the role of the local branches was to enrol members, to collect money, and 'to determine the particular form which the Branch would wish their aid to take in time of war'. A pamphlet issued on the constitution and aims of the re-constituted Red Cross referred to 'the nature of the aid likely to be furnished by the Society in time of war, as illustrated by particulars of that provided in the late war in South Africa'.[29] This was indeed a far cry from the Japanese model; and, as it had been stated at the inaugural meeting that the society was to be 'entirely voluntary' and independent of the War Office in time of peace, it was difficult to imagine how the British Red Cross could ever be brought to the desired state of war preparedness.

In 1907, however, the launching of R.B. Haldane's territorial scheme opened up new possibilities of co-operation between voluntary agencies and the army, for the territorials were not, in principle, a professional military organisation. The County Associations which administered them were presided over by their respective Lords Lieutenant: the prospect dawned of a perfect symmetry, not to say marriage, between a military organisation emanating from the Lord Lieutenant, and a medical aid organisation emanating from his wife. By the autumn of 1907 R.B. Haldane and Keogh had initiated discussions with Frederick Treves, Chairman of the Red Cross Executive, on linking the Red

Cross with the territorial medical services; the entire Executive met Haldane at the War Office at the end of November to set up a working party. It was agreed that the Red Cross would undertake to find supplementary quarters, equipment, and personnel 'mainly consisting of men' for the fourteen territorial general hospitals, to set up convalescent homes, and to organise transport for the sick and wounded and food depots along the lines of communication. These proposals were officially embodied in a War Office circular to the Territorial Force Associations of 4 May 1908, inviting their secretaries to establish contact with their local Red Cross branches.[30]

WOMEN, PATRIOTISM AND VOLUNTARY AID

On 16 August 1909 a new era opened for the voluntary aid movement when the War Office issued its 'Scheme for the Organisation of Voluntary Aid in England and Wales', with an appendix on the organisation and resources of the Red Cross Society of Japan. The new scheme was to be entrusted to male and female Voluntary Aid Detachments, 'just as in the case of the relief detachments of the Japanese Red Cross Society, and the voluntary aid companies of Germany'. It was to supply certain gaps in the territorial medical service. 'Clearing hospitals' and transport facilities were to remedy the lack of any connection between field ambulances and railway lines. Rest stations and temporary hospitals were to be set up along evacuation routes. Buildings and staff were to be prepared for the expansion of territorial general hospitals. The Men's Detachments, consisting of a Commandant, Quartermaster, Medical Officers, Pharmacists and up to forty-eight ordinary members each, were to prepare means of road transport and convert buildings to hospital use. The Women's Detachments were to consist of a Medical Officer/Commandant, a Quartermaster, two lady Superintendents, and twenty women of whom two were to be fully trained nurses. They were to set up rest stations, taking charge temporarily of soldiers too ill to travel; they might also be employed in ambulance trains, and in nursing and cooking duties in clearing hospitals. All detachments were to be organised for their local Territorial Force Association by the Red Cross, and to receive preliminary training in first aid and nursing from the St John's Ambulance Association.[31]

All this appeared as the logical extension of previous planning for the Territorial Force. The published scheme even included the statement that the territorial medical services' 'incompleteness is intentional, because it was eminently to be desired that every opportunity should be given to the British Red Cross Society and other societies of taking a share in the work appropriate to those who in all civilized countries seek to mitigate the lot of the sick and wounded in war'. But the VAD scheme was, in fact, less a product of governmental forward thinking than a response to earlier popular initiatives – and in particular to female initiatives. It did not spring fully formed from the heads of either Haldane or Keogh. Keogh had originally envisaged turning to the Red Cross only for 'charwomen, maidservants, labourers *et hoc genus omne*'. His first ideas on supplementary aid had not sketched out any significant role for women beyond fundraising. And he had certainly not intended detachments to include trained female personnel.[32]

Previous army medical plans for supplementary voluntary aid had focussed not on the Red Cross, but on the Order of St John and its subsidiary organisations the St John Ambulance Association and the St John Ambulance Brigade. After the Anglo-Boer War the brigade maintained its own Bearer Companies, and in 1905 members formed a Royal Naval Sick Berth Reserve.[33] Despite these signs of official approval, the St John movement as a whole still smarted over the War Office's rejection of its female volunteers during the Boer War. The members of the SJAB Nursing Divisions, proud holders of certificates in first aid and home nursing, had been turned down for want of a three-year certificate of hospital training, and felt this as unfair discrimination: like many others, they were convinced that society women with lesser qualifications than theirs had nevertheless managed to obtain nursing positions in South Africa. From 1903 onwards the women of the brigade began to discuss the possibility of organising the members of the Nursing Divisions as military nursing reserve. A Brigade Nursing Officer sparked off much sympathetic comment when she wrote to *First Aid* in 1907:

I have been greatly interested in articles . . . connected with Red Cross work in Japan, and the part that women take in connection with it in that country. Cannot the ambulance women of this country have a part found for them in defence of hearth and home. . . . Surely it would not be difficult to form an Auxiliary Branch of Queen Alexandra's Imperial Military Nursing Service, in which the St John Nursing Sisters might be enrolled and permitted to occasionally undergo instruction at a military hospital.

She added that her request was[34]

In no way connected with the Female Suffrage movement, for the ladies of which I entertain a very strong measure of contempt, for the way in which they are lowering the prestige of women amongst all self-respecting classes of society.

The writer may have known that a year earlier, the medical superintendent of the Portsmouth Guardians had enrolled some of his workhouse infirmary nurses as an SJAB Nursing Division with a view to getting them recognised as a military nursing reserve unit; this proposal was ultimately sanctioned neither by the War Office nor by St John.[35] The Nursing Divisions must have been somewhat disappointed by the news in May 1907 that the Order, in conjunction with the War Office, was forming a Military Home Hospitals Reserve to replace the officers and men of the RAMC serving abroad in time of war. The scheme covered only male nursing in the home hospitals of the regular service, and although in 1908 there was some talk of incorporating the women of the Nursing Divisions also, this project did not materialise.[36]

The Order now turned its attention away from the regular army, and began to devise schemes to supplement the territorial organisation. Adeline Duchess of Bedford, a Lady of Grace of the Order, wife of the Lord Lieutenant of Bedfordshire, and a member of the Council of the British Red Cross Society, proposed the formation of a 'Women's Aid Service' as auxiliary to the Territorial Force Nursing Service in case of invasion. Nursing Division sisters already holding the first aid and home nursing certificate of the SJAA would be given a further course of training, to include practical instruction in hospitals and dispensaries. She visited France in order to investigate the work of women in such organisations as the Association des Dames Françaises and the Union des Femmes de France, and received encouragement and co-operation from Ward at the War Office, and from Keogh, who was also a Knight of Grace of the Order. In early 1909 she, Sir Richard Temple, Assistant Director of the SJAA and Sir Herbert Perrott,

Secretary of the Order, visited Elizabeth Haldane to discuss the project with her, and above all to canvass the claims of partially trained, but 'competent women' to complement the work of fully trained nurses in wartime.[37]

By March 1909 Elizabeth Haldane was, as she wrote to her mother, 'bombarded with letters and suggestions'.[38] An enormous groundswell of opinion was lifting the technical discussion of gaps in military-medical provision on to a completely different emotional plane. Women in particular began to take initiatives of their own: the earliest and most flamboyant move had been made in 1907 by the founders of the First Aid Nursing Yeomanry Corps. In its first incarnation this appears to have been a rather select club for girls, the Islington Drill Brigade Girls' Yeomanry, described in 1908 as 'a development of the Islington Drill Brigade, which has for its founder Captain Baker, a well-known advocate of physical culture and a thorough disciplinarian.' The girls wore an extremely dashing and expensive uniform 'consisting of a crimson zouave, with the usual badges, crossed spurs &c., on the sleeve, blue riding skirt and riding boots, yellow sash, red and blue service caps, with chin straps, a natty riding whip completing the equipment.' They were all 'strong and efficient riders'. The adult corps which succeeded this organisation was supposed to train women for the mounted rescue of wounded soldiers. The corps soon found friends in useful quarters. Col. F.C. Ricardo, of the Grenadier Guards, who later became their CO, inspected them, and they were given space to drill at the Albany Barracks. By early 1909 it was reported that a 'busy band of aristocratic amazons' was engaged in recruiting work; prominent among them was Lady Ernestine Hunt, daughter of the Marquis of Aylesbury, who reportedly 'had considerable experience in the field hospitals of South Africa and Egypt'. By the end of the year she and a Mrs St Clair Stobart had broken away from FANY and formed a second military-medical organisation, the Women's Sick and Wounded Convoy Corps.[39]

Within the pre-1914 military ambulance movement, the FANY always remained a group apart, not least because of the expenses consequent on membership. But although the corps was absorbed into neither the VADs nor the territorial medical service, its ambitious example, which received a good deal of publicity, undoubtedly spurred other women into action. In many different parts of Britain women were assuming the right to participate in

Haldane's defence scheme, and demanding the training and organisation that would enable them to do so effectively. Early in 1909 the female relatives of the soldiers of a Cheshire Territorial regiment requested a special course of instruction in first aid and nursing in order to make themselves useful to their menfolk in time of war. This was duly organised through the SJAA. In London, Viscountess Esher began to arrange similar courses of instruction for ladies.[40] In April 1909 Elizabeth Haldane received a letter from a lady in Scotland:

> we have decided to form a small corps of mounted women, with a foot section of all who do not wish to learn the riding. So many ladies were keen on the First Aid work, but hesitated at the riding.

She had, she wrote, received a flood of applications from all over Scotland, and offers of help from territorial medical officers. They were going to learn stretcher drill, and day and night signalling. Was it possible that they could obtain 'some sort of official recognition'? They had already discussed the question of uniform and 'distinction marks'.[41] Other enthusiastic women wrote in a similar vein directly to Haldane himself, or to Keogh.

These developments made an enormous impression on Keogh. On 12 March 1909 he wrote to Elizabeth Haldane:

> Some time ago a lady wrote to Mr Haldane regarding the formation of classes of instruction in first aid for women, the wives of officers, NCOs and men of the 6th Cheshire Regt. I was asked to reply to her. (She asked for the grant of a medal to those who passed as qualified in first aid). I replied sympathetically, but said that the S of S could not recognise her movement apart from that on similar lines already undertaken by the Order of St John. I am very sorry I did not keep a copy of the letter. It was an error for I fully recognise the value of the movement not only on account of its intrinsic utility but because it was likely to afford the women of the Country an opportunity of 'joining' the T.F. and so of compelling their husbands and brothers and sons to join . . . I think we have a chance if we work warily, of starting a great popular movement. We have first of all to bring the St John people with us, next to conciliate the nursing profession, prone to view with disfavour the amateur nurse.

Ten days later, Keogh proposed bringing this question before the Advisory Council of the TFNS: 'we can extend the organisation of women for Home Defence in very many directions.' The following month he wrote about forming a 'Woman's Society' or 'National Corps' of women to fill in the gaps in the medical organisation of home defence, in conjunction with the County Association; 'next we must stir up the Country.'[42] Keogh's enthusiasm was fuelled by the British Red Cross Society's utter failure to develop grass-roots activities, and his instinct to seize the moment to build a patriotic movement among women was a sound one. The year 1909 was extraordinary for manifestations of nationalist panic and crusading zeal. Early in the year, Gerald du Maurier's play about an invasion of the British Isles, *An Englishman's Home*, had inspired thousands of young men to join the Territorial Force; and, perhaps, more important, it had fostered a general state of exaltation in which other members of society searched for ways of discharging a new-found sense of patriotic mission. 'We have had a wonderful time in London,' noted Viscount Esher. 'Quite a revivalist fortnight. As some one said, the most exciting since the late Moody and Sankey. Gerald du Maurier's play began it.' In February and March it became general knowledge that the German naval programme threatened Britain's long-assumed global superiority in battleships; a different kind of agitation, linked to the jingoistic music-hall war-cry 'We want eight and we won't wait' launched an expensive supplementary Dreadnought construction programme.[43]

Women's responses to this wave of feeling took a variety of forms, but the military ambulance movement was the one which gave their aspirations practical and concrete expression. A path of usefulness opened up for women who had perhaps already begun to envy the territorial nurses their designation as 'the only women who can take any part in national defence'.[44] Haldane and Keogh were not alone in seeing that a purely voluntary territorial organisation would fail if the non-combatant women of the country could not be persuaded to support it. But few other officials recognised that women's support would be most valuable if linked to regular and demanding activity, and real responsibility, within a permanent military organisation. They thus acted as midwives at the birth of one of the most important 'women's movements' of the immediate pre-war years.

BUILDING A MOVEMENT

Throughout the period 1910–14, roughly two-thirds of Voluntary Aid Detachment members were women. The predominantly female membership reflected the prior claim of the Territorial Force on the patriotism of male volunteers under the age of 40. 'The difficulty all round is getting the men,' as an administrator in the London area wrote in November 1910. All Red Cross branches reported problems in recruiting men, and apathy amongst those enrolled; some branches had no male detachments at all before 1914.[45] Both in their origins and in their subsequent history, therefore, the VADs may justly be characterised as a 'women's movement', although its national direction was always in the hands of men. The numbers involved were large: around 8,000 women by the end of 1910, around 26,000 by early 1912, rising gradually to just under 50,000 on the eve of the war.[46] The activities of the detachments had an influence far beyond their immediate membership, as will be seen in the next chapter; here it is proposed to deal chiefly with the organisation and training of detachments, and their relation to the defence system as a whole. By early 1912 there were nearly 300 regular army nurses in the QAIMNS, and slightly under 3,000 women enrolled in the TFNS.[47] Alongside them the VADs mustered 26,000 women, ready in principle to be mobilised to assist the territorial medical services in an invasion or other national emergency. What was expected of these women, however, and whether they were to be integrated within the defence system as nurses, orderlies or a reservoir of unskilled labour, remained a largely unanswered question.

The VAD organisation was not strongly centralised. Detachments were formed by Territorial Associations acting through local branches of the Red Cross. In July 1901 the VADs were designated a section of the Technical Reserve of the Territorial Force, but they continued to be left very much to their own devices: unlike the territorial units, they received no funding whatever from central government. The 1909 circular asked for a national network of detachments, but laid down no target for membership. Annual inspections by military authorities were stipulated, and initially members were required to obtain the first aid and home nursing certificates of the SJAA before enrolling;

however, no guidelines were laid down for post-enrolment training. Commandants were told to study the 1909 circular, and then given 'a perfectly free hand to take such steps as may seem best to train the Detachments, knowing and keeping in view the duties they must be prepared to perform'.[48] The Red Cross made no official training manual available before the end of 1911, by which time other bodies shared the responsibility for organising detachments. From the outset the Red Cross and the Order of St John had disagreed over the qualifications required of new recruits. St John withdrew from the joint scheme in mid-1910 and was subsequently allowed to organise detachments independently. In addition, some detachments were organised directly by the Territorial Associations acting with little reference to either voluntary agency.[49] By far the majority of detachments were, in fact, organised by the Red Cross – 1110 out of a total of 1318 in February 1912 – but their local circumstances and social resources varied enormously. The Red Cross for its part decided in 1910 to recognise preliminary qualifications granted by a wide variety of national and local certifying bodies, finally recognising itself as one in 1911.[50] There were, in consequence, widely divergent interpretations of the 1909 circular, of the position of the VADs within the territorial system, and of the role of women within the VADs. The pattern of training opportunities offered to women was by no means uniform, and conclusions drawn from local experience are not necessarily applicable to the movement as a whole.

The 1909 circular stated that 'each detachment should be capable of being used either as a clearing hospital, or as a rest station, or as an ambulance train personnel, as the circumstances of the moment may demand in time of war', and 'should therefore be trained in such a manner as will enable it to perform any of these functions'. The only clear demand it made of recruits was the preliminary qualification in first aid and home nursing. Early in 1910 men were exempted from the latter qualification; and later that year the requirement of a preliminary qualification was relaxed altogether. In order to speed up the formation of detachments, a 'probation' system was devised by which each new recruit had to promise to obtain the appropriate certification within twelve months of joining.[51] In one way this solved the question of what the newly formed detachments were supposed to do: members spent much of their time working for their preliminary certificates. Keen detachments might meet weekly; all met at least once a month. The next stage of their training was often rather repetitive of the first:[52]

> In order to gain the necessary experience, the members practise putting on bandages and splints, arresting haemorrhage, and other matters which they have learnt in their first aid classes, and which require much practice in order that they may be done efficiently with comfort to the patient and with neatness. The bandaging class lasts about forty minutes, and is followed by drill, which lasts from thirty to forty minutes. The drill is of great use in helping members to see the need of combined action in work, for discipline and, last but not least, for smartness. Silence is maintained, and marching in single and double file, forming fours and other simple manœuvres are gone through. Stretcher drill is undertaken, . . . On another evening bed-making and the careful moving of sick and injured persons in bed under the careful supervision of a trained nurse takes up the first forty minutes, and is again followed by drill.

Some detachments were reported to have been content to go no further than this; but others clamoured for more preparation for their wartime responsibilities. As an unofficial detachment manual asked in 1912, how many women had yet been trained to assist at an operation, 'or can look upon a shell wound without fainting? . . . Wash a helpless patient, or lift him on and off a bed pan and clean it afterwards?'[53] These skills could only be acquired in civil hospitals in peacetime. In 1911 the Red Cross set up a sub-committee on nursing tuition, and the SJAB designated Lady Perrott, wife of Sir Herbert, 'Lady Superintendent in charge of Nursing Corps and Divisions'. She obtained from a number of metropolitan and provincial hospitals the privilege of detachment training in wards and out-patients' departments; by September 1912 she had in some cases been able to arrange a fortnight's residential training.[54] Usually VAD hospital training involved a couple of hours' ward work a week, 'making beds with real sick or injured persons in them, taking temperatures and charting them, putting on fomentations and simple dressings.' One Red Cross VAD in Pontypridd recalled going to 'the local hospital and besides doing ward work, I mean any kind of ward work that had occurred, the doctors let me go into the operating theatre and were very good about explaining.' Obviously some detachments were better placed to gain this kind of experience than others; remoter rural detachments had to make do with lectures from their local district nurse, and they were occasionally able to accompany her on her rounds.[55]

The purely domestic aspect of hospital work was also an important feature of VAD training. The 1909 circular proposed that women VADs should be taught how to prepare invalid diets. By 1910 they were also expected to take responsibility for laundry work. In autumn 1909 Cantlie's lectures at the Regent Street Polytechnic went into considerable detail on the care of clothing in general, and that of the regular and territorial soldier in particular: VAD members learned the skills of washing, mending, darning, sewing, knitting and disinfection.[56] In Berkshire and London, VADs spent winter sessions cutting out and sewing pillow-cases, hot-water-bottle covers, bedjackets and dusters, which were either stored or donated to hospitals. Detachment members also studied home hygiene and sanitation, food values and 'housewifery'.[57] It is clear that many VADs saw these domestic functions as something which detracted from 'real' detachment work, and even lowered its prestige. In 1910 a new regulation exempted four cooks per detachment from all preliminary qualifications, giving support to the idea that a full member of a detachment had higher priorities to consider; and at a Kent VAD camp held in 1913, only two out of 126 campers demonstrated any proficiency in cooking. Some commandants thought it important from the point of view of discipline and self-sufficiency for members to acquire such skills as cooking and washing up; others thought it a waste of valuable camping time, if they could find servants to do it for them. A move to co-opt laundresses who, like cooks, should be exempt from preliminary qualifications, was quashed by the Technical Reserve Committee in 1912.[58]

Had VAD work and training involved nothing more than elementary nursing skills and housewifery, it is most unlikely that it would have attracted women in as large numbers as it did: similar opportunities, after all, had been available through the SJAB Nursing Divisions for several years. But cutting across the fairly simple development of an auxiliary hospital function was the popular presupposition of 1909, officially endorsed by the War Office, that the country was in danger of invasion and dislocation of normal services. Training exercises and field displays were organised, often in conjunction with local territorial units, where members were told to imagine that

21 and 22 Pre-war field days: VADs in Sussex (21) and Lancashire (22) (British Red Cross Society)

a battle was supposed to have taken place near the Northumbrian coast. The invaders were forced to re-embark on account of the appearance of the fleet, while the defenders rushed to the coast, leaving the 'wounded' behind to be dealt with by the ambulance parties. . . . The engagement occurred somewhere about three o'clock, and soon after a heavy roll of casualties was reported;

or that

a party of revolutionaries, well armed, had assembled at Wimbledon Common at a time of national peril, and that on their attempting to damage the South-Western Railway a force of Territorials had dispersed them, with a number of killed and wounded on both sides.

VAD women were taught to look after the wounded in hospital tents. They were put in charge of field kitchens, and given instruction in 'improvised cooking arrangements on ordinary fires and in the open'.[59]

Thus, neither domestic nor nursing training necessarily confined the VAD within four walls; weeks spent under canvas became as important as weeks spent in hospital. The first residential camps for Red Cross VADs were held in Glamorgan and Wiltshire in 1911, and sparked off widespread enthusiasm. A summer camp organised by the County of London branch in July 1913 taught its members to pitch and strike tents, dig trenches for camp fires, load wagons, and make beds and straw mats for the wounded. A member of the Kent camp of 1913 rhapsodised: 'The joy of those nights in camp! the freshness of them! . . . Friendships were made that tend to draw the county together in one bond of Voluntary Aid sisterhood.'[60] Improvisation and spontanaeity were the key words of the movement. Members took their cue from the 1909 circular's recommendations on adapting local resources for the purposes of sick accommodation and transport. This approach was most vividly expressed by Cantlie in April 1913, at a conference of St John Nursing Officers:[61]

You may be isolated from your detachment on the country-side. . . . You find you have to make a stretcher. But you say you have nothing to make it with. You must get some pitchforks, (they are probably the only things you will find in a country district), knock the heads off the forks and rope the handles together. How are you going to rope them together? You have no rope. The military have commandeered every scrap of rope and leather and strap and there is not a piece to be found anywhere. What are you to do? There is a strawstack. You can make a straw rope, and so everyone should know how to sit down behind a strawstack and make a straw rope. . . . You have used up all the dressings that were in your havresac. You have nothing to tie your splints with. Yes, you have your straw rope; it is easily made and goes round nicely, and for dressings you must take some straw and burn it and thus get some wood ash, and you can use that; it is the best ambulance dressing in the world.

This was indeed a far cry from domestic duties and hospital routines. Instead of restricting women VADs to a modest auxiliary role, these open-air exercises encouraged them to develop initiative, and to envisage taking command of a situation in an emergency. Their training offered them a position of leadership of sorts within their own communities. They were invited to take their own decisions on the best use of local resources, and to look at their immediate environs with a new eye:[62]

Let us suppose that the School-house, the Church, or the Hall will hold forty wounded. Forty beds must be provided. Are there forty inhabitants who will give a bed and bedding for each of these? Are there ten women who will nurse them? Are there three women who will cook for them? Is there a minister of religion who will give them spiritual comfort and consolation? Is there a village carpenter who will prepare splints for the mangled limbs, and are there children who will roll the bandages to envelope them? . . . Is there anyone whose help is not required? Not one. Where is his or her place, what does he or she do? That will be told them. . . . We can give the knowledge, we can provide the organisation.

These aspects of women's VAD work – outdoor activities, improvisation, training in leadership – were accentuated by the failure of men to enrol in the movement in the expected numbers, except in areas organised exclusively by the SJAB. In their absence a women's detachment could at any moment find itself the sole agency in charge of transport of the sick and wounded, classically the male function in military-medical organisation. The male organisers of the movement found this situation unacceptable. By 1910 the County Director of the Rutland Red Cross had instructed the quartermasters of women's detachments to get twelve local men trained in stretcher drill, and not to wait for a proper male detachment to be formed. The Oxford branch was co-opting members of local Fire Brigades for this purpose in 1911. The Executive of the Red Cross finally responded to these local initiatives only in February 1914, when it authorised the women's detachments to recruit and register 'bearer squads' of six men.[63] But not all women's detachments acted on these instructions. Women members were often young and strong – the minimum age for joining was 17 – and could compare their lifting capacities favourably with those of male detachment members aged over 40. By 1912 male organisers were reacting with alarm to reports of women's stretcher practice. Many medical instructors thought that stretcher work for women was 'altogether contraindicated', but, if absolutely unavoidable, should be carried out by four women per stretcher. Cantlie's official manual stipulated no less than 'six women bearers, one at each end of the stretcher, and four more supporting the sides of the stretcher'.[64] The sole purpose of stretcher drill for women was said to be for discipline and smartness, and to enable them to give instruction to others, less skilled than themselves, in emergencies. A meeting of the Technical Reserve Committee at the War Office in November 1912 reiterated that women were to be discouraged from this work, and some counties devised ingenious modifications of stretcher drill, and invented wheeled or specially lightweight stretchers. The indisputable fact remained, however, that women detachments expected to take responsibility for what had previously been considered essentially 'men's work'; and they felt justified in doing so by their growing certainty that the next war would take every able-bodied man into the firing line.[65]

How were the VADs viewed by civilian nurses? Keogh had anticipated the need to 'conciliate the nursing profession'; and the movement recognised the importance of trained nurses in many ways. The 1909 circular stipulated that there should be at least two in every detachment of twenty women members; the 1910 edition stated that the lady superintendent was to be a trained nurse. In 1911 the Director-General stressed the importance of obtaining qualified nurses as superintendents: the ruling might sometimes have to be relaxed, but not 'where the enrolment of a trained nurse as lady superintendent is merely a matter of trouble, difficulty, or alleged unsuitability'.[66] In the remoter rural branches, this office had to be filled by the district nurse; elsewhere, retired nurses or members of the TFNS were called upon. Their role was originally expected to be supervisory only; early in 1910, however, they were invited to undertake training functions as well.[67]

The reasons for this change were largely financial. While in some areas patriotic doctors lowered their costs or lectured free of charge, in most they insisted on charging the fees which they had in the past received for lecturing and examining St John classes. 'What an impossible handicap to a women's VAD in a country district would be a fee of £21 – for the first aid and Nursing' wrote a lady organiser from Scotland to Elizabeth Haldane, and another organiser wrote to the secretary of the Red Cross, 'It is out of the question to charge villages 7s.6d. and 9s.6d. a head.' In 1913 the BMA resolved to insist on a fee of five guineas per course, which again caused dismay and the prospect of disbandment among many detachments. The services of a trained nurse, on the other hand, were nothing like so expensive. In July 1910, at the request of the Red Cross, the War Office sanctioned the employment of trained nurses as home nursing instructors in a published amendment to the VAD scheme.[68] The replacement of doctors by nurses was a major bone of contention between the Red Cross and St John, and one of the chief reasons for the latter's withdrawal from the joint operation of the scheme in that year. St John accused the Red Cross of pursuing quantity rather than quality in the formation of detachments, and refused to recognise nurses as instructors until June 1914.[69]

Although qualified nurses were members and instructors of detachments, and many hospitals accepted VADs for training, relations between nurses and women VADs remained highly ambivalent. Even where nurses were not ardent registrationists, they resented any kind of 'playing at nurses' by amateurs which could reduce the status of what was to many a vocation, and to some a profession. On a practical level, there was a real danger that nurses' wages, which were as yet hardly generous, would be further depressed if large numbers of semi-trained women were on the outbreak of war employed either in military hospitals, or in civilian hospitals as replacements for those called away on Territorial duty. Registrationists naturally feared that their struggle might receive a setback from which it would never recover. Anxieties focussed on the title 'nurse' and the type of uniform worn by VADs. Lady Perrott insisted that the St John VADs were never called 'nurses', but the term was widely employed in the Red Cross. Princess Christian, ever the champion of nursing professionalism, wrote to Lord Esher in December 1912 to ask 'whether the term *Nurse* could not be altered to Nursing Aids – or Nursing Aid Sister, or some such term'. Soon afterwards the War Office wrote to the County Presidents of the Red Cross forbidding the improper use of the term 'nurse'.[70] In January 1913 the magazine *First Aid* organised a competition to find the best alternative title, the prize going to 'Vadet'; but this does not appear ever to have passed into common parlance. One wartime territorial matron is said to have insisted on using the term for the VADs assigned to her hospital, but her patients pointedly refused to follow her example.[71] Uniform was equally a source of resentment, and both St John and Red Cross VADs were criticised bitterly for apeing the appearance of the professional nurse. No single uniform appears to have been compulsory: detachments sometimes designed their own, and appeared in a remarkable variety of headgear. They certainly looked a good deal more like nurses than soldiers; and in April 1914 the Advisory Sub-Committee on Voluntary Aid was asked to devise a new uniform which should be distinguishable from that of the hospital-trained nurse.[72] They were soon, however, to be burdened with more pressing tasks.

The extent of the trained nurses' anxiety can be gauged from a report of a meeting between the Assistant County Director of the Somerset branch of the Red Cross and 'a number of fully-trained nurses in West Somerset':[73]

The general feeling of the meeting was one of sympathy with the aims of the Society, but a plea that in case of a national strike of nurses members of VAD's might not be employed as blacklegs was strongly urged, and a case was cited where VAD members had been known to interfere with a case under the care of a professional nurse. Considerable feeling was exhibited at a proposition to delete the words 'three years' from the regulation *re* the qualification of a nurse lecturer . . . and the suggestion was abandoned. Two resolutions, to be sent to headquarters, were then carried unanimously: – 'That examinations ought to be held at local centres at the same time throughout the United Kingdom, and . . . set and marked by a matron (such as a Territorial F.N.S. matron) the questions being compiled from the Nursing Manual.' 'That the Nursing Manual in present use (Cantlie, No. 2), should be replaced by one that is up-to-date and written by a nurisng authority.'

The nursing community was very far from wanting to boycott or suppress the VADs: as always where military matters were concerned, trained nurses wanted an opportunity to emphasise the importance of the contribution that they alone could make to the state. The same nurses who feared 'scabbing' wanted to be more involved in VAD training. There was certainly scope for intervention. Even among the Red Cross detachments, there were enormous variations in the content of lectures, the standard of examinations, and the amount of practical work undertaken. Attempts to remedy this lack of uniformity were half-hearted. In May 1912 the County of London branch proposed a centralised three-year training scheme, which included courses in home nursing and hospital attendance; in July the Red Cross Council approved the scheme, with its system of ribbons and bars for proficiency, but did not make it compulsory. In 1911 and 1912 the Red Cross had finally published its own training manuals, Cantlie's *Red Cross First Aid* and *Red Cross Nursing*, but the latter in particular was widely criticised for being too technically advanced: detachments reported a falling-off in attendance, and begged to return to the simpler publications of the SJAA. Some VADs working from Cantlie's manual were expected to be able to give hot air baths and hypodermic injections, carry out nasal feeding, and know the Latin names for diseases.[74] Others were undergoing a much less demanding training in unrealistic conditions: they practised their bandaging on clothed limbs only, and their patients never presented disgusting or distressing complaints, but were all too often 'delightful Boy Scouts in the best of health!' On 8th July 1914 these matters were aired by a deputation of trained nurses to the War Office Advisory Sub-Committee on Voluntary Aid.[75] Their proposals for reform were all too soon overtaken by events.

BEHIND THE LEGEND

Because they were the medium of female recruitment for a huge variety of non-combatant tasks in the First World War, the VADs have passed into popular legend, and certainly the mainstream literary canon, as the epitome of enthusiasm, dedication and efficiency. However, this retrospective view severely distorts the history of the pre-war movement. Although it certainly generated keenness, excitement and hard work, it was also beset with confusion, incompetence and acrimony. Finance was a particular nightmare. The relatively small number of St John detachments, mostly based in cities, were able to build successfully on previous traditions of voluntary funding, but the Red Cross detachments, especially the more rural ones, frequently floundered. It was not just a question of the fees to be paid for medical instruction; bandages had to be renewed, the expenses for travel to competitions, displays and examinations had to be met, tents and other camp equipment had to be purchased or hired. In 1910 the Devonshire Red Cross VAD handbook suggested that 'patriotic individuals' might be willing to foot the entire bill, and occasionally they did so. Two Surrey detachments, for example, were entirely funded by the assistant county director, Lt-Col. Longstaff. Together with the local branch treasurer, he paid for all the equipment which on 1 August 1914 appeared to be needed for the coming emergency. Other branches managed to raise smaller funds, which paid for specialised hospital equipment.[76]

Detachments were under-staffed as well as under-financed. It was difficult to obtain the regulation complement of medical officers and trained nurses willing to act as commandants and superintendents, and the commitment of ordinary members was by no means sustained or uniform. Mrs Longstaff recalled that a year after the Wimbledon detachment was founded, only she, her husband, her daughter and a female neighbour were available for committee work.[77] Between 1910 and 1912, the vice-presidents and county committee of the County of London branch of the Red Cross did not meet, and the average attendance at detachment drills was reported to be less than 50 per cent of membership. In Wimbledon, and doubtless in many other branches, it was understood that members were free to resign at any time. By November 1913 the Exeter branch had created a reserve section for members 'unable to continue on the active list'. Many 'active' members did not even turn up for War Office inspections, and those who did often performed unimpressively, and with inadequate equipment.[78]

Detachments complained bitterly of the lack of interest shown in their problems by Red Cross headquarters, and in particular of the lack of any central finance support.[79] Central leadership was certainly very weak. In part this was attributable to the schism between the two great voluntary agencies. It is difficult at this distance in time to appreciate the bitterness of the dissension between the Red Cross and St John: a Red Cross account of the pre-war period, published in 1917, had to be suppressed in order not to prejudice the continued co-operation between the agencies for the duration of the war.[80] The quarrel drained the energies and enthusiasm of the Red Cross Executive and Council, and subjected many of them to a paralysing conflict of personal loyalties, as many of them were also members of the Order of St John. Knights and Ladies of Grace served on the Red Cross Council, as Lords Lieutenant and their ladies, as chairmen of Territorial Associations and St John county sections, and as directors of Red Cross county branches: 'as many offices as the famous character in the *Mikado*, in vain struggling to reconcile their duty in one office with their obligations to the others.'[81]

The leadership was also demoralised by lack of government funding. In March 1912 Treves resigned from the chair of the Red Cross executive, and from all his responsibilities in connection with military nursing, on grounds of ill-health: he subsequently felt free to speak publicly about the War Office's refusal to supply the VADs with any equipment. Esher was deeply depressed by the movement's failure to achieve the official standing of its Continental counterparts: this would have involved not only government funding for military preparations, but also a larger role in peacetime ambulance work. In April 1912 he went so far as to invite Queen Alexandra to reconsider her connection 'with an organisation which may fail, when called upon, to fulfil expectations': Treves's resignation would leave the British Red Cross Society to 'crumble to pieces'; the conflict with St John made it impossible to organise the detachments on a sound financial and administrative basis; the society had no national relief function, and too narrow a social base. Soon after writing thus, he resigned his position on the Red Cross Council.[82]

There can be little doubt that the fundamental cause of the VAD movement's malaise was the lack of encouragement and direction it received from the War Office. The movement, having been created exclusively to deal with the emergency of invasion (or possible internal insurrection) was, by 1911, clearly somewhat marginal to the planning of the General Staff and the Committee of Imperial Defence. These bodies now anticipated a Continental engagement to check a German threat to France – a purpose for which the Territorial Force as a whole was not explicitly designed, but to which it could, none the less, easily be adapted. Both Haldane and Keogh possessed a strong sense of the intrinsic value of popular enthusiasm harnessed to a voluntary war effort; neither of them had thought that the VAD movement needed to be directly integrated with a British expeditionary force. Keogh, however, left the Army Medical Services in 1910, was briefly Organising Secretary of the British Red Cross Society, and then became Rector of Imperial College; Haldane left the War Office in June 1912 to become Lord Chancellor. Without their backing, the VADs seemed increasingly quixotic and irrelevant. What need was there for a nationwide network of detachments if only those cities designated Territorial General Hospital Centres were likely to be involved in a war medical scheme?[83] Moreover, the VADs' methods of work and training caused some disquiet to the traditional military mind; there was too much spontaneity, too little discipline – and as one RAMC officer wrote, too free a hand given to women:[84]

> When one or more Voluntary Aid Detachments combine to form a temporary hospital, and if the commandant of the most senior detachment is a lady, will she command any men's detachment that may be attached to her unit? This may seem a point of minor importance, but some grading of officers commanding Voluntary Aid Detachments appears to be necessary, and personally I do not think it would be wise for a woman to act in any capacity other than a nursing sister or matron.

The early discussions between the War Office and the Red Cross had anticipated a close connection between the VADs and the territorial medical service as a whole. The Red Cross Executive expected most of its branch work to be carried out in or near towns in which the territorial general hospitals were situated. According to the 1909 circular, the VADs were not only intended to plug the gaps between the field ambulance and the base hospitals, but also to provide 'supplementary personnel' for the latter; moreover, local Red Cross branches were expected to equip the general hospitals, and to assist the Territorial Associations in earmarking accommodation for them. In July 1912, however, the War Office withdrew all responsibility for territorial general hospitals from the Red Cross.[85] The severance of the connection left the VAD movement adrift and rudderless. There was no coherent or necessary relation between the regional branches. Central government offered no concrete projection of a national emergency in which each detachment would have its definite part to play. There were no opportunities to develop any forms of division of labour, or specialisation, between branches. A plea to the War Office for clarification and guidance in forward planning met with a distinctly discouraging response at the beginning of 1913:[86]

as it is impossible to forecast the locality or intensity of the fighting or the number of sick and wounded at any given time or place, it is equally impossible to say how many VADs will be required, where or when they will be wanted, or what will be the best method of utilizing their services . . . it is not possible nor is it desirable to assign specific duties to individual Detachments.

In the meantime, the Territorial Force medical service was beginning an agitation of its own to take charge of the VADs. It was argued that the county organisation of voluntary aid was incompatible with the divisional organisation of the territorials, and that the VADs were still largely unprepared for the task of setting up clearing hospitals. A national VAD congress supported these arguments, and passed a resolution in favour of coming in from the cold, stressing[87]

the desirability of Voluntary Aid Detachments being administered by the British Red Cross Society according to Territorial Force Divisions and organised by the War Office with reference to mobilisation and to lines of communication; and on the need of financial aid being given in peace time to Voluntary Aid Detachments by the War Office, and on the necessity of an adequate staff being provided by the War Office for the direction and training of Voluntary Aid Detachments.

The War Office responded in March 1913 by announcing that a territorial cadre would be established in each division to help in co-ordinating, training, and eventually mobilising detachments. At the end of the year the Wessex Territorial RAMC proposed a new scheme of linked reception, clearing and general hospitals, and hinted as strongly as possible that the detachments as such no longer had an independent role to play in war:

> These plans are in no way antagonistic to the general scheme for the peace organisation of Voluntary Aid, but individual Voluntary Aid Detachments must be looked upon as training units and not as the completed personnel of a Temporary Hospital, which will have to be made up according to the size and requirements of the Temporary Hospital in question, and will often necessitate the selection of individuals from different detachments.

By February 1914 this memorandum had been submitted to Red Cross headquarters, and accepted pending War Office approval. The memorandum was a very public repudiation of the original ethos of the VADs. At a regional conference of VADs at Salisbury on 25 February the County Director for Devonshire gave it a particularly enthusiastic welcome, which sounded the death knell to the aspirations of many female members:[88]

> it puts an end once and for all to the idea that women would ever be used in the field; consequently it does away with the doctrine that improvisation is better than the use of proper appliances on every and all occasions; detachment members should work up to the highest standards with the understanding that they would be used in buildings, as nurses, not on the field as first aiders; and improvisation would only be resorted to as a last resource, as for instance if traffic were so congested that supplies were cut off.

In June 1914 the War Office set up a committee under the chairmanship of Sir Walter Lawrence to inquire into the multiple difficulties encountered by the VAD movement.[89] War broke out before its deliberations could be concluded, and indeed rendered them largely irrelevant. Although voluntary fundraising continued, the VAD movement henceforth received government financial support. The Red Cross and St John patched up their quarrels for the time being. The pattern of duties to be performed by VAD members evolved with the course of the war. The trained nurses might continue to resent the VADs whom the patients addressed as 'nurse', and who undercut their wages by working gratuitously or for small grants; but they could hardly be so unpatriotic, or so impractical, as to refuse to have them in the hospitals. Over two and a half million sick and wounded soldiers were treated in hospitals in the United Kingdom alone between 1914 and 1919;[90] the careful distinctions originally made between the functions of regular, regular reserve, territorial and VAD nursing were broken down by the sheer scale of the work, the geographical spread of hostilities, and the failure of invasion to materialise.

By 1914 few people thought of military nursing as a man's job. The TFNS had been constructed on an all-female basis, and the VAD scheme had quickly deleted its original provision for supplementary male hospital staff. At least 32,000 women served as military nurses between 1914 and 1919;[91] but it was not they who were seen as substitutes for men, freeing them to go to the front. In 1915 a new area of VAD work, the General Service Section, was set up to perform precisely this function within the army hospitals: 'By the adoption of a system of replacement by women of men now employed, it will be possible to transfer non-commissioned officers and men to other medical units at home and abroad.' The General Service Section moved women into the hospitals as dispensers, as dental, laboratory and X-ray assistants, as clerks, telephonists, laundresses, cleaners and cooks. At least 11,000 women were General Service VADs:[92] but it is arguable that, in the perspective of 1899, the majority of the 32,000 hospital nurses also released men for combatant and ambulance service. It is outside the scope of this chapter to discuss the role of other VADs who played little or no part in the military-medical system, except to note that the many women employed as drivers in France via the detachments, and via the FANY, did not drive ambulances near the front: here the pre-war division of labour stood firm, and the work remained a male preserve.

The war needed nurses as it needed soldiers: not just in large numbers, but quickly. The VAD system routinised a basic form of training in hospital work which could be completed in three or four months; and for all its imperfections, it provided for the war hospitals in a way that the TFNS, much less the QAIMNS and

Reserve, could not. About 23,000 VADs served as military hospital auxiliaries:[93] the pool of trained civilian nurses available in 1914 could not possibly have furnished this number. The VAD scheme had proved to be an instrument of expansion second to none, a flexible, nationwide organisation adapted to local circumstances. It would be hard to find a better example of the voluntary principle of social action than the organisation in its pre-war form: largely decentralised, financially independent, for the most part lacking higher governmental direction or uniformity of method. It seems highly appropriate that it should have been an agency of this kind which attempted to form a state military reserve out of women, the least 'conscripted' section of society. VAD work required no previous connection with the army, and little formal education or previous training in practical skills; it positively favoured women who were not in state employment, and who were, indeed, outside the labour market altogether. Why not, therefore, as one girl asked herself in 1914, 'go and learn to be a nurse while the Kitchener men were learning to be soldiers?'[94]

CHAPTER 10

++++++++++++++++++++

EMANCIPATION OR MILITARISATION?

++++++++++++++++++++

The period between the Anglo-Boer War and the outbreak of the First World War was one of intense political ferment in Britain. Socialism and feminism directly challenged many of the fundamental tenets of the parliamentary system; but the issue of national defence also stimulated a radical reappraisal of social and political institutions.[1] Near-defeat in South Africa, the massive manpower requirements of the ultimate victory, and a post-war wave of invasion scares, led to a popular movement for the introduction of male military conscription. The National Service League, formed by Lord Roberts in 1903, not only argued for this measure on strategic grounds, but also described it as the means of overriding class divisions and uniting the manhood of the country. The League posited and popularised an arms-bearing model of citizenship, rather than an electoral one.[2] Conscriptionists tended to be conservative in their political views; but, as we have seen, the concept of 'the Nation in Arms' also held great appeal for liberals such as R.B. Haldane, who saw in his creation of the Territorial Force the potential for a unifying and even egalitarian social movement. It might seem that this political discourse was one from which women were by definition excluded. But it was in fact so pervasive that women of all political complexions or none were drawn into it and compelled to debate its premises.

On both sides of the pre-war debate on women's suffrage, huge importance was attached, and much ink spilt, on the 'physical force' argument. Anti-suffragists argued that the state could not exist unless it could be physically defended, and that only those who could personally take up arms on the state's behalf were entitled to citizenship. Since women did not perform this function, they could never be regarded as the political equals of men.[3] Suffragists were adept at picking holes in the 'physical force' argument. They pointed out that the vote was not withdrawn from men when they became aged or infirm, and that society debarred certain men, such as prime ministers and generals, from personal engagement in conflict.[4] Nevertheless, many of the premises of the 'physical force' argument were shared by the suffragists with their opponents. They were largely committed to the maintenance of the empire, and they did not disbelieve in the threat of invasion; and many of them were prepared to argue for equal suffrage on the grounds that women could and did play a necessary role in warfare. This was particularly the case in certain nursing circles. Many nurses who fought for the improvement of their professional status through state registration were also suffragists, and anxious to demonstrate the utility to the state of the fully trained nurse. War nursing continued to be the most obvious example of an area of state need. As Isla Stewart, president of the Matrons' Council, said, to nurses alone 'came the honour of removing the reproach that women were of no use in time of war';[5] and Elizabeth Haldane thought that 'we women can do work for our Army as really as if we shouldered the musket and handled the sword'.[6] As has been seen, R.B. Haldane himself publicly stated that women's nursing services in war furnished convincing evidence of their fitness for equal citizenship. That war nursing was more than a philanthropic or cosmetic gesture was constantly hammered home in the years when the TFNS was being built up. Nurses were not being enrolled to be kind to soldiers, but to keep up the numerical strength of armies, to repair and replace the losses of the battlefield as quickly as possible.[7]

There were indeed observers, the suffragette Emmeline Pethick Lawrence among them, who realised that modern conditions of warfare rendered much of the 'physical force' argument obsolete: who agreed with von der Goltz's *Nation in Arms* that not just armies, but whole nations went to war, and that nursing was only one of the auxiliary services which would be required of women and other non-combatants. The successful prosecution of war depended utterly on the work of those in the rear who would feed, clothe and arm as well as nurse the soldiers.[8] But this thesis was not invoked by suffragists in the nursing lobby, who shared the general preoccupation with personal military service and the risking of self in the larger cause. A nurse entered into a direct physical relationship with the wounded soldier, like him taking her life in her hands; her contribution was at the same time intensely personal and selfless. No matter how necessary they might be to the war effort, the same symbolic importance could never be attached to the functions of transport and supply.

It seems reasonable to assume that the logic of these suffragist arguments about women's personal war service would have made some impression on the 'antis' in the years preceding the First World War. If, as we have been led to believe, it was women's contribution to the war effort which made the case for the granting of the vote to some women in 1918, might we not expect to find some signs of conversion to suffragism among those who were witness to the growth of the TFNS and the VADs before 1914? In fact, quite the reverse seems to have been the case. The leadership and ranks of the voluntary aid movement were peopled by some of the most vocal anti-suffragists of the period. No matter where logical reasoning might lead, in practice there was no inevitable connection between female war service and female political equality. The St John's Ambulance Brigade gave evidence of this before the Boer War; the movement considered its female Nursing Divisions eligible for war service, but denied its Nursing Officers any part of the framing of their own regulations; and after the war those who called again for an auxiliary military role for the Nursing Divisions condemned unequivocally the demands and the propaganda methods of the suffragettes.[9] Even more striking was the post-war link between the Red Cross and anti-suffrage sentiment. The female leadership was often identical in the Red Cross and the National League for Opposing Women's Suffrage: thus for example the Duchess of Montrose was simultaneously President of the Scottish Women's National Anti-Suffrage League and of the Scottish Council of the BRCS, as well as being Vice-President of the Advisory Board of the TFNS; Lady Wantage was head of the Red Cross and the Anti-Suffragists in Berkshire; Lady Jersey occupied the same positions in Oxfordshire.[10]

Perhaps it is not to be wondered at that such ladies, usually the wives of the lords lieutenant of their respective counties, should have espoused socially conservative views; nevertheless it seems strange that these views should not have been modified by experience. Like Kipling, who eulogised in verse the heroism and sacrifices of the British nurses of the Anglo-Boer War, but became a strong supporter of the anti-suffrage movement,[11] these women proved capable of preparing each other for war and kindred emergencies without seeing themselves in a different political light. Katherine Lady Tullibardine, one of Elizabeth Haldane's most faithful co-workers in the Scottish VAD movement, told a Glasgow meeting of the NLOWS in November 1912: 'I do not think that we, who are incapable of taking upon ourselves the burden of national defence, should have the decisive voice in questions of peace and war.' And she reiterated these opinions in a speech at Edinburgh in January 1914: the business of government rested 'on forces in which it is impossible that we should serve.'[12] Another prominent anti-suffragist, Violet Markham, seems actually to have seen in the Red Cross movement a symbol of all the forces antithetical to female enfranchisement. She wrote to Elizabeth Haldane in 1912:[13]

> I don't feel I *could* go through the work of a General Election if I had anything nearly or remotely to gain from it. To me life rests on such vast paradoxes and I do believe that what one renounces is given back. . . . When they [women] go into battle I want them to be the Red Cross Legion – fearless where the struggle is fiercest but withal self-denying and consecrated.

If it is surprising to find that prominent Red Cross ladies resolutely ignored the possible political implications of their work, it is even more remarkable to note that many of the most active suffragists virtually ignored the existence of what was, if only numerically, the most significant of contemporary women's organisations. Very few bridges were built between the two movements. VADs were hardly ever mentioned in the suffrage press. The suffragist Mrs St Clair Stobart, whose Women's Sick and Wounded Convoy Corps was a registered VAD in the County of London branch of the Red Cross, and Dr Elsie Maud Inglis, the founder of the Scottish Women's Suffrage Federation, who was Commandant of an Edinburgh VAD in this period,[14] were exceptional in their participation in preparations for war service. When R.B. Haldane attended recruiting meetings for the Territorial Force, and when he addressed an international conference of nurses in London on the connection between war nursing and women's emancipation, he faced fierce heckling by suffragettes: but they were there to demand votes for women, not to hear his speeches on the likelihood of war, or to consider the implications of his schemes for the future role of women in society.[15]

It seems paradoxical that at a time when defence issues and the physical force argument were so much in the air, large numbers of women were nevertheless able to divorce the concepts of auxiliary military service and the right to the franchise. But it must be remembered that participation in parliamentary elections was not the only model of citizenship and political activity being canvassed in this period. The Boer War effort raised, for women as well as for men, the prospect of the nation organised as a fighting unit: both sexes and all classes could accept their allotted roles and work together towards the single end of maintaining the integrity of nation and empire against external challenges.[16] This was presented by organisations such as the National Service League and the Navy League as the most urgent of political tasks; even the liberal and philanthropic Elizabeth Haldane wrote of it as 'an end which includes every minor end within its embrace'.[17] Thus it was perfectly possible for the women involved in Red Cross work to feel that they were already fulfilling the highest duties of citizenship, and that they need look for no further forms of public recognition. Learning how to do stretcher drill, to set up temporary hospitals, to organise entire communities for the emergency reception of the wounded, qualified a woman as an actor on the public stage; the external signs of uniforms, badges and field displays confirmed her in this opinion of herself. VADs longed less for the vote than for the outbreak of war, when they would be reassured that their work was of real use and of central importance to a great national enterprise.

The main focus of ambition was thus not Parliament, but the army. Grace Ashley-Smith, the chief architect of the FANY, was not a suffragist, although her organisation and methods were very similar to those of Mrs St Clair Stobart; and in pursuit of her military objectives she took measures which before the Anglo-Boer War would certainly have earned her the label of feminist, and would have brought upon her corps the ridicule and failure which attended the efforts of the Women's Volunteer Medical Staff Corps of 1894. She insisted on her members wearing divided skirts for astride riding, and wrote of one of her organisation's weaker links, 'who insisted on wearing white drawers with frills under her khaki skirt', that 'she had to go; no women's movement could have survived those white frilly drawers on parade.'[18] But the goal of Grace Ashley-Smith's 'women's movement' was not emancipation for political purposes; and, although her members gleefully accepted invitations to all-male officers' 'smokers', she was not working to break down barriers between the sexes in society at large. She summed up her ambitions in a description of a church parade at a Guards' summer camp in 1914 which the FANY were the first women ever to attend:[19]

> I was thrilled and bursting with pride to be there at last with the FANY, the Grenadiers on one side, the Coldstreams opposite, the Scots Guards on our right, and the Irish Guards alongside. There are certain supreme moments in every one's life, that was one of mine. It was worth all the labour and slogging, and self-denial and discouragement – all the ups and downs, all the jeers and sneers and laughter – to be there at last – part of the army – yes and with the best of it.

It is a remarkable illustration of the difference in British social life before and after the Anglo-Boer War that Grace Ashley-Smith and the FANY could survive the jeers and sneers – as the WVMSC had not – to earn the goodwill and co-operation of these sections of the military. It was an equally remarkable sign of the times that women VADs, though costumed more like nurses than soldiers, and working within a more sexually stereotyped framework, were positively encouraged and trained to work closely alongside their local territorial units. Neither the FANY nor the women VADs lacked their detractors. All military and medical authorities insisted that the FANY would not be allowed to serve at or near the front, and that the VADs should neither exceed a subordinate role in the territorial hierarchy, nor attempt to perform unfeminine feats of strength. But the forces of opposition were far outweighed by those of encouragement and approval. The marked change in male perceptions of women's potential for war service which took place between 1899 and 1909 cannot be explained simply by the competence and hardiness displayed by the female nurses in South Africa, or by the new military importance attached to medical services in the wake of the Boer War's disastrous losses through disease. The explanation lies at least in part in the generalised sense of crisis which in this period afflicted those who were accustomed to wield power in Britain, or at least to benefit by its customary exercise; who now feared the demise of that power internally amidst the rise of new political classes and pressure groups, as well as its external collapse in the face of international competition.

In this political emergency, auxiliary forces had to be co-opted; but in such a way as to strengthen the existing leadership without throwing its dominant position into question. Perhaps the most paradoxical example of this expedient was the National League for Opposing Women's Suffrage, which was founded by men who then proceeded to recruit redoubtable women to campaign for their own continuing political subordination. But the auxiliary women's section of a male organisation was a well-established feature of British society long before the Boer War. Both the Liberal and Conservative parties had their female sections, the Women's Liberal Federation and the women's section of the Primrose League respectively, although neither party adopted female suffrage as official policy. The big patriotic leagues of the Edwardian period, the Navy League and the National Service League, also formed strong women's sections, although neither proposed that women should take part personally in the task of national defence. These organisations offered women the vicarious occupations of fund-raising and publicising male activities from which they themselves were debarred. In 1909, the *annus mirabilis* of nationalist agitation, women established several 'vicarious organisations' of their own. The British Women's Patriotic League pledged its members 'to bring in at least one recruit for the Territorial Association'.[20] The Women's Aerial League urged women to raise the level of public interest in aviation, and to give financial support to students undertaking appropriate professional training; and its organ, the *Aerial Observer*, solemnly warned 'Will readers please note that the Women's Aerial League is *NOT* a society for the encouragement of flying among women.'[21]

The women's voluntary aid movement broke with this convention by offering its members a personal involvement with the activities of the Territorial Force; but it did so within a framework which did not, in principle, challenge the existing sexual division of labour. The woman who ministered to the wounded soldier and returned him to the front was indeed supporting men, but was not assuming a male role. Not even the most adventurous devotee of female ambulance work proposed taking up arms herself. VAD women – usually the wives and daughters of the upper and middle classes – symbolised the crisis of Britain's *'ancien régime'*, and its remedy. In December 1910 Lord Meath addressed a meeting of the British Women's Patriotic League, formed the previous year by Lady West and Mrs Wollerson. He called for the help of all 'loyal and patriotic women' in working against the 'softening, weakening, and disintegrating influences of modern social and national life'. The nation could only rise 'through the possession by its citizens of those virile virtues which are engendered by poverty, hardships and suffering. . . . Those of us who are rich need not necessarily be soft, selfish or indisciplined.'[22] Thus, in order to compensate for some men's weaknesses, the right sort of women had to be strong. The sight of women lifting stretchers, wearing khaki or quasi-military uniform, participating in military camps and performing mounted rescue work in military gymkhanas was not necessarily anathema to every male defender of the status quo: on the contrary, it might be a source of reassurance and hope.

Military nursing was the auxiliary function *par excellence*. Because it was the means of co-opting women for war service without threatening gender roles and hierarchies, it was perceived by many civilians as a successful model for co-option in other social spheres. In particular, it provided an attractive model for the incorporation of young girls into the adult world. One of the most striking features of the girls' movements which sprang up in Britain at the beginning of the century was the extent to which they adopted either the military nurse, or the first-aider, or both, as role-model for their members. The 'Church Red Cross Brigade', founded in 1901, was a sister organisation to the Anglican Church Lads' Brigade.[23] The boys' organisation drilled in a pseudo-military uniform; around 1911 this was changed to khaki and its wearers taught how to use a rifle.[24] The girls wore 'a special kind of Uniform having resemblance to the Yeomanry pattern'; this included bushwhack hats, and skirts which stayed well clear of the ground. They were taught home nursing, hygiene and first aid, and by 1912 were 'in many country and colliery districts . . . working under Medical supervision, . . . fulfilling all the duties hitherto performed by a paid Parish Nurse'. They were also considered by their founders to constitute 'A Young Women's Volunteer Ambulance Corps, available for Public Service either in Peace or War'. By 1909, they had attracted the approving eye of

278

Director-General Keogh and had received an inspection by an official of the RAMC. The girls undertook street first aid duty on the occasion of Edward VII's funeral, and were reported 'able to stand the strain and heat even better than the regular ambulance men'. All these activities were advertised as demonstrating 'the great value of these Brigades as a means of reaching and influencing the Young People of our Nation, and bringing them under sound and healthy moral and religious influences'.[25] Other, non-conformist, organisations for girls which were founded in the immediate wake of the Anglo-Boer War, such as the Girls' Guildry, a counterpart to the Boys' Brigade, and the Girls' Life Brigade, a sister organisation to the Boys' Life Brigade, also offered their members a mixture of quasi-military uniform, marching, drill and first aid instruction, but do not seem to have attracted the Anglican organisation's share of official attention.[26]

After the launching of the Territorial Force, a new impetus was given to the formation of youth organisation. Early in 1908, Baden-Powell published his *Scouting for Boys*, outlining a scheme to develop courage and endurance, chivalry and a love of the outdoor life among boys, and was disconcerted to find that by November 1909 around 6,000 girls had begun to form Scout groups. His plans contained no provision for girls, but he felt it necessary to respond to such an overwhelmingly popular demand, as well as to prevent any dilution of his original scheme for boys. The Girl Guide organisation was conceived as 'A suggestion for character training for Girls' which would produce better mothers and wives for 'the future manhood of the country'. The scheme 'might be started either independently, or possibly as a cadet branch, or feeder to the Territorial Organisation of Voluntary Aid', and would convey instruction to girls in 'hospital nursing, cooking, home nursing, ambulance work'.[27] This adult response was a great disappointment to the many girls who had been forming Scout patrols on their own initiative. They recalled:[28]

Armed with staves the Girl Scouts set off to look for adventure. It was found in leaping over dykes, and crawling about in fields on hands and knees, or even on one's tummy. . . . We also had a great idea that these poles would be useful to help us to jump across rivers and even to make bridges, . . . we were reluctantly changed from being Scouts to Guides . . . [a process which involved the re-naming of all girls' companies]. It seemed rather a come-down to be flowers instead of animals, and the ideal of womanliness had no appeal for us at that age.

Although in its early years the Girl Guide movement placed great importance on camping and other open-air pursuits, its founders were determined to protect themselves from the charge of turning little girls into Amazons or tomboys. The voluntary aid movement provided the perfect peg on which to hang a programme of activities for the Guides. The possibility of invasion was used as a spur to efficiency in learning tracking, signalling and first aid: a pamphlet published around 1910 began:[29]

> Girls! Imagine that a battle has taken place in and around your town or village . . . what are you going to do? Are you going to sit down, and wring your hands and cry, or are you going to be plucky, and go out and do something to help your fathers and brothers, who are fighting and falling on your behalf?

When in 1912 Baden-Powell's sister Agnes published *The Handbook of the Girl Guides*, it was subtitled 'How girls can help to build up the Empire'. Outdoor activities for Guides were grouped under the heading 'Finding the Injured', and indoor practices under that of 'Tending the Injured'. The Guides' contribution to the Children's Welfare Exhibition at Olympia in 1913 was virtually a replica of a VAD field display:[30]

> The Guides gave displays on First Aid, signalling, fire-drill, stretcher-drill, and physical exercises. The great feature was a hospital tent, in which were demonstrated roller-bandaging, poultice-making, and the changing of sheets. The enclosure was arranged as a camp; with tent-pitching, camp-fire cooking, and the washing of clothes going on.

The Guides even went so far as to play war games. In 1910 one wrote:

> We were so glad we were called to render First Aid, where Boy Scouts were having a sham fight. The brigands were trying to capture the country, and we bandaged the Scouts, who were supposed to be hurt.

Just as the more adventurous women VADs provoked expressions of alarm from male observers, so these energetic joint activities

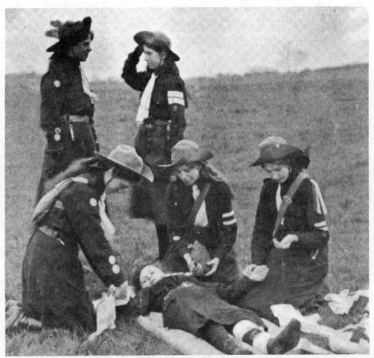

23 1st Darlington Guide Company at First Aid work, 1911. These girls
were following much of the VADs' programme of work. Their hats
recall Treves's nurses in South Africa. (Bodleian Library)

with Scouts provoked a guarded reaction from the pursed lips of Agnes Baden-Powell:

> I am very glad to hear that the Girl Guides have been so useful and active in ambulance work and First Aid at the field days recently held by Boy Scouts. Although the Guides would never think of marching with the Scouts, and do not join with them in any of their pursuits, they proved themselves very capable and businesslike in binding up the wounded, and also in carrying despatches when required. A Guide would be horrified to think she was mistaken for an imitation Scout, or that she was mimicking boys' sports, and the girls have decided to give up all the *fleur-de-lys* badges that they got from the Boy Scouts, and are returning them, and getting the Guides' pretty 'trefoils' in their place.

And a group of 'so-called Girl Guides' who were so far carried away by their enthusiasm for war games that they 'made a raid on a Boy Scouts' camp at midnight' were completely disowned.[31]

Despite Baden-Powell's original intentions, and despite the imitative nature of much of the Guides' programme, the Guides did not ever become part of the VAD movement. A variety of affiliation schemes was discussed: in 1910 it was suggested the Girl Guides be enrolled in Cadet Voluntary Aid Detachments, and re-named 'Girl Cadets of the British Red Cross Society'; in 1912 the Advisory Committee on Voluntary Aid considered 'the question of attaching a certain proportion of Boy Scouts to VADs'.[32] As we have seen, the Boy Scouts often played a prominent role in territorial and VAD field days; but an official attachment was finally ruled out by both the War Office and Baden-Powell. The Red Cross began to discuss forming its own cadet branches at the end of 1910, and 'Red Cross Cadets' first made their appearance in Glamorgan in 1911, 'something like girl scouts but with Red Cross work and home nursing more developed'.[33]

The military nurse was the auxiliary of the soldier; the VAD was the auxiliary of the military nurse; the Girl Guide aspired to be the auxiliary of the VAD. The anticipated needs of the wounded soldier structured the recreation, education, and 'political' ambitions of an ever-increasing number of women and girls between the end of the Anglo-Boer War and 1914. On the basis of the services they were to offer in wartime, they were incorporated in the army as non-combatants and 'non-effectives', and in the state as pseudo-citizens. But how realistically did they envisage the emergency in which the soldiers' wounds would require their tending? May Cannan saw the VADs as making 'tentative plans for an occurrence that was only half believed in'.[34] Their involvement with the territorial organisation did not lead them to seek information on national and international political questions; they drilled and studied for the most part without any sense of urgency. Many of them, as we have seen, were slack in attending meetings and inspections. Perhaps they were influenced by the ridicule of the uninvolved,[35] and by the declining interest of the War Office as the threat of invasion receded. Yet the newspapers were there for them to read. May Cannan was, however, unusual in sensing, by the end of 1913, that war was imminent:[36]

> I called on the Headmaster and asked for it [Magdalen College School] as a Hospital 'in the event of mobilisation for war'. He asked in a half sardonic jocular way when I expected that to be and I answered, 'after the harvest in 1914. The Kiel Canal will be finished by then.'

Grace Ashley-Smith was more typical of her peers, blithely setting off on a cruise to South Africa on 25 July 1914, just three days after a War Office interview in which she had begged for a recognised auxiliary position with the RAMC for her FANY.[37]

Preparation for war was for many of the women first aiders little more than a pretext for enjoyable activity and public recognition. The spurious 'equality' and camaraderie with men which it conferred did not inspire in them the desire to control or influence men's decisions as to when, or whether, their detachments would be mobilised. Engagement in war was seen as an unproblematical, non-political act. Given the fact that the Territorial Force and the VADs were explicitly designed to meet the danger of invasion, this was understandable; participation in purely defensive warfare posed no political or moral problems for the vast majority of the population. The possibility of taking part in war on the Continent – the advisability or otherwise of using war as an instrument of policy – were topics which were barely touched on in public discussion of territorial activities. For most women VADs, war was only an opportunity for action, not an occasion for the exercise of political and moral choice. Katharine Furse, a member of a London VAD and of the BRCS sub-committee on training, responded to the threat of secession and civil war in Ireland by forming an Ulster Hospital Corps of volunteer nurses. She naively assured the press that there was 'no political bias' behind the enterprise, and reflected many years later:[38]

> I did not analyse situations carefully . . . as I look back now I see that my main motive in wanting to help Ulster was my wish to put my Red Cross work into practice.

Grace Ashley-Smith rushed to offer the FANY's services to Sir Edward Carson, who was organising the Ulster resistance to Irish Home Rule, without realising that there were 'five ardent Sinn Feiners in our ranks' – who promptly resigned. Pat Beauchamp spoke for those who remained: 'it's all the same to me as long as I'm there for the show.'[39]

It cannot be said that the suffragist sisterhood as a whole was much better informed on internal and international politics than the majority of Red Cross volunteers, or more alive to the immediacy of militarist and pacifist issues. For the militant Women's Social and Political Union, war was chiefly a metaphor employed to describe and justify their own tactics of martyrdom and violence – the latter being practised almost exclusively against inanimate targets. They extolled the spirit of conflict and struggle: indeed, as Sylvia Pankhurst said of the movement after some of its members seceded to form the Women's Freedom League:[40]

> The spirit of the W.S.P.U. now became more and more that of a voluntary army at war. . . . Processions and pageantry were a prominent feature of the work, and these, in their precision, their regalia, their marshals and captains, had a decided military flavour. Flora Drummond was called the General and rode at the head of processions with an officer's cap and epaulettes.

There seems to have been little reflection on the practical applications of organised military force. If the WSPU spared any consideration to armed strife between the nations, it was chiefly as a stick to beat male society with: how could the powers that be condemn the WSPU when they themselves were armed to the teeth?[41] The more moderate Women's Freedom League published pacifist articles in its newspaper, The Vote. These argued in general terms that war was futile, but did not suggest that war was imminent and that women might want to organise opposition to it.[42]

Both the WSPU and Mrs Fawcett's moderate National Union of Women's Suffrage Societies espoused a liberal imperialism, assuming that the British Empire was a force for world progress which was held together less by the exercise of military coercion than by the consent of the governed.[43] This was not a theoretical framework which could help feminists to understand or anticipate the outbreak of war between competing imperialist powers: it could not be imagined that Britain would need to resort to violent means in Europe to retain or expand her position elsewhere in the world. Moreover, despite the pervasive propaganda about invasions, and the tension building up in Ulster, war was still seen as a disaster happening far away, and to other less fortunate peoples. The Balkan wars of 1912 were reported and discussed throughout the suffrage press. Red Cross teams, hospital nurses, and Mrs St Clair Stobart's WSWCC went to the theatre of war to alleviate the sufferings of soldiers and non-combatants. The fact that the horrors of war weighed heavily on Bulgarian women and children was seized on by suffragists as a further refutation of the 'physical force' argument: wars affected non-combatants as much as soldiers, and the former had, therefore, as much right to vote on questions of war and peace as the latter.[44] But it was only a debating point; not a foreboding.

Mrs St Clair Stobart returned from her seven weeks in the Balkans daunted neither by the Bulgarian military authorities' refusal to allow her corps to 'convoy the wounded from field to base hospital, as they were qualified to do' nor by the boycott practised on them by the Turkish inn-keepers.[45] Her encounters with mutilated soldiers and destitute civilians convinced her that war was an unmitigated evil, and reinforced her belief in the necessity of feminism:[46]

> It is an evil thing that men only should witness the results of war. Wars will never cease till women – at whatever cost to themselves – are admitted behind the drop-curtain, and discover, amongst the cardboard scenery and the grease-paints which glorify for the public the tragedy of war, the brutal realities which are the secrets of those behind the footlights.

She went on to argue that women could only be mobilised as a force against war *after* they had become more fully integrated with the existing war services of the state. Women 'must no longer be played with, as at present, by the British Red Cross Society's scheme of Voluntary Aid Detachments. They must be trained and adopted wholeheartedly by the Territorial Army.' They should be 'enlisted and paid as men are paid in the Territorial Army, and *real* work, not play work, must be exacted by those who understand the kind of work which would be required in military eventualities.' She gave these arguments as the grounds for her resignation from both the County of London branch of the Red Cross, and the WSWCC.[47] Her somewhat perverse line of reasoning found no echo in the writings of other feminists; though individuals could certainly be found within the Red Cross movement who sincerely believed that 'if you wish for peace, prepare for war', or at the very least, that 'voluntary aid in itself could never bring war nearer'.[48]

Katharine Furse was, in retrospect, highly critical of these assumptions. She herself had a most distinguished career in the First World War, leading the first VAD corps to visit France in October 1914, returning to London in 1915 to take charge of the whole organisation of the VADs, and in 1917 becoming first head of the Women's Royal Naval Service. But she looked back on the past without complacency:[49]

> I realise more than ever the danger, as well as the value, of preparation; not being able to distinguish in my own mind whether what we went through was not greatly due to the excitement in which we had been indulging for some four years; the glamour of the chance to put what we had learnt into practice; the glamour of feeling important and superior and the glamour of assisting H.M. Forces. We did not want men to be sick or wounded, but we thought that, if men had to be sick or wounded, we would do our best to help them, so that, when war seemed to be imminent, we were boiling over with our desire to put into practice what we had learnt.

It is difficult to disagree with her judgment. Whatever half-heartedness was observable in the pre-war female membership of the VADs disappeared the moment that war was declared: it was 'playing at war' which had seemed futile, not war itself. The VAD organisation did more than facilitate the mobilisation of women for war service in the technical sense. It also mobilised them psychically, preparing thousands to look forward to a time when their public importance would be intensified – when they would be real actors in the world 'show'. The VADs of August 1914 were marked out as the vanguard for other women to follow; theirs was the organisation which made it theoretically possible for any woman to become a war nurse, at a time when 'every shop that sold a cape and apron was literally besieged by those who wanted, at least, to possess a uniform'.[50]

When Grace Ashley-Smith and her fellow passengers on board ship for South Africa were informed of the outbreak of war:[51]

> I was the first to speak: 'Thank God it's come now.' My inmost thought was that it had come *whilst I was young enough to be in it*. In my usual heedless way I did not explain this, and the captain turned his sombre gaze on me with a glint of anger.

It is true that many inexperienced boys of military age might have used exactly the same words to describe their feelings. Yet it would not have been amiss for those whose chosen function was to heal and not to kill, and who would not themselves be in the front line of physical anguish, to have paused in the summer of 1914 to consider the full implications of their government's decision to declare war. Before the war was over Katharine Furse had begun to experience doubts, and even remorse over her own role. She was proud of her decorations, her Royal Red Cross and her Order of the British Empire, but as she received them 'there was always a queer haunting feeling in my heart that as women we were profiting by the sacrifice of men.'[52]

What profit did the war bring most women? The conventional wisdom is that it brought them the parliamentary vote and a new freedom in social relations – in short, that war succeeded where pre-1914 feminist organisations had failed. The experiences of the military nurses and their professional and amateur colleagues suggest, tentatively at least, some dissenting conclusions. The pre-war history of the military nursing reserve and the VADs certainly throws into question the equation between the recognition of the value of women's war services and the recognition of their right to the parliamentary vote. Large numbers of men in leading positions in Parliament and the government, the War Office and the army, the Army Medical Department and the medical profession before 1914 were fully aware of the essential role that women nurses would perform in the event of war, but this did not make them suffragists. Many of the women who were most active in Red Cross preparations were themselves often vocally anti-suffragist.

Politicians knew very well that women would volunteer for war service whether or not they were enfranchised; none suggested, while international tension was mounting, that it would be wise to ensure women's co-operation by giving in to the militant feminists' demands. The thousands of women already organised for war nursing showed that women's patriotism and usefulness could be taken for granted. After the war, women's war service certainly gave several politicians a graceful public excuse for dropping their opposition to a measure of female suffrage in 1918; but if war service was really the decisive factor in enfranchisement, why should the vote have been, as it was under the terms of the Representation of the People Act 1918, limited to women over the age of thirty? The whole question of the cause of this major shift in the political landscape will remain the subject of an endless debate. It would seem that the conventional explanation in terms of the political recognition of women's war service needs to be reassessed in the context of unspoken issues, as yet relatively unexplored by historians, of national and internal party politics.[53]

The pre-war organisation of military nursing not only did not prepare the ground for the political incorporation of women in British society, but it may actually have defused the movement of women towards sexual equality. British women and girls of the upper and middle classes were at the turn of the century growing closer to their male peers in education, in interests, and in physical strength. The Girl Guides, as we have seen, started life as a spontaneous movement of girls wishing to emulate the Boy Scouts. A young woman joined the FANY because 'I was country-bred and I adored horses. I have always regretted that I had not been born a boy.'[54] A schoolgirl wrote to *Votes for Women*:[55]

> I am an average girl of the day. I have two cousins about my own age in the Territorials. In the case of one I am actually stronger than he, . . . I am sure I could fight as well as many of my boy or men friends if I had to – at any rate, I am quicker and have more presence of mind.

A wellspring of ambition and energy which might have been channelled into demands for political and economic equality was drawn off into a range of subordinate activities within a rigidly hierarchical male organisation. The desire for efficient, useful and professional forms of female occupation was catered for by the business of preparing for war; a concern to exercise a responsible public role was diverted away from the realm of civic and international issues.

The memoirs of VADs such as May Cannan and Vera Brittain show how bitter was the sense of let-down these women experienced when the war was over and their services were no longer required. Once disbanded, it was not easy for them to find a rewarding public role or full-time occupation. They were now as marginal to society as they had been before 1909.[56] Grace Ashley-Smith, who emigrated to Rhodesia with her husband at the end of 1919, wrote a semi-autobiographical novel describing her post-war depression. Her heroine[57]

> had undergone long hours of exposure in blinding rain and stinging cold, she had required nerve and courage and endurance – she had cleaned her car with fingers numbed with cold, and toiled over a stiff engine on freezing nights; she had helped to carry heavy stretchers, driven on pitch dark nights with shells dropping round, held the dying and the delirious. All this seemed to go for nothing now – it did not help her to make bread, or to explain to the boy how to wash clothes, or how to iron. . . . Her courage that had risen high to danger and excitement, threatened to fail her now . . . and she gave way to constant fits of crying.

The same sense of anti-climax must have been experienced by many demobilised men, especially those who faced unemployment and homelessness; but they were not, as women were, subject to the further insult of being labelled 'the surplus two million'[58] who must defer to the needs of the surviving members of the opposite sex. Women munition workers and engineers had their own share of disappointment, as they were forced to resign their jobs in favour of men, and encouraged to return to domestic service;[59] but the pill may have been less bitter to swallow for women who had not been keyed up for a public role well in advance of the war.

Like the Representation of the People Act 1918, the Nurses' Registration Act 1919 was a reform for which many women had worked for decades; and, like the former measure, this reform was also achieved in a way which disappointed pre-war hopes, especially those of the suffragist registrationists. Nurses such as Mrs Bedford Fenwick had thought that the military needs of the state would produce the most convincing arguments in favour of uniform professional standards in nursing; but in fact the war had shown how easily the state could override the nurses' criteria of professionalism, by 'diluting' hospital staffs with barely trained VADs. In the post-war period, governments were concerned to provide medical staff and services for the poorer classes in general, rather than only the small number who were treated in large voluntary hospitals.[60] When in 1925 the nursing Register was established it contained six sections, each with its own training requirement; a training syllabus had been drawn up, but was not made compulsory; and, in Abel-Smith's words, 'nearly every major decision in implementing the Nurse Registration Act was taken not by the General Nursing Council but by the Minister of Health or the House of Commons'.[61] The Registration Act was certainly a milestone in the history of women and of nursing; it was far from being a triumphal arch of progress.

From the viewpoint of some women's struggle for equality and for a peaceful world before 1914, the Red Cross armlet was a charm which drew the sting out of feminism, thwarted aspirations to professional distinction, and stifled objections to war. But we must not ignore the histories of countless women and girls whose home backgrounds denied them access to political activities and professional competence and who, but for their VAD work, might not have ventured beyond tennis parties and fundraising bazaars:[62]

> after I got home from school we were very gay from 1910 to 1914 and I'm afraid rather selfish. . . . I'm afraid we were very carefree. . . . Most of my friends were secretaries of various charitable organisations, the NSPCC and various things of that kind. . . . I think we joined the VAD because it was something quite new. It was practical work which appealed to so many of us. . . . We all threw our heart into it, you know.

Such voices were probably a majority among the pre-war VADs. They were neither preparing themselves for political emancipation nor setting off on the path to political disillusion. They did not concern themselves with events outside their family circles and their local communities, but worked cheerfully towards the day of their own bereavements; and the war, when it came, was experienced by them as a multitude of purely private tragedies.

THE NURSING OF OFFICERS

‡‡‡‡‡‡‡‡‡‡‡‡‡‡‡‡‡‡‡‡‡‡‡

Throughout the period covered by this book, the soldiers treated in military hospitals came overwhelmingly from the private ranks. Officers were expected to make their own arrangements for sickness and injury, for two reasons: first, because their private incomes were presumed such as to make resort to state provision unnecessary and unjustifiable; second, because the army medical system was designed to root out malingerers and penalise the victims of venereal disease, and it was not thought appropriate to place men of the officer class within this coercive framework. This was not always understood by the Victorian public. In 1855 Sidney Herbert felt compelled to defend Florence Nightingale from the accusation 'that she refused to give her assistance to the officers, and, for the sake of more popularity, wishing to devote herself to the men'. He added the gloss that he had 'advised her strongly herself not to do so, and with regard to the ladies engaged with her, not to allow them to attend upon the officers, or else there would be imputations and scandal soon abroad.'[1] As he spoke, however, the House of Commons was proposing that the army hospitals provide special wards for sick and wounded officers returning from active service; and the new general hospitals built at Netley and Woolwich contained a small number of individual rooms for these invalids.[2]

While the War Office acknowledged an obligation to officers needing treatment as a direct result of military operations, no allowance was made for the accidents and illnesses of everyday service. Director-General Muir was by 1878 anxious to get 'beds for officers returning from India authorized at Netley – with a couple of Female nurses – which will be a great boon to those concerned'; whether this was because Indian service was in general very debilitating, or because the officers of the Indian army were a more impecunious group than those based in Britain, is not clear.[3] In November 1881 the Netley PMO refused to admit a group of sick officers recently disembarked from India on the grounds of insufficient accommodation; the incident received wide publicity, and he was subsequently severely censured.[4]

The issue of officers' treatment came to prominence again during British military campaigns in the Middle East between 1882 and 1885. Lady Strangford's voluntary hospital at Cairo accepted many officers as patients:[5]

> The hotels as fast as they opened were rapidly filled with English officers, and among these many sickened. Every day came a fresh entreaty for nurses to attend some bad case, and all the nurses were at work within two days of their arrival. . . . I was forced to bring English officers out of the hotels into our Hospital if they were to be nursed by my nurses.

On the whole, however, it was not considered dignified or, indeed, morally correct for members of the higher social classes to be the beneficiaries of charitable donations. The National Aid Society catered only for the private ranks in Egypt, and an irate mother wrote to its chairman that the British public would 'do nothing for the *officers*, tho' everything for the men who do not want it'. Those officers who did qualify for admission to army hospitals in Egypt and the Sudan had to accept 'no carpet to set foot on', bed linen 'of the coarsest Tommy Atkins description . . . coarse British pottery. Their food is A1, but what invalid can eat out of a coarse cup?'[6]

The Director-General had mixed feelings about the demand for special hospital facilities in wartime. On the one hand he thought that

> No distinction should be made in field hospitals, except that Officers should have the use of separate tents. But as all sick and wounded should have the best that is practicable, I think the Officers should be satisfied with what is provided for them.

On the other hand he was resigned to the inevitability of continued pressure for separate arrangements, in war and peace, in field, general, station hospitals and hospital ships, and to the requisite changes being embodied in the new medical regulations framed after 1883.[7]

This development raises several questions of interpretation. It may have been the case that by the 1880s, the officer and gentleman who would once have been content to be cared for in his own quarters by his manservant had become aware that higher standards of nursing care were available in some hospitals. The tropical fevers and enteric disorders to which the guardians of empire were particularly prone may have increased the demand for constant professional nursing attendance. However, it may also have been true that those demanding military hospital facilities were less wealthy than their brother officers, and that after 1871, when the purchase of commissions was abolished, the number of officers able to afford highly skilled private treatment began to decline. It should not simply be assumed that the social classes from which the officers were drawn had wholeheartedly accepted the practice of hospitalisation at this stage. Sir Robert Loyd-Lindsay of the National Aid Society complained in 1882 that[8]

> some of the wounded Officers have chosen to place themselves under Civilian surgeons, rather than under the very skilful military surgeons at Netley. In doing this I cannot but think that they have been ill advised in their own interests, for the arrangements at Netley Hospital are admirable, and the reputation of such men as Professor Longmore and Dr McClean and others, for skill in gun shot wounds stands high in the estimation of every army in Europe.

Although the military evidence suggests that institutional treatment no longer inevitably carried the stigma of poverty, prejudice was still quite strong in this area.

Hospital provision for officers remained a live issue for the rest of the century. Financial arguments continued to prevail against opening officers' wards, even after a severe outbreak of typhoid in the Dublin station in 1891; and the suggestion was never made that officers might be treated alongside the men. In practice, a working compromise was hammered out whereby GOCs could, on the recommendation of their PMOs, authorise the admission of special cases to the station hospitals. Finally in 1902 the army medical reorganisation following the Anglo-Boer War came down firmly in favour of constructing officers' wards.[9] Questions as to the propriety of allowing ladies to minister to bed cases of their own social class appear to have been laid to rest. Sidney Herbert had thought the risk of scandal self-evident: the early Army Nursing Service had been designed to create an impassable social (and by extension sexual) gulf between sister and patient. In the 1880s, Catherine Grace Loch had forbidden her Indian Army nursing sisters to accept officers' invitations to balls, but had eventually been overruled. In 1889 Sister Mary Cole had, indeed, overstepped the mark by admitting sick officers into nurses' quarters and indulging in games of cards[10]; but a few years later the *Navy and Army Illustrated* could see nothing but good in the provision of Netley nursing for officers:[11]

> the secret of their healing power lies not so much in their wholesome presence and their medical training, as in the fact that they belong to the same class as the officers who have faced death and danger side by side with their patients. . . . In the absence of their own near relatives, the ladies on the nursing staff are not Sisters in name only, but in deed and truth.

One can at least speculate that the hospitalisation of officers to some degree enhanced the ANS's attractiveness to middle- and upper-class women at the turn of the century. The official records, unfortunately, furnish virtually no evidence either of impropriety or marriage between sisters and patients.

A NOTE ON SOURCES

The secondary literature on British military nursing before 1914 is extremely scanty. Ian Hay's *One Hundred Years of Army Nursing* (London 1953) and Juliet Piggot's *Q.A.R.A.N.C.* (London 1975) contain only brief sections on the nineteenth century. In part, the lack of interest shown in this area is due to the general, somewhat obsessive literary and historiographical concentration on the career of Florence Nightingale, a veritable 'cult of personality' which takes too many of her successes for granted. Military nursing has, so to speak, been relegated to a footnote in Nightingale history. However, it is also true that there are daunting obstacles in the way of research. The records on military nurses are meagre and dispersed, and reflect all too clearly their status 'in but not of' the army.

Official sources are very disappointing. The War Office holdings include two files and a scattering of general correspondence on the Crimean nurses, and reports of inquiries held on the ANS in 1868, 1893 and 1902. The first of these deals with the superintendence of Jane Shaw Stewart; all other documents bearing on her case appear to have been destroyed. The indexes to correspondence WO 139/2 and 139/7 state that three files were destroyed between February and April 1901; no reasons are disclosed for this. The 1931 published guide to War Office records list two further files on the Shaw Stewart period, both in the WO 32 class, which seem to have completely disappeared in the reorganisation of this class, although there is no written evidence of their destruction. The War Office files include two nominal and seniority rolls for the

ANS before and after 1902. The first gives the date but only very occasionally the place of birth of individual nurses: entries give no information on education, training, previous occupation or father's occupation. Entries also contain annual summaries of quarterly reports (since destroyed) on the conduct of each nurse, with remarks on her fitness for promotion. The main purpose of these records was to establish eligibility for pensions; as most nurses stayed less than three years in the ANS, entries for only a minority of nurses survive. The post-1902 file does give details on education, training and father's occupation, as well as details on promotion, but does not comment on individual conduct. The Paymaster-General's files on nurses' pensions add very little to the information in these rolls.

After 1902 an Army Nursing Board was set up to deal with the structure and conditions of service of the QAIMNS; a similar board was set up after 1908 for the TFNS. Neither these bodies nor the VADs left records in central official repositories. The TFNS and VADs were administered through County Associations, and together made up the largest organisation of war nursing staff in the period covered by this thesis. It is hoped that this book will stimulate attempts to discover military nursing records which may have been locally preserved.

An oblique light is of course thrown on the Army Nursing Service by several classes of War Office documents dealing with army hospital administration, the ambulance service, and the male nursing staff, known successively as the Medical Staff Corps, Army Hospital Corps and Royal Army Medical Corps in this period. Printed regulations for both the male and female services are also a valuable source, as are the reports of Parliamentary inquiries made into the army hospital system after the Crimean War, the Egyptian campaign of 1882–3, and the Anglo-Boer War.

Neither the Army Medical Department, the ANS, the QAIMNS, nor the military general hospitals, appear to have retained series of documents on female nurses. Senior medical officers took much of their official correspondence away with them on retirement. As Surgeon-General Munro wrote proudly in 1887: 'I have in my possession every letter that the Director-General wrote to me, in which there is any reference to duty.'[1] It was through private channels that papers such as those of Inspector-General John Hall and Professor Thomas Longmore were deposited at the Muniment Room of the RAMC Library at Millbank, London. (This collection has now been transferred to the RAMC Museum at Aldershot.) Many collections remain in private hands, or are lost.[2] There are no unpublished collections deposited with the RAMC,

QARANC, or the Ministry of Defence. The Royal Herbert Hospital, Woolwich, still in use as a military hospital, has no records other than those of currently serving nurses. The army withdrew from the Royal Victoria Hospital, Netley, in 1966, and the whereabouts of its records are unknown. In 1950 the Commandant wrote to the biographer of Sir Almroth Wright that 'all our records seem to have disappeared'.[3]

The uncertain official status of the army sisters was underlined by the heavy involvement of voluntary agencies in furnishing wartime auxiliaries. This has the compensation for the historian of offsetting the paucity of official collections. The holdings of private organisations and individuals often contain War Office documents, as well as much other important information. Thus some deficiencies in the public records for the period 1854–85 can be made good from Florence Nightingale's correspondence, and that of her Training School. The papers of Sir Robert Loyd-Lindsay (later Lord Wantage), who was MP, Financial Secretary to the War Office, and first president of the National Society for Aid to the Sick and Wounded in War (later the British Red Cross Society) are an indispensable source on voluntary and regular military nursing from 1870 to the end of the century. Both the British Red Cross and the St John's Ambulance Association helped to organise medical and nursing aid during the Anglo-Boer War, and published detailed reports on their work. The two organisations were also involved in the VAD scheme between 1909 and 1919: their files contain records of War Office decisions, and texts of War Office and AMD circulars not easily located elsewhere. Another non-official source for the pre-war period is the correspondence of Elizabeth Haldane, whose brother was Secretary of State for War 1906–12. She sat on the Nursing Board of the TFNS and was the confidante of the Director-General of the Army Medical Services and of the Matron-in-Chief, QAIMNS. The texts of many official and voluntary agency proposals are to be found in her papers. Finally, a source which could perhaps be classified as simultaneously official and non-official, the Royal Archive at Windsor Castle, offers some material on military nursing: but it is rather less than might be hoped, given the active personal interest and patronage bestowed in this area by Princess Christian and Queen Alexandra. Sadly, much relevant correspondence appears not to have been preserved.

None of these sources makes it very easy for us to hear the voices of the nurses themselves. Reading between the lines of regulations and training curricula, we see something of what was expected of the nurses; and official reports, and the Nightingale, Shaw Stewart and Deeble letters, help us to see how far expectations were translated into practice. We are also helped by the fact that the period covered by this book included a number of wars: these have the great advantage for the historian of inspiring memoirs and rapportage from individuals who might not ever have put pen to paper in other circumstances. But these glimpses of real personalities are as frustrating as they are illuminating. The history of nursing in general is still very much in its infancy: research has barely begun in the field of nursing practice and biography before the 1880s.[4]

From that decade onwards, however, the picture changes: the nursing community at last generated professional organisations and the readership for several periodicals, most notably the 'Nursing Mirror' section of the *Hospital*, and the *Nursing Record* (continued as the *British Journal of Nursing*). Both publications appeared weekly, furnishing a copious source of individual biography, conditions of work, and the controversy over state registration, to which the 'Nursing Mirror' was opposed. They provide, through articles and letters contributed by nurses, an unparalleled insight into the large and small issues of the nursing world. They show how varied and wide-ranging were the interests and aspirations of British nurses at the turn of the century: articles on medicine and hospital care are interspersed with features on literature, social and public health issues, the contemporary women's movement, and foreign travel and adventure. No other women's publications in this period – certainly not the weeklies produced by the suffrage movement – offer so much evidence of broad-mindedness, optimism and practicality. This writer can only feel grateful for the opportunity to make the acquaintance of so lively-minded and courageous a body of women.

NOTES AND REFERENCES

INTRODUCTION

1 G. Flaubert to George Sand, 11.3.71, quoted in F. Steegmull, ed., *The Letters of Gustave Flaubert 1857–1880* (London 1982), p. 170.
2 E. Hobsbawm and T. Ranger, eds., *The Invention of Tradition* (Cambridge 1984).

CHAPTER 1 BEFORE THE NIGHTINGALES

1 J. Woodward, *To do the sick no harm* (London 1974), pp. 29–30; J.F. South, *Facts Relating to Hospital Nurses* (London 1857), p. 11; W. Brockbank, *The History of Nursing at the M.R.I., 1752–1929* (Manchester 1970), p. 1.
2 See J. Williams, ed., *The Autobiography of Elizabeth Davis, a Balaklava Nurse* (London 1857), 2v.
3 K. Jones, *A History of the Mental Health Services* (London 1972), pp. 120, 141; B. Abel-Smith, *A History of the Nursing Profession* (London 1960), p. 6; South, *op. cit.*, pp. 7, 9, 11, 13–14.
4 WO 25/264, Testimonials to nurses: papers of C. Grieg, surgeon of Clifton, near Bristol; South, *op. cit.*, pp. 12–13, 17; B. Abel-Smith, *The Hospitals 1800–1948* (London 1964), p. 43; J.R. Gillis, 'Servants, Sexual Relations, and the Risks of Illegitimacy in London, 1801–1900', *Feminist Studies* V, no. 1, 1979, pp. 147–8.

5 Abel-Smith, *The Hospitals*, pp. 43–5; M.J. Peterson, *The Medical Profession in mid-Victorian London* (Berkeley 1978), pp. 14–15; South, *op. cit.*, pp. 10, 14–15.

6 Abel-Smith, *The Hospitals*, p. 46; E.G. Thomas. 'The Old Poor Law and Medicine', *Medical History* 24, 1980, p. 5; A. Digby, *Pauper Palaces* (London 1978), p. 44.

7 Digby, *op. cit.*, pp. 41, 44, 169; Thomas, *op. cit.*, p. 9.

8 R.G. Hodgkinson, *The Origins of the National Health Service* (London 1967), pp. 153, 163, 169–70, 649–51, 659–61.

9 E.H. Sieveking, *The Training Institutions for Nurses, and the Workhouses* (London 1849), pp. 9, 13, 16, 22.

10 G. Anderson, 'An Oversight in Nursing History', *Journal of the History of Medicine* 3, Summer 1948, p. 421.

11 Sarah Trimmer, *The Economy of Charity* (London 1801), vol. II, pp. 57–8; Sieveking, *op. cit.*, p. 10.

12 W.R. Ward, *Religion and Society in England 1790–1850* (London 1972), pp. 7–8; G. Kitson-Clark, *Churchmen and the Condition of England 1832–1885* (London 1973), p. 196.

13 M. Stanley, *Hospitals and Sisterhoods*, (London 1854).

14 J.N. Murphy, *Terra Incognita* (London 1873), p. 165; E. Bolster, *The Sisters of Mercy in the Crimean War* (Cork 1964), pp. xvii-xviii; J. Rose, *Elizabeth Fry* (London 1980), pp. 178–80; E.W. Morris, *The London Hospital* (London 1926), p. 186; Woodward, *op. cit.*, p. 34.

15 P.F. Anson, *The Call of the Cloister* (London 1964), pp. 220–1, 239–41; Stanley, *op. cit.*, pp. 42–3. The Anglican Nursing Sisterhood of Christ Church, Coatham, to which Dorothy Pattison – 'Sister Dora' – belonged, was founded in 1858; J.G. Manton, *Sister Dora* (London 1971), p. 150.

16 Stanley, *op. cit.*, p. 46; R. Few, *A History of St John's House* (London 1884), p. 5.

17 *Rules of the Training Institution for Nurses for Hospitals, Families and the Poor*, St John's House, Queen Square, Westminster (London 1855), pp. 8–11.

18 WO 43/963 f.222, Florence Nightingale to Hawes, 1.5.55: 'Ladies are with difficulty to be found, whose qualities, experience and health fit them for the task'; MR 801/9/9, Nightingale to Col. Clark Kennedy, 14.6.61, objecting to 'making it a test of a person's devotion to any service that he or she will perform it gratuitously' and to 'a Civil Institution in London, admirable in almost every other respect, which makes "Ladies" (who can pay) "Sisters", by right of that condition.'

19 P. Deane and W.A. Cole, *British Economic Growth 1688–1959* (Cambridge 1962), p. 142, Table 3; see also L. Davidoff, 'Mastered for Life: Servant and Wife in Victorian and Edwardian England', *Journal of Social History* 7, 1974; C. Hall, 'The Early Formation of Victorian Domestic Ideology' in S. Burman, ed., *Fit Work for Women* (London 1979); M.H. Darrow, 'French Noblewomen and the New Domesticity 1750–1850', *Feminist Studies* V, 1979.

20 F.K. Prochaska, *Women and Philanthropy in 19th Century England* (Oxford 1980); A. Summers, 'A Home from Home – Women's Philanthropic Work in the Nineteenth Century', in S. Burman, *op. cit.*

21 Quoted in M. Hill, *The Religious Order* (London 1973), pp. 282–3.

22 Rev. J.S. Brewer, 'Workhouse Visiting', in Rev. F.D. Muarice, ed., *Lectures to Ladies on Practical Subjects* (Cambridge 1855), pp. 276–7.

23 These biographical details are drawn from E.T. Cook, *The Life of Florence Nightingale* (London 1913) vols I and II.

24 Nightingale to Elizabeth Herbert, 14.10.54; quoted in Cook, *op. cit.*, vol. I, p. 151.

25 N. Cantlie, *A History of the Army Medical Department* (Edinburgh and London 1974), vol. I., p. 440. On the pre-Crimean army, see H.F.A. Strachan, *Wellington's Legacy: the Reform of the British Army 1830–1854* (Manchester 1984).

26 Cantlie, *op. cit.*, vol. I, pp. 3, 439–40, 443–4.

27 See Appendix, 'The nursing of officers'.

28 J.W. Fortescue, *A History of the British Army* (London 1930), vol. XIII, p. 30; Strachan, *op. cit.*, p. 244.

29 Cantlie, *op. cit.*, vol. I, p. 444; A.R. Skelley, *The Victorian Army at Home* (London and Montreal 1977), p. 47.

30 *General Regulations and Orders for the Army*, 1811, pp. 137–8; Cantlie, *op. cit.*, vol. I, p. 4; Skelley, *op.cit.*, p. 42.

31 J. Dobson, 'The Army Nursing Service in the 18th Century', *Annals of the Royal College of Surgeons of England*, XIV, 1954, pp. 417–19; M. Trustram, *Women of the Regiment* (Cambridge 1984), pp. 12–13; Cantlie, *op. cit.*, vol. I, p. 445. I have not been able to trace the regulation cited.

32 GLRO, H.I./ST/NC.8/1, ff.10,17; WO 25/264, Bundle 'B', letter from Mrs Gordon, 30.11.54; BL Add.MSS 45761 ff.228–228b, Nightingale to D. Galton, 4.12.63.

33 BL Add.MSS 43397 f.148, Nightingale to Lady Cranworth, 21.12.56.

34 Trustram, *op. cit.*, pp. 30–2.

35 B.C. Hacker, 'Women and Military Institutions in Early Modern Europe: a Reconnaissance', *Signs* VI, 1981, pp. 645–8, 655; Trustram, *op. cit.*, pp. 3, 11–12.

36 *General Regulations and Orders* . . . 1811, pp. 137–8.

CHAPTER 2 THE CRIMEAN EXPERIMENT

1 The biographical literature on Florence Nightingale is immense. The popular image of 'The Lady with the Lamp' is liable to be formed for the foreseeable future by Lytton Strachey, *Eminent Victorians* (London 1918) and Cecil Woodham-Smith, *Florence Nightingale* (London 1950). Serious historians will continue to rely on E.T. Cook, *The Life of Florence Nightingale* (London 1913), 2 vols, and the most recent study, F.B. Smith, *Florence Nightingale, Reputation and Power* (London and Canberra 1982) will prove valuable if read in conjunction with it. Other useful studies of Florence Nightingale are by S.A. Tooley (London 1904), L.R. Seymer (London 1950) and E. Huxley (London 1975).

2 The medical history of the Crimean War is exhaustively treated in N. Cantlie, *A History of the Army Medical Department* (Edinburgh and London 1974), vol. II, chapters 1–3. I have based my account on his, except where otherwise stated.

3 H.F.A. Strachan, *Wellington's Legacy: The Reform of the British Army 1830–1854* (Manchester 1984), pp. 232–3, 236, 244, 245; review article, 'The Report from the Select Committee on the Army before Sebastopol and the Report on the State of the Hospitals of the British Army in the Crimea and Scutari', *British and Foreign Medico-Chirurgical Review*, XVI, 1855, pp. 291, 300–1, 303.

4 R.J. Morris, 'Religion and Medicine: the Cholera Pamphlets of Oxford, 1832, 1849, 1854', *Medical History* 19, 1975, p. 264; N.D. Lankford, 'The Victorian Medical Profession and Military Practice: Army Doctors and National Origins', *Bulletin of the History of Medicine*, 54, 1980, p. 254; C. Lloyd and J.L.S. Coulter, *Medicine and the Navy 1200–1900* (Edinburgh and London 1963), vol. IV, pp. 141–2; *Medical and Surgical History of the British Army which served in Turkey and the Crimea*, PP 1857–8 XXXVIII, p. 48. For an account of the state of knowledge on contagion in this period, see M. Pelling, *Cholera, Fever and English Medicine 1825–65* (Oxford 1978).

5 (Frances Margaret Taylor), *Eastern Hospitals and English Nurses, by a*

Lady Volunteer (London 1856), vol. I, p. 230, vol. II, pp. 113, 115-6; Sister Mary Aloysius Doyle, *Memories of the Crimea* (London 1897), pp. 36-7.

6 *Report upon the State of the Hospitals of the British Army in the Crimea and Scutari*, PP 1854-55 XXXIII, Appendix, pp. 84-5, 125, 128, 147.

7 R.G. Richardson, ed., *Nurse Sarah Anne* (London 1977), p. 95.

8 Cook, *op. cit.*, vol. I, p. 227; Cantlie, *op. cit.*, vol. II, pp. 87-8.

9 Cook, *op. cit.*, vol. I, p. 131.

10 Richardson, *op. cit.*, p. 105.

11 Cook, *op. cit.*, vol. I, pp. 150-4. In 1854 the two offices of Secretary at War and Secretary for War existed side by side. After the war they were combined.

12 'Since the sick soldiers of our army in the Crimea were saved by the skill and patience of the nurses who gave themselves freely to that work of mercy, it has been impossible surely to cast discredit before English hearers on voluntary female charity, or on the organisation which a proper discharge of its duties requires': *Guardian*, 16.10.61, p. 937. General works on the sisterhoods include P.F. Anson, *The Call of the Cloister* (London 1964) and M. Hill, *The Religious Order* (London 1973); see also the chapter on sisterhoods in M. Vicinus, *Independent Women* (London 1985).

13 E. Bolster, *The Sisters of Mercy in the Crimean War* (Cork 1964), pp. 13-14.

14 Cook, *op. cit.*, vol. I, pp. 158-9; Smith, *op. cit.*, pp. 25, 27-8; GLRO, H.I./ST/N.C.8/1 Military nurses, ff. 17, 19, 22.

15 Cook, *op. cit.*, vol. I, p. 158; for Mary Stanley's subsequent philanthropic career, see the memoir at the end of A.P. Stanley, *Memoirs of Edward and Catherine Stanley* (London 1880).

16 M. Stanley, *Hospitals and Sisterhoods* (London 1854) pp. 44-5; Cook, *op. cit.*, vol. I, p. 158.

17 Margaret Goodman, *Experiences of an English Sister of Mercy* (London 1862), p. 61.

18 WO 25/264, Testimonials to Nurses, Bundle N.

19 J.F. South, *Facts Relating to Hospital Nurses* (London 1857), pp. 13-15; BL Add.MSS 43402, Florence Nightingale, Notes on Nurses, ff. 6-7, 23; GLRO HI/ST/N.C.8/1, Military nurses, ff. 4, 5, 10; M.G. Spencer, *Westminster Hospital* (London 1924), p. 67.

20 Smith, *op. cit.*, pp. 16-17, throws strong doubt on Florence Nightingale's claims to have worked in the Middlesex Hospital in

1854; her only other working experience would have been in Germany and at Harley Street.

21 BL Add.MSS 43397 f. 93b. Florence Nightingale to Lady Cranworth, 22.2.56; GLRO, H.I./ST/N.C.8/1 Military nurses, ff. 9, 11, 19.

22 WO 25/264 Bundle S, Jane Shaw Stewart to Mary Stanley, 6.11.54; WO 43/963 f. 218, Lady Canning to B. Hawes 30.4.55; Taylor, *op. cit.*, vol. I, pp. 9–10.

23 Cook, *op. cit.*, vol. I, p. 152.

24 WO 6/70 f. 31, Newcastle to Raglan, 11.12.54; Cantlie, *op. cit.*, vol. II, p. 75; WO 43/963 f 196.

25 WO 43/963 f. 186; Cook, *op. cit.*, vol. I, pp. 188, 191; J. Williams, ed., *The Autobiography of Elizabeth Davis, a Balaklava Nurse* (London 1857), vol. II, pp. 94–5.

26 Bolster, *op. cit.*, pp. 49–50, 63.

27 BL Add.MSS 43393 f. 149b, Nightingale to Sidney Herbert, 12.2.55; Cook, *op. cit.*, vol. I, pp. 191, 252; Woodham-Smith, *op. cit.*, p. 194.

28 The fatalities among the ladies were Martha Clough and Miss Smythe. Three nurses, one Catholic nun and one Anglican sister also died.

29 Taylor, *op. cit.*, vol. II, pp. 270–1; GLRO H.I./ST/N.C.8/1, Military nurses, f. 20; F.C. Devas, *Mother Magdalen Taylor* (London 1927), pp. 17, 24.

30 GLRO, H.I./ST/N.C.8/1, Military nurses, f.6; Rev. W.F. Hobson, *Catharine Leslie Hobson, Lady-Nurse, Crimean War, and her Life* (London 1888), pp. 29, 34, 38–9, 49, 51–2; BL Add.MSS 43397 f.76b, F. Nightingale to Mrs Bracebridge, 4.11.55.

31 RA F1 f.106, Rev. C.E. Hadow to Chaplain General, 12.1.55; *Report of the Select Committee on the Army before Sebastopol*, PP 1854–5, IX, p. 304; Goodman, *op. cit.*, p. 106.

32 Doyle, *op. cit.*, p. 33; Cook, *op. cit.*, pp. 188–93; Smith, *op. cit.*, pp. 34, 39.

33 Taylor, *op. cit.*, vol.I, p. 100.

34 WO 43/963 f. 296b, Fitzgerald, *Confidential Report*; R. Roxburgh, 'Miss Nightingale and Miss Clough: Letters from the Crimea', *Victorian Studies* 13, 1969, pp. 76–7; BL Add.MSS 43402, Notes on Nurses, f. 19.

35 Taylor, *op. cit.*, vol. II, pp. 150–2, 164.

36 WO 43/963 f. 218, Lady Canning to B. Hawes, 30.4.55; J. Shepherd, 'The Civil Hospitals in the Crimea', *Proceedings of the Royal Society of Medicine* 59, 1966, pp. 199–204.

37 Smith, *op. cit.*, p. 40; WO 43/963 f. 197, letter of Florence Nightingale, 5.3.55.

38 BL Add.MSS 43393 f. 159, Nightingale to Herbert, 15.2.55.

39 WO 43/963 f. 199, Nightingale to Panmure, 5.3.55; Lord Stanmore, *Sidney Herbert, a Memoir* (London 1905), vol. I, p. 414. A draft reply to Florence Nightingale in the War Office files, dated 22 March 1855, states that the Ladies of Mercy at Scutari are under her control and that of the Principal Medical Officer. A draft reference to Koulali and Balaklava has been firmly struck out: see WO 43/963 f. 201.

40 BL Add.MSS 43393 f. 188, Nightingale to Herbert, 12.3.55; WO 43/963 f. 205, letter of Florence Nightingale, 2.4.55; f. 209, War Office to Nightingale, 20.4.55; GLRO H.I./ST/N.C.8/1, Military nurses, f.6.

41 *Florence Nightingale at Harley Street*, Introduction by Sir H. Verney, Bt (London 1970), pp. 17, 26–7; Cook, *op. cit.*, vol. I, pp. 134–5; Smith, *op. cit.*, pp. 11,13.

42 WO 43/963 f. 218, Lady Canning to B. Hawes, 30.4.55.

43 Williams, *op. cit.*, vol. II, pp. 132–3.

44 Smith, *op. cit.*, pp. 63, 65; BL Add.MSS 43397 ff. 76–7, Nightingale to Cranworth, 14.1.56; (Martha Nicol), *Ismeer, or Smyrna, and its British Hospital in 1855, by a Lady* (London, 1855), pp. 173, 336–8.

45 WO 43/963 f. 280, War Office to Hall and Smith, 25.2.56; Cook, *op. cit.*, vol. I, pp. 292–3.

46 Cook, *op. cit.*, vol. I, pp. 194–5.

47 *Report . . . Hospitals . . .* , p. 30; Cantlie, *op. cit.*, vol. II, pp. 88–9; Strachan, *op. cit.*, p. 245. The purveyor was in principle responsible for the cleaning of the hospitals, and for hospital servants.

48 Cook, *op. cit.*, vol. I, p. 186; Taylor, *op. cit.*, vol. I, pp. 203–4; Bolster, *op. cit.*, p. 141.

49 Cook, *op. cit.*, vol. I, p. 196; Stanmore, *op. cit.*, vol. I, p. 408. Mother Bridgeman's sisters, for the good of their orderlies as much as of their patients, took charge of the alcoholic stimulants: Bolster, *op. cit.*, p. 141.

50 Florence Nightingale, *Subsidiary Notes as to the Introduction of Female Nursing into Military Hospitals in Peace and in War* (London 1858), Introduction, pp. 15–16.

51 WO 43/963 f. 222 Florence Nightingale to B. Hawes, 1.5.55; f. 225, Nightingale to Hawes, 10.5.55.

52 Taylor, *op. cit.*, vol. II, p. 23; Stanmore, *op. cit.*, vol. I, p. 407.

53 S.M. Mitra, *The Life and Letters of Sir John Hall* (London 1911), p. 452.

54 G.H.B. Macleod, *Notes on the Surgery of the War in the Crimea* (London 1858), p. 54.

55 *Ibid.*, pp. 52–4; Doyle, *op. cit.*, p. 73; Nicol, *op. cit.*, p. 61.

56 WO 43/963 f. 300, Fitzgerald, *Confidential Report*.

57 Florence Nightingale, *Subsidiary Notes*, pp. 6, 32.

58 *Report . . . Hospitals*, Appendix, p. 331; Goodman, *op. cit.*, pp. 105–6.

59 Taylor, *op. cit.*, vol. I, pp. 276–8; Doyle, *op. cit.*, p. 65; Nicol, *op. cit.*, pp. 314–15.

60 Taylor, *op. cit.*, vol. I, pp. 284–5, 288; Goodman, *op. cit.*, pp. 129–31, 102–3; Nicol, *op. cit.*, p. 63.

61 Doyle, *op. cit.*, pp. 53–4.

62 Richardson, *op. cit.*, p. 127; Taylor, *op. cit.*, vol. II, p. 23; Cook, *op. cit.*, vol. I, p. 238; Bolster, *op. cit.*, p. 151.

63 Williams, *op. cit.*, vol. II, pp. 92–3; Taylor, *op. cit.*, vol. I, p. 13.

64 Florence Nightingale, *Subsidiary Notes*, Introduction, p. 23.

65 Roxburgh, *op. cit.*, p. 76.

66 Doyle *op. cit.*, p. 21.

67 Nicol, *op. cit.*, pp. 6–8, 89–91.

68 Mrs Motherly, *The Servant's Behaviour Book* (London 1859), pp. 12, 19, 23–4.

69 Taylor, *op. cit.*, vol. I, p.37.

70 Nicol, *op. cit.*, pp. 8, 89–90.

71 Taylor, *op. cit.*, vol. I, p. 37.

72 Stanmore, *op. cit.*, vol. I, p. 373; Taylor, *op. cit.*, vol. I, pp. 38–9; Nicol, *op. cit.*, pp. 85–6. Mrs Butler was a nurse in the accident ward at Bart's; despite her early display of obligingness, she was sent home for 'misconduct' in July 1855. Julia Gunning had nursed in hospitals in Paris as well as in a workhouse cholera ward. She was invalided home from Smyrna; her sight was said to have been 'weakened by a cannon ball in the Paris Revolution'. GLRO H.I./ST/N.C.8/1, Military nurses, f. 16.

73 Stanmore, *op. cit.*, vol. I, p. 377; Taylor, *op. cit.*, vol. I, pp. 48–9; Nicol, *op. cit.*, pp. 308–9. Mrs Suter may have been the wife of the Mr Suter who wrote on behalf of 'friends' – an apothecary and his wife – who wished for posts in the east. WO 25/264, Bundle S.

74 Nicol, *op. cit.*, p. 91; Taylor, *op. cit.*, vol. II, pp. 13–14.

75 Taylor, *op. cit.*, vol. II, p. 20; Nicol, *op. cit.*, p. 89; Williams, *op. cit.*, vol. II, pp. 112, 126–8.

76 Taylor, *op. cit.*, vol. I, pp. 162, 164–5; Stanmore, *op. cit.*, vol. I, p. 373.

77 Stanley, *op. cit.*, pp. 54–5.

78 Nicol, *op. cit.*, pp. 89–90.

79 Taylor, *op. cit.*, vol. II, pp. 19–20, 117–118; vol. I, pp. 13–21; Nightingale, *Subsidiary Notes*, p. 62.

80 WO 43/963 f. 232, Nightingale to Hawes, 1.5.55; f. 218, Lady Canning to Hawes, 30.4.55.

81 Printed in Williams, *op. cit.*, vol. II, pp. 217–23.

82 WO 43/963 f.235.

83 Cook, *op. cit.*, vol. I, p.151.

84 *Report . . . Hospitals . . .* , p. 409.

85 *Ibid.*, p. 409; *Report of the Proceedings of the Sanitary Commissioners dispatched to the Seat of War in the East 1855–6*, PP 1857, IX, p. 337; 'The Report . . . , *British and Foreign Medico-Chirurgical Review*, XVI, 1855, p. 300 suggests that the arrival of auxiliary civilian surgeons in spring 1855 also helped to reduce death rates.

86 Lloyd and Coulter, *op. cit.*, vol. IV, pp. 61–3, 140, 147, 149; C. Bryce, *England and France before Sebastopol* (London 1857), pp. 26–7, 95; *Medical Times and Gazette*, 14.6.56, pp. 604–5.

87 WO 1/374 ff. 7–8, Raglan to Panmure, 12.5.55; ff. 31–2, Panmure to Raglan, 11.6.55; Taylor, *Eastern Hospitals*, vol. II, pp. 227–8; Cantlie, *op. cit.*, vol. II, pp. 150, 233.

CHAPTER 3 LADY INTO NURSE

1 The fullest published account of the episode is in C. Woodham-Smith, *Florence Nightingale* (London 1950), pp. 479–80. For the problems in tracing documents on Jane Shaw Stewart, see *Note on sources*, p. 295.

2 *Report upon the State of the Hospitals of the British Army in the Crimea and Scutari*, PP 1854–5 XXXIII; *Report of the Proceedings of the Sanitary Commissioners dispatched to the Seat of War in the East 1855–6*, PP 1857, vol. IX; *Report of the Committee on the Pathology of the Diseases of the Army in the East*, PP 1857 XVIII; *Report to the Director-General of the Army Medical Department on the Sanitary Condition of the Army in the East*, PP 1857–8 XXXVII; *Medical and Surgical History of the British Army which served in Turkey and the Crimea*, PP 1857–8 XXXVIII; *Report of the Commissioners appointed to enquire into the Regulations affecting the Sanitary Condition of the Army, the Organisation of Military Hospitals,*

and the Treatment of the Sick and Wounded, PP 1857–8 XVIII; *Report on the Site of the Royal Victoria Hospital, near Netley Abbey*, PP 1857–8 XIX.

3 They included Dr John Sutherland, head of the sanitary commission despatched to the seat of war in 1855, later Florence Nightingale's amanuensis; Sir John NcNeill and Col. A.M. Tulloch, who reported for the sanitary and Commissariat commissions; Dr Thomas Alexander, Smith's successor as Director-General of the Army Medical Department; Col. J.H. Lefroy, scientific adviser to the Secretary of State for War, despatched by Panmure to report privately on the state of the war hospitals, who later worked with Alexander and others on plans for an Army Medical School; Col. Clark Kennedy, Assistant Adjutant General at Lord Raglan's headquarters, who was asked by a mutual friend to report on the French military hospitals on Florence Nightingale's behalf, and who was Commandant of the Military Train, with headquarters at Woolwich, after the war.

4 *Report of the Commissioners appointed to enquire into the Regulations affecting the Sanitary Condition of the Army, the Organisation of Military Hospitals, and the Treatment of the Sick and Wounded*, PP XVIII 1857–8. Hereafter cited as *Report . . . Sanitary Condition*. See also E.T. Cook, *The Life of Florence Nightingale* (London 1913) vol. I, pp. 362–5.

5 *Report . . . Sanitary Condition*, p. 42; A.R. Skelley, *The Victorian Army at Home* (London and Montreal 1977), p. 47.

6 On the history of the Nightingale Training School, see M.E. Baly, *Florence Nightingale and the Nursing Legacy* (London 1986), and the same author's unpublished PhD thesis, 'The Influence of the Nightingale Fund from 1855 to 1914 on the Development of Nursing', London University 1984.

7 R. Few, *A History of St John's House* (London 1884), p. 8; S.F. Holloway, 'The All Saints' Sisterhood at University College Hospital, 1862–99', *Medical History* 3, 1959, p. 147; F. Garnett, *Florence Nightingale's Nuns* (New York and London 1961) pp. 180–3.

8 See, for example, Frances Margaret Taylor, *Eastern Hospitals and English Nurses* (London 1856), vol. II, pp. 272–3. For protests against this denigration of paid nurses, see J. Williams, ed., *The Autobiography of Elizabeth Davis, a Balaklava Nurse* (London 1857), vol. II, p. 291, and G.H.B. MacLeod, *Notes on the Surgery of the War in the Crimea* (London 1858), pp. 52–3.

9 BL Add.MSS 43397 f. 148, Nightingale to Cranworth, 21.12.56; f. 152b, Cranworth to Nightingale, 27.12.56.

10 *Report on the Site of the Royal Victoria Hospital, near Netley Abbey* PP 1857–8 XIX, p. 476.

11 Printed in G. Douglas and G. Dalhousie Ramsay, eds, *The Panmure Papers* (London 1908), vol. II, pp. 381–4.

12 WO 33/6A pieces 23 and 24.

13 WO 33/7 piece 2, Report on the Volume of Proposed Regulations for Army Hospitals, 5 February 1859, f. 50, refers to this earlier report, but I have been unable to locate it.

14 *Regulation for the Duties of Inspectors-General and Deputy-Inspectors General of Hospitals*, 1859, pp. 3, 13.

15 WO 33/7, *loc. cit.*

16 For the report of the AHC Committee see WO 33/13 piece 218; for its schemes for general hospitals see BL Add.MSS 43395 ff. 282–9.

17 *The Times*, 1 August 1861, p. 10, col. 2.

18 WO 139/2, Index to Correspondence. Entry under 'Hospitals – Servants and Nurses: Herbert Hospital, Woolwich': Nursing Staff appointed. 6911/376, 17 October 1861. This date is corroborated roughly by Col. Wilbraham's reference in a letter of 3 December 1863 to two years of the female nursing system: see WO 33/20 piece 371, Instructions to the Committee of Inquiry into the State of the Nursing Service at the Royal Victoria Hospital, Netley, 1868 (hereafter cited as Instructions . . .) ff. 149–50. In this letter he refers to a staff of six female nurses.

19 *Report of the Army Medical Department for 1863*, p. 273; WO 33/20, Instructions. . . . ff. 149–50; Quarterly Army List for April 1863, p. 150. This milestone had been completely forgotten by the end of the century. Mrs Deeble was mistakenly claimed to have been the first woman, other than the Queen, to reach the Army List in e.g. *Navy and Army Illustrated*, vol. 3, 1896–7, pp. 208–9; *Sunday Strand*, July 1900, pp. 45–6.

20 *The Times*, 17 October 1866, p. 10, col. 6; WO 33/20, Instructions . . . ff 145–6.

21 Sutherland to Nightingale, 28 July 1868, BL Add.MS 45753, f. 59.

22 Biographical information on Jane Shaw Stewart and her family drawn from: *BP*; M. Stenton, *Who's Who of British M.P.'s*, (London 1976), vol. I; J. Foster, *Members of Parliament for Scotland* (London and Aylesbury 1882); F. Boase, *Modern English Biography* (London 1965), vols. III and VI; *Guardian*, 6 June 1900, p. 811; *Illustrated London News*, 18.8.1900, p. 250; *D.N.B.* Jane died in mid-March 1905, by which time her work was largely forgotten. *The Hospital 'Nursing*

Section' 1.4.05, p. 1, referred to her being at Netley until 1863. See also *British Journal of Nursing*, 25.3.05. p. 232.

23 BL Add.MSS 45774 f. 65, Shaw Stewart to Nightingale, 26.5.59.

24 WO 43/963 f. 296, Fitzgerald, *Confidential Report*.

25 BL Add.MSS 45774 f. 37, Shaw Stewart to Nightingale, 16.3.57.

26 *Ibid.*, f. 41, the same, 21.1.57; f. 65, the same, 26.5.59; f. 3, the same, 6.8.56; ff. 7, 9, the same, 18.8.56.

27 WO 25/264 Bundle S, Shaw Stewart to Stanley, n.d., probably November 1854.

28 BL Add.MSS 45774 f. 62, Shaw Stewart to Nightingale, 26.5.59; ff. 21, 21b, 25, the same, 16.3.57; BL Add.MSS 43395 f. 319, Shaw Stewart to Herbert, 10.7.61.

29 WO 43/963 f. 312, Shaw Stewart to Nightingale, 21.1.56.

30 BL Add.MSS 45744 ff. 17–18, Shaw Stewart to Nightingale, 24.11.56.

31 M. Stanley, *Hospitals and Sisterhoods* (London 1854), pp. 44–5.

32 BL Add.MSS 45774 f. 51, Shaw Stewart to Nightingale, 1.1.59; f.8, the same, 18.8.56; ff. 61, 64b, the same, 26.5.59.

33 This was one of the volumes of her *Notes affecting the Health, Efficiency, and Hospital Administration of the British Army*. The first three chapters of *Subsidiary Notes* are taken word for word from Shaw Stewart's lengthy 'Confidential Memorandum', BL Add.MSS 45774 ff. 21 *et seq.*, 16.3.57; three other chapters on French hospital construction and military nursing are based closely on her writings in the same MS volume. Cook has labelled the 'Confidential Memorandum' as Florence Nightingale's MS for *Subsidiary Notes*; another hand (presumably Woodham Smith's) correctly identifies it as Jane Shaw Stewart's, but Woodham Smith does not discuss the implications, or treat Shaw Stewart as anything but a shadowy figure, in her own biography of Nightingale. It is impossible to confuse the handwriting of the two women, and Shaw Stewart never acted in a purely secretarial capacity for Nightingale. The sections on experiences in Scutari in the published work were added by Nightingale (Shaw Stewart never served in Turkey), who also deleted Shaw Stewart's many approving references to the Church of England. Cook, *op. cit.*, vol. I, p. 347, notes Mrs Gaskell's unwitting appreciation of a characteristic of Shaw Stewart's style – 'the quiet continual devout references to God which make the book a holy one.'

34 BL Add.MSS 45774 ff. 61–64b, Shaw Stewart to Nightingale, 26.5.59. In 1859 Mrs Smith, Florence Nightingale's aunt, wrote to Jane Shaw Stewart saying that she was not to write to Florence, or hear from her, again: the state of her health required that third parties

should open Jane's letters to her. See BL Add.MSS 45774 f. 214, Shaw Stewart to Nightingale, 30.7.70. In fact the correspondence seems to have continued between 1860 and 1863; see BL Add.MSS 43395 f. 318, Shaw Stewart to Herbert, 10.7.61; 45761 ff.103–5, Nightingale to Galton, 4.9.63.

35 BL Add.MSS 45774 f. 15, Shaw Stewart to Nightingale, 22.10.56.

36 WO 33/6A, Regulations . . . 1858, ff. 282, 288–90, 390–1; Douglas and Dalhousie Ramsay, *op. cit.*, vol. II, p. 384.

37 WO 33/6A, Regulations for the Duties . . . ff. 288–90, 398.

38 J.F. South, *Facts Relating to Hospital Nurses* (London 1857), pp. 28–31; *British Medical Journal*, 1874, Part I, pp. 243–4, 283, 619–20; Few, *op. cit.*, pp. 20–5, 48–53.

39 Anon., 'The Employments of Women', *Gentleman's Magazine*, 1855, pp. 488–9.

40 WO 43/963 f. 222, Nightingale to Hawes, 1.5.55; f. 225, the same, 10.5.55; BL Add.MSS 45774 f. 35, Shaw Stewart memorandum, 16.3.57.

41 BL Add.MSS 43402 ff. 3, 5, Florence Nightingale, Notes on Nurses.

42 *Report . . . Sanitary Condition*, pp. 468; 477, second footnote: italics in original.

43 *Ibid.*, p. 468; *Report on the Site of the Royal Victoria Hospital near Netley Abbey*, PP XIX 1857–8, pp. 345, 346, 496; WO 33/6A piece 31, f. 679, Report on the Victoria Hospital, Netley; F.B. Smith, *Florence Nightingale* (London, 1982), pp. 93–4.

44 *Subsidiary Notes*, p. 22; BL Add.MSS 45774 f. 29b, Shaw Stewart to Nightingale, 16.3.57; 45751 f. 174, Nightingale to Sutherland, 28.1.61.

45 BL Add.MSS 45774 ff. 35, 26, Shaw Stewart to Nightingale, 16.3.57; WO 33/6A, Regulations for the Duties . . . f. 391.

46 BL Add.MSS 45774 f. 66, Shaw Stewart to Nightingale, 26.5.59; f. 210b, the same, 10.8.70, referring to leaving St John's House for Woolwich in 1861; 43395 f. 318, Shaw Stewart to Herbert, 10.7.61 45751 f. 195, Nightingale to Sutherland, *c.* 16.7.61.

47 MR 801/9 pieces 6, 6a, Nightingale to Clark Kennedy, 8.6.61.

48 BL Add.MSS 45774 f. 25, Shaw Stewart to Nightingale, 16.3.57; f. 65, the same, 26.5.59; 43395 f. 319, Shaw Stewart to Herbert, 10.7.61: emphases in original.

49 WO 33/20 f. 137, Instructions . . . ; ff. 149–50, Appendix C, letter from Wilbraham, 3.12.63.

50 BL Add.MSS 45761 ff. 103–5, Nightingale to Galton, 4.9.63; ff. 115–115b, the same, 15.9.63.

51 WO 33/20 Instructions . . . f. 148; BL Add.MSS 43397 ff. 272b–274, Nightingale to Lefroy, 25.11.64.

52 WO 33/20, Instructions . . . , Appendix C, ff. 149–50, letter of Wilbraham to Under Secretary of State for War, 20 February 1864; BL Add.MSS 45753 f. 32, Nightingale to Sutherland, c. 16 March 1868.

53 WO 33/6A f. 282, Regulations for the Duties . . . ; WO 33/20, Instructions . . . f. 148.

54 BL Add.MSS 45754 f. 72b, Nightingale to Sutherland, c. 15.2.70; ff. 89b–91, the same, c. 24.2.70; 45775 ff.1–2, Deeble to Nightingale, 30.11.69; ff 10–10b, the same, 13.1.70.

55 BL Add.MSS 45752 f. 80, Nightingale to Sutherland, c. 1865; 45825 ff. 126–126b, note by Sutherland, c. 1861.

56 WO 33/20 ff. 144–5, Instructions . . . ff 144–5; Horse Guards Circular Memorandum 258, At Home and Abroad, 13 May 1863. Peculation and corruption in the handling of linen and all other military hospital stores remained endemic: see the memoir of an AHC man, William Morrison, 'Glimpses of Life from Within from 1860–1895', *Journal of the Royal Army Medical Corps*, 120, 1974, pp. 17, 121; 121, 1975, pp. 42, 46.

57 WO 33/20, Instructions . . . ff. 14–15, 147, 152.

58 *Lancet*, 1870, Part II, p. 100; Quotation from the manuscript by L. Davidoff in 'Class and Gender in Victorian England: the Diaries of A.J. Munby and Hannah Cullwick', *Feminist Studies* V, no. 1, 1979.

59 WO 33/20, Instructions . . . Wilbraham to Scott Robertson, Purveyor in chief, 3 December 1863, Appendix C ff. 149–50.

60 *Medical Times and Gazette*, 1.8.68, p. 130.

61 Army Medical Department, Report for 1860, in PP 1862 XXXIII, p. 208; the same, Report for 1862 in PP 1864 XXVI, p. 336; Myna Trustram, 'Marriage and the Victorian Army at Home: the Regulation of Soldiers' Relationships with women, and the Treatment of Soldiers' Wives', unpublished D Phil thesis, Bristol University, July 1981, p. 217.

62 WO Circular 849. Home and Foreign, 30 January 1864.

63 WO Circular, 849. Home and Foreign, 30 January 1864.

64 *Lancet*, 1868, part II, p. 93.

65 *Lancet*, 1866, part I, p. 448; *The Times*, 17 October 1866, p. 10, col. 6; *Lancet*, 1867, part I, p. 24; *Medical Times and Gazette*, 31.8.67, pp. 230–1.

66 *Lancet*, 1868, part I, p. 593.

67 WO 33/20, Instructions . . . ff. 146; 139–40; 144.

68 High as the turnover was, the 'case for the prosecution' exaggerated it. The list of forty-one nurses produced for the inquiry included eight whose departures in 1866 were not resignations: they accompanied Jane Shaw Stewart to inaugurate the female nursing service at the Royal Herbert Hospital, Woolwich. The largest block of resignations – fourteen, of whom nine had served under twelve months – took place in the year 1867, for most of which Jane was actually absent from Netley, and preoccupied with the Woolwich nurses; a substitute Superintendent, who resigned in September 1867, served in her place. Moreover, if, as seems probable, the class of nurse coming to Netley was not the head nurse type, but the less experienced under-nurse, then the turnover rate becomes less remarkable. Florence Nightingale insisted, in fact, that there had not been as many changes among the Netley nurses as there were in every civil hospital. *The Times*, 17.10.66, p. 10, col. 6; WO 33/20, ff. 146, 150, Instructions . . . ; South, *op. cit.*, p. 17; BL Add.MSS 45754 f. 120, Nightingale to Galton, 1.5.68.

69 Anon., 'Maids and Mistresses', *Temple Bar*, XI, 1864, p. 50, 'A Lady', 'Servants *vs.* Mistresses', *Churchman's Family Magazine*, VIII, 1866, p. 165; Offences Against the Person Act 1861, 24. and 25 Vict. C. 100.

70 WO 33/6A f. 391, Regulations for the Duties . . . ; WO 33/20 ff. 139–40, Instructions . . . , BL Add.MSS 45763 ff.215b–217b, Nightingale to Galton, 9.8.66.

71 BL Add.MSS 45774 ff. 128b–129, Shaw Stewart to Nightingale, 21.10.69, f. 147b, the same, 30.10.69; f. 212b, the same, 10.8.70.

72 WO 33/20 Instructions . . . f. 145; BL Add.MSS. 45774 f. 212b, Shaw Stewart to Nightingale, 10.8.70; GLRO, H.I./ST/NTS/C1.2, f.7. M. Baly, 'The Nightingale Nurses 1860–1870', *Bulletin of the History of Nursing Group at the Royal College of Nursing* 8, Autumn 1985, p. 22 indicates that probationers were sent from St Thomas's to Netley for training.

73 WO 33/20 f. 138, Instructions . . . ; regrettably, the records on the St Thomas's nurses who entered the service in this period are very scanty, and no records have been traced for the other entrants. St John's House, which might be thought to be a likely source given Shaw Stewart's stipulation as to church membership, has no record of any of her nurses.

74 WO 33/20, Instructions . . . ff. 138, 146, 148–50.

75 Cook, *op. cit.*, vol. II, p. 194.

76 BL Add.MSS 45775 ff. 1b–2, Deeble to Nightingale, 30.11.69,

f. 10, the same, 13.1.70; ff. 27b–28, the same, 8.3.70.

77 R. Strong, *Reminiscences* (Edinburgh, privately printed 1935), pp. 5–6. Mrs Strong later had a distinguished career in nursing in Scotland. As matron of Glasgow Royal Infirmary, she was a pioneer in the field of preliminary training for women intending to take up hospital work; she was also a supporter of state registration for nurses; See R.M. Hallowes, *Nursing Mirror* 25.11.1955, pp. xi–xii.

78 BL Add.MSS 45753 f. 83, Nightingale to Sutherland, *c.* September 1868. The War Office wanted Mrs Deeble and six women trained at the Nightingale Training School for Netley. This was embarrassing, as the normal practice of the School was to accept candidates on merit only.

79 BL Add.MSS 45754 f. 19, Nightingale to Sutherland, *c.* 1.11.69; emphases in original.

80 War Office Circular 715, Royal Warrant for Army Hospital Corps, 27.9.61; BL Add.MSS 45754 ff. 90b–91, Nightingale to Sutherland, 24.2.70; Strong, *op. cit.*, p. 8.

81 War Office Circular, 1 January 1870, Clause 33.

82 BL Add.MSS 45774 ff. 123–87, letters and memoranda of Shaw Stewart to Nightingale, 1869; 45754, f. 3, Nightingale to Sutherland, 1.10.69; f. 22b, the same, *c.* 13.11.69. On the 1885 and other amendments to the regulations, see next chapter.

83 Wantage Papers on Egypt, Mrs Deeble to Lady Loyd-Lindsay, 21.6.85; 21.11.85; 27.11.85.

84 BL Add.MSS 45772 ff. 51, 55, Florence Nightingale notes, *c.* December 1883.

85 Few, *op. cit.*, passim; Holloway, *op. cit.*, p. 152; S.A. Plotkin, 'The Crisis at Guy's Hospital', *Guy's Hospital Gazette* 75, 1961, pp. 45–50.

CHAPTER 4 UNEASY TRUCE

1 F.E. Fremantle, *Impressions of a Doctor in Khaki* (London 1901), p. 115.

2 See Chapter 6.

3 WO 33/53, A. 265. Report of the Committee Appointed to Consider the Subject of the Nursing Service of the Army, 1893; *Nursing Record*, 6.9.88, p. 307 (quoting the *Echo*); H. Morten, 'Her Majesty's Nursing Sisters', *Illustrated Naval and Military Magazine*, May 1890, p. 72; *The Hospital 'Nursing Mirror'*, 29.10.98. p. 51.

4 WO 32/9337, A. Higgins to the Lords Commissioners of the Treasury, describing one Superintendent and two Sisters as the official establishment for a military hospital with a hundred beds and over.

5 N. Cantlie, *A History of the Army Medical Department* (Edinburgh and London 1974), vol. II, pp. 284, 288, 358; personal communication, QARANC HQ.

6 *Report of the Royal Commission appointed to consider and report upon the Care and Treatment of the Sick and Wounded during the South African Campaign*, PP 1901 XXIX, p. 376.

7 *Nursing Record*, 16.7.98. p. 43; 22.10.98, p. 326; 6.5.99, p. 357; 9.9.99. p. 203.

8 This procedure was laid down as early as 1859: WO 33/6A, Regulations for the Duties of Inspectors-General and Deputy-Inspectors-General of Hospitals . . . and for the Duties of Officers, Attendants and Nurses, f. 399.

9 *Regulations for the Army Medical Services*, 1894, p. 65; the *Regulations* up to 1889 had enjoined only 'ready and efficient assistance' on the orderlies.

10 *Nursing Record*, 25.6.98, p. 520.

11 *The Hospital 'Nursing Section'*, 22.3.02, p. 333.

12 *The Hospital 'Nursing Mirror'*, 27.4.01. p. 57.

13 WO 33/53, Report . . . 1893, pp. 5–6.

14 *Regulations for the Army Medical Services*, 1894, p. 35; 'Arrangements should be made for the continuous presence of a nursing sister in the hospital throughout the day'; *The Hospital 'Nursing Mirror'*, 25.8.00, p. 282; *The Hospital 'Nursing Section'*, 22.3.02, p. 333.

15 *Regulations for the Medical Department of H.M. Army* (1878), No. 133, WO 33/53, A.265. Report . . . 1893, *Nursing Record*, 25.6.98, p. 519; *The Hospital 'Nursing Mirror'* 25.8.00, p. 282; *The Hospital 'Nursing Section'*, 22.3.02, p. 333.

16 *Nursing Record*, 25.6.98, p. 520; WO 33/53, Report . . . 1893, p.9; William Morrison, 'Glimpses of Life from Within, from 1860 to 1895', *Journal of the Royal Army Medical Corps*, 120, 1, January 1974, pp. 209–10.

17 *Report of a Committee appointed by the Secretary of State for War to inquire into the Organisation of the Army Hospital Corps*, PP 1883 XVI, p. xxviii.

18 *Nursing Record*, 25.6.98, p. 518.

19 Fremantle, *op. cit.*, p. 444.

20 *Nursing Record*, 25.6.98, p. 518.

21 *Nursing Record*, 3.2.00, p. 96, quoting *British Medical Journal*; *Nursing Record*, 5.4.02, p. 276, quoting *St John's House Gazette*.

22 BL Add.MSS 45775 ff. 32b–33, Mrs Deeble to Florence Nightingale, 20.3.70.

23 *Report . . . Army Hospital Corps* PP 1883 XVI, p. 509, question 12,765; WO 33/53. Report . . . 1893, p. 13; WO 25/3955, Nominal and Seniority Roll, Army Nursing Service, ff.1–3.

24 *Report . . . Army Hospital Corps* PP 1883 XVI, p. 511, question 12,820; BL Add.MSS 45775 ff. 32b–33, Deeble to Nightingale, 20.3.70.

25 *Report of the Army Medical Department for 1870*, Appendix XIX, pp. 544–6.

26 M.E. Baly, *Florence Nightingale and the Nursing Legacy* (London 1986), pp. 43, 151–2.

27 For example, Westminster Hospital established its training school, based on that of the Liverpool Royal Infirmary, in 1874; J. Langdon-Davies, *The Westminster Hospital 1719–1948* (London 1952), pp. 134–7. Training reform began at Guy's with the appointment of Miss Burt as Matron in November 1879; S.A. Plotkin, 'The Crisis at Guy's Hospital', *Guy's Hospital Gazette*, 75, 1961, pp. 45–50. Training at the London Hospital was instituted in 1880 with the appointment of Miss Lückes as Matron; E.W. Morris, *The London Hospital* (London 1926), p. 190. The restructuring of training methods at the Nightingale Training School is described in Baly, *op. cit.*

28 Cantlie, *op. cit.*, pp. 233, 235; *Broad Arrow*, 26.12.91, p. 769; *Report . . . Army Hospital Corps*, PP 1883 XVI, p. 509, question 12,754.

29 *Nursing Record*, 25.6.98, p. 520; *The Hospital 'Nursing Section'*, 21.10.01, p. 29; *Nursing Record*, 25.4.02, p. 276, quoting *St John's House Gazette*.

30 Dame Maud Piper McCarthy, MS paper on military nursing, n.d., no pagination; presumably inter-war; in QARANC Museum, Aldershot; W.S. Inder, *On Active Service with the St John's Ambulance Brigade in the South African War, 1899–1902* (Kendal 1903), p. 63.

31 *Report of the Royal Commission on the War in South Africa*, PP 1904 XLI, p. 218, question 15,567; p. 219, question 15,569.

32 WO 32/9338, War Office Actuaries' Report No. 745, 19.7.01, p. 3.

33 WO 33/53, Report . . . 1893, p. 6.

34 Rev. C.J. Hardy, *The Five Talents of Women* (London 1888), p. 227.

35 WO 25/3955, Nominal and Seniority Roll, ff. 29–30.

36 *Royal Commission . . . the Sick and Wounded . . .* PP 1901 XXIX, p. 637; *The Hospital 'Nursing Section'*, 16.11.01, p. 103.

37 In 1887 the top nursing salaries at St Thomas's, the London Hospital and Bart's were £260, £250 and £240 respectively; IOR, L/MIL/7/11316 f. 11, memorandum, Surgeon-General Payne, 30.10.87. Some matrons were said to be earning £300 p.a. in 1894; *Nursing Record*, 6.10.94, p. 238.

38 E. McCaul, 'Some Suggestions for Army Reform', *Nineteenth Century*, April 1901, p. 582.

39 Hardy, *op. cit.*, p. 225.

40 WO 25/3955, Nominal and Seniority Roll, ff. 58, 102.

41 C. Maggs, *The Origins of General Nursing* (London 1983), pp. 126–7.

42 *Nursing Record*, 6.9.88, p. 307, quoting the *Echo*; *Royal Commission . . . the Sick and Wounded . . .* PP 1901 XXIX, p. 637; see also WO 30/133, A Report upon the Condition of the Chief Military Hospitals in Great Britain, 1903, *passim*.

43 WO 25/3955, Nominal and Seniority Roll, f. 79.

44 *The Hospital 'Nursing Mirror'* 29.10.98, p. 51; *Nursing Record*, 9.7.98, p. 23.

45 *Report of the Army Medical Department for 1867*, Appendix XIII, p.371; *Medical Times and Gazette*, 31.8.67, p. 230.

46 E.E. Cuthell, 'Nursing in Indian Military Hospitals', *Army and Navy Magazine* XIII, 1886–7, pp. 135–7; *Nursing Record*, 5.5.92, pp. 352–3.

47 BL Add.MSS 45807 ff.267–74, Roberts to Nightingale, 29.7.86; IOR, L/MIL/7/11316 f. 84, Adjutant-General in India to Secretary to the Government of India, Military Dept., enclosure, 21.8.86.

48 IOR, L/MIL/7/11316 f. 80, Military Department memorandum, 1.11.86; *ibid.*, f. 78, Military Department minute, 22.11.86; Cuthell, *loc.cit.*

49 IOR, L/MIL/7/11316 ff.8–10, India Office memorandum, Mr Hardie, 8.11.87.

50 H. Morten, 'Her Majesty's Nursing Sisters', *Illustrated Naval and Military Magazine*, May 1890, p. 76; *Nursing Record*, 24.2.94, p. 125; *Catherine Grace Loch*, p. 218; *Nursing Times*, 21.9.07, p. 816; *The Times*, obituary of Countess Roberts, 22.12.20, p. 13.

51 *Catherine Grace Loch*, pp. 5, 318; *The Hospital 'Nursing Section'*, 22.8.03, p. 265.

52 By 1899 a brief first aid course had been devised for orderlies prior to their secondment from the regiments: *The Hospital 'Nursing Mirror'*, 12.8.99, p. 256, quoting the *Civil and Military Gazette* of Lahore.

53 *Catherine Grace Loch*, pp. 210–11.

54 *Ibid.*, pp. 210, 214, 303; see quotation in *Nursing Record*, 30.6.92, p. 524.

55 *Nursing Notes*, 1.5.94, p. 67; *The Hospital 'Nursing Mirror'*, 4.9.97, p. 200; *ibid.*, 12.8.99, p. 256, quoting the *Civil and Military Gazette* of Lahore.

56 Cantlie, *op. cit.*, vol. II, pp. 379–80. In the Tirah Campaign of 1897–8, there were 1065 hospital admissions for venereal disease and 948 for gunshot wounds.

57 *Catherine Grace Loch*, pp. 34, 37–8, 40–1, 68–9, 76, 211–12, 214, 350–1.

58 *The Hospital 'Nursing Mirror'* 4.9.97, p. 200; *Nursing Record*, 4.9.97, pp. 188–9, quoting the *Indian Medical Record*.

59 IOR, L/MIL/7/11316 f. 84, Adjutant-General to Secretary to the Government, Enclosure, 21.8.86; f. 80, Military Dept. to Viscount Cross, India Office; f. 69, memorandum, Surgeon-General Payne.

60 *Catherine Grace Loch*, pp. 8, 95–8, 351; *Nursing Record*, 18.11.93, p. 259; *The Hospital 'Nursing Mirror'*, 4.9.97, p. 200.

61 *Catherine Grace Loch*, p. 33; *Nursing Record*, 18.11.93, p. 253.

62 *Nursing Record*, 18.11.93, p. 259; *Catherine Grace Loch*, p. 351.

63 *Nursing Record*, 8.12.94, p. 374.

64 *Nursing Record*, 6.9.88. p. 307, quoting the *Echo*.

65 Wantage Papers on Egypt, Mrs Deeble to Lady Wantage, 21.6.85.

66 WO 33/208, Discussion of the War Office Committee on the Reorganisation of the Army Medical and Army Nursing Service, July 1902, p. 133.

67 *Black and White Budget*, 23.12.99, p. 6; *Illustrated Naval and Military Magazine*, July 1885, p. 49; *Navy and Army Illustrated*, vol. 3, 1896–7, pp. 208–9; *British Journal of Nursing*, 31.3.06, p. 251.

68 See WO 25/3955, Nominal and Seniority Roll; military connections are hinted at where place of birth is mentioned as e.g. Lucknow or Carrickfergus; most names do not have place of birth appended.

69 *WWW*; IV p. 152, *Catherine Grace Loch*, p. 1.

70 *Report . . . Army Hospital Corps*, PP 1883 XVI, p. 510, question 12,775.

71 Wantage Papers on Egypt, Mrs Deeble to Lady Wantage, 21.6.85.

72 BL Add.MSS 45775 f. 169, Sybil Airy to Florence Nightingale, 28.4.85. Exclamation marks in the original!

73 *Nursing Record*, 6.10.94, p. 239.

74 *Regulations for the Army Nursing Service*, 1.3.88, Section II; IOR, L/MIL/7/11316 f. 48b, Surgeon-General Madden, note, 5.5.87; WO 33/53, Report . . . 1893, p. 14.

75 WO 33/53, Report . . . 1893, p. 12.

76 *Ibid.*, p. 6.

77 *Medical Times and Gazette*, 20.11.80, p. 596; *British Medical Journal*, 1882, pt I, p. 484.

78 War Office Circulars 1.6.70, 14.11.70. *Report of the Army Medical Department for 1867*, Appendix XIII, p. 371, prints a suggestion of 1866 for employing Indian Army wives and widows in 'female hospitals'. Cuthell, *op. cit.*, p. 138, suggests that the scheme was implemented. In 1887 Surgeon-General Payne described the failure of a scheme to train soldiers' wives as nurses in hospitals in Calcutta: 'order was preserved with difficulty among them, and few of them had had so much education as would enable them even to begin to learn'. It is unclear, however, whether it had been proposed to employ them in female hospitals or in military hospitals proper. IOR, L/MIL/7/11316 f. 69, Surgeon-General Payne, memorandum, 6.1.87.

79 See Chapter 6.

80 *Nursing Record*, 2.10.90, p. 164.

81 *Nursing Mirror*, 4.1.08, p. 220.

82 *Regulations for the Army Nursing Service*, 1888 and 1891; *Nursing Record*, 2.7.91, p. 18; WO 25/3955, Nominal and Seniority Roll, *passim*.

83 *Nursing Mirror*, 3.9.10, p.347.

84 Fremantle, *op. cit.*, pp. 79–80.

85 *Catherine Grace Loch*, p. 351.

CHAPTER 5 PHILANTHROPY AND THE BATTLEFIELD

1 On the differences between military and civilian life, see: E.M. Spiers, *The Army and Society 1815–1914* ((London and New York 1980); M. Trustram, *Women of the Regiment: Marriage and the Victorian Army* (Cambridge 1984); A. Summers, 'Militarism in Britain before the Great War', *History Workshop Journal* 2, 1976, pp. 108–10.

2 M. Goodman, *Experiences of an English Sister of Mercy* (London 1862), pp. 111, 218–19.

3 C. Marsh, *Memorials of Captain Hedley Vicars, 97th Regiment* (London 1856); O. Anderson, 'The Growth of Christian Militarism in mid-Victorian Britain', *English Historical Review*, 86, 1971, pp. 46–72.

4 O. Anderson, *op. cit.*, p. 59; A.P. Stanley, *Memoirs of Edward and Catherine Stanley* (London 1880), pp. 242–3; Sister Mary Aloysius Doyle, *Memories of the Crimea* (London 1897), p. 50, fn;

Rev. W.H. Hobson, *Catharine Leslie Hobson* (London 1888), pp. 64, 80.

5 See H. Cunningham, *The Volunteer Force* (London 1975).

6 Cunningham, *op. cit.*, p. 72; B. Rose, 'The Volunteers of 1859', *Journal of the Society for Army Historical Research*, vol. 37–8, 1959–60, p. 103; Anonymous, 'The National Rifle Association', *Macmillan's Magazine*, XVI, 1867, p. 186; T.H. Hayhurst, *A History and Some Records of the Volunteer Movement* (Bury and Manchester 1887), pp. 164–5. See also the many cartoons on these themes in *Punch* 1860–2.

7 On these developments, see M. Howard, *The Franco-Prussian War* (London 1960), ch. I; and B. Bond, 'Mechanized warfare and the growth of pacifism' in A. Briggs, ed., *The Nineteenth Century, the Contradictions of Progress* (London 1970).

8 R.E. and T.N. Dupuy, *The Encyclopaedia of Military History* (London 1980), pp. 829–30; G. Moynier and P.L. Appia, *Help for the Sick and Wounded* (London 1870), p. 428; T. Longmore, 'On the Geneva Convention of 1864', *Journal of the Royal United Services Institute* X, 1866, pp. 177–8; Anonymous, 'Military Reform', *Fraser's Magazine* 74, 1866, p. 690.

9 B. Bond, 'Recruiting the Victorian Army 1870–1892', *Victorian Studies*, 5, 1962, p. 332.

10 *Memoirs of Margaret Fuller Ossoli* (London 1852), vol. III, pp. 212–13, 243; Jessie White Mario, 'Experience of Ambulances', *Fraser's Magazine* XV, 1877, pp. 771–3.

11 H. Brackenbury, 'Philanthropy in War', *Blackwood's Edinburgh Magazine* CXXI, pp. 155–7; W.G. MacPherson, 'The Role of the Red Cross Societies in Peace and War', Royal United Services Institute lecture, 6 February 1907, p. 11.

12 J.A. Davis, 'Garibaldi and England', *History Today* 32, December 1982, pp. 21, 23–5; *The Volunteer Rifleman's Magazine*, No. 1, August 1860, pp. 25–6; G.J. Holyoake, *Bygones Worth Remembering* (London 1905) vol. I, p. 245; W. Lamont, *Volunteer Memories* (Greenock 1911), p. 50.

13 D. Hewlett, *Elizabeth Barrett Browning* (London 1953), pp. 241, 324–5, 331; A. Hayter, *Mrs Browning* (London 1962), pp. 124–5, 128–9, 137–8, E.A. Daniels, *Jessie White Mario, Risorgimento Revolutionary* (Ohio 1972), pp. 7, 9, 21–3.

14 D.F. Mackay, 'The Influence of the Italian Risorgimento on British Public Opinion, 1859–61', unpublished D Phil thesis, Oxford University 1959, p. 223; *Victoria Magazine* VII, 1866 pp. 466–7;

Emma Pearson and Louise McLaughlin, 'Under the Red Cross', *St James's Magazine*, n.s. IX, 1872, pp. 124–5; Jessie White Mario, 'Garibaldi in France', *Fraser's Magazine* XVI, 1877, p. 607.

15 F.C.P., 'The Decoration of the Royal Red Cross', *Illustrated Naval and Military Magazine* I, 1884, p. 65.

16 E.T. Cook, *The Life of Florence Nightingale* (London 1913), vol. II, pp. 106, 116; MR, Longmore Papers 54/12, Florence Nightingale to Thomas Longmore, 14.2.67; BL Add.MSS 45750 f. 16, Florence Nightingale to the Princess Royal, 22.9.66.

17 *Victoria Magazine* VII, 1866, p. 369; Mrs Craven, *The Life of Lady Georgiana Fullerton* (London 1888), p. 315; F.C. Devas, *Mother Magdalen Taylor* (London 1927), p. 69.

18 J.H. Dunant, *Un Souvenir de Solferino* (Geneva 1862).

19 Brackenbury, *op. cit.*, p. 155.

20 Longmore 1866, p. 177.

21 E. King and H. Luke, *The Knights of St John in the British Realm* (London 1967), pp. 143–4; *The Statutes of the Sovereign and Illustrious Order of St John of Jerusalem, Angliâ* (London 1864), pp. 34–5; *First Annual Report of the Order of St John of Jerusalem in Angliâ* (London 1868), p. 17.

22 *First Annual Report*, p. 19; *Annual Report of the Secretary-General*, Order of St John of Jerusalem (London 1869), p. 16; the same, 1870, p. 16; Longmore 1866, pp. 177–8; *Memoir of the Bailiwick of Brandenburg of the Order of St John of Jerusalem* (London 1868), pp. 4, 10–12, 14–17; Brackenbury, *op. cit.*, p. 156.

23 *The Times*, 18.7.70, p. 8; 22.7.70, p. 7.

24 *Report of the Chapter* presented to the Chapter-General of the Order of St John of Jerusalem in England (London 1871), p. 5; *Lord Wantage, V.C., K.C.B., A Memoir by his Wife* (London 1907), p. 176. Henry Brackenbury was at this time lecturing in military history at the Royal Military Academy, Woolwich. He was a keen supporter of Cardwell's army reform, and after 1873 was identified as a member of Sir Garnet Wolseley's 'Ashanti Ring', accompanying Wolseley on his campaigns in Zululand and the Sudan. His other appointments included private secretary to Lytton while he was Viceroy of India; military attaché to the Paris Embassy; head of Army intelligence 1886–91; Director-General of Ordnance during the South African War. Whether his own enthusiasm for the improvement and augmentation of military medical services communicated itself to Wolseley or *vice versa* is unknown; both were converts to the cause of civilian aid by 1877. He was also a correspondent of Longmore's. He

was thought of in some quarters as '*the* cleverest man in the British Army'. See *DNB.*; J. Luvaas, *The Education of an Army* (Chicago, 1964), p. 182; MR, Longmore Papers 51/54, Muir to Longmore, 31.1.80.

25 T. Longmore, 'On the Geneva Convention of 1864, in relation to . . . the late Franco-German War', *Journal of the Royal United Services Institute* XVI, 1873, p. 216; Brackenbury, *op. cit.*, pp. 160, 170; *Lord Wantage*, pp. 180, 188, 203; V.A.J. Swain, 'The Franco-Prussian War of 1870–1; Voluntary Aid for the Wounded and Sick', *British Medical Journal* 111, 1970, pp. 511–13.

26 *Lord Wantage*, pp. 186–7.

27 W. Maccormac, *Notes and Recollections of an Ambulance Surgeon* (London 1871), p. 86; *Lord Wantage*, p. 188; Wantage Papers on Franco-Prussian War, Princess Christian to Mrs Loyd-Lindsay, 15.9.70; 22.9.70; 2.10.70. This chapter does not attempt to list all the British nurses of the war. Two who are also worth mentioning are: Clara Lowe, born in 1818 on St Helena, the daughter of Sir Hudson Lowe, who although not a trained nurse, went in the 1860s to live and nurse among the poor of London's East End; after the war, she helped in the work of an emigration scheme and a small-pox hospital in Canada, and in the work of a Christian mission in India, before returning to East End 'rescue work' (see *The Hospital 'Nursing Section'* 21.5.04, p. 105); and Elizabeth Barclay, who later trained at St Thomas's Hospital for a year (GLRO HI/ST/NC3/SU162, Nightingale to McNeill, 27.8.1872) – I am indebted to Martha Vicious for this reference; at the end of 1872 Florence Nightingale sent her to superintend the nursing at the Edinburgh Royal Infirmary. A year later, 'a wreck of a woman addicted to both alchohol and opium', she was relieved of her post (M.E. Baly, *Florence Nightingale and the Nursing Legacy* (London 1986), p. 164).

28 R. Loyd-Lindsay, *On Aid to the Sick and Wounded in War*, lecture, 31.3.71, privately printed; MR, Longmore Papers L 110/3, Cuttings on Franco-German War, p. 25.

29 Wantage Papers, collection on Franco-Prussian War, Mrs Capel to Loyd-Lindsay, 4.10.70; *Questions on the Operations of the British National Society for Aid to the Sick and Wounded in War* (London 1871), pp. 76–7, 91–4.

30 Major C. Burgess, 'Recollections of the Red Cross', *Illustrated Naval and Military Magazine* I, 1884, pp. 414, 416.

31 *The Hospital 'Nursing Mirror'*, 15.5.97, p. 61, published a notice of *The Narrative of my Experience as a Volunteer Nurse in the Franco-German*

War of 1870–1 'by Anne Thacker; with a sketch of her life by James M. Menzies, M.A.' This book is in the British Library catalogue but, sadly, is on the list of those printed books destroyed during the Second World War. No other copy has been traced.

32 *Nursing Notes* 7, 1.4.94, p. 41; 1.11.94, p. 144; 1.12.94, p. 157; J. Donnison, *Midwives and Medical Men* (New York 1977), pp. 177–8.

33 F. Lees, 'In a Fever Hospital before Metz', *Good Words*, 1873, pp. 322–7; *Victoria Magazine* XVII, 1871, pp. 169–70: BL Add.MSS 45754 ff. 75–6, Florence Nightingale to Dr Sutherland, *c.* February 1870; E.A. Pratt, *Pioneer Women in Victoria's Reign* (London 1897), pp. 135–6; Sarah Tytler, 'Girls who won Success', *Atalanta*, August 1888, p. 639; *Nursing Times*, 31.3.06, p. 262; *Nursing Mirror*, 23.12.1955, pp. iii–iv.

34 E. Pearson and L. McLaughlin, *Our Adventures during the War of 1870–1* (London 1871), 2 vols; J.G. Manton, *Sister Dora* (London 1971), pp. 258, 328–9; *The Times*, 12.6.93, p. 6; MR, Longmore Papers L 110/3 Cuttings on Franco/German War, p. 32; *Victoria Magazine*, VIII, 1871, p. 90; E. Pearson and L. McLaughlin, *Service in Servia under the Red Cross* (London 1877); W.C. Dowling, 'The Ladies' Sanitary Association and the Origins of the Health Visiting Service', unpublished MA thesis, London University 1963, p. 224.

35 Brackenbury, *op. cit.*, pp. 159–9; MacPherson, *op. cit.*, p. 2.

36 WO 33/23 piece 0487, p. 221, 'Report on the Medico Military Organisation of Prussia' by Deputy Inspector-General J.H. Ker Innes, 30.3.71; J. Fleetwood, 'An Irish Field Ambulance in the Franco-Prussian War', *Irish Sword* 6, 1963–4, pp. 139–40.

37 *The Times*, obituary, 28.3.87, p. 10.

38 F. Nightingale, *Notes on Nursing* (London 1860), p. 75.

39 *Hospital Training for Ladies, an Appeal to the Hospital Boards in England*, by the Right Honourable Viscountess Strangford (London 1874), pp. 3–4.

40 *Report of the Chapter*, . . . 1874, pp. 3, 8; *Nurses for the Sick Poor*, Report of the Committee of the Order of St John of Jerusalem in England (London 1873).

41 *Hospital Training for Ladies*, p. 16.

42 *Report of the Chapter* . . . 1877, pp. 10–11; D. Anderson, *The Balkan Volunteers* (London 1968), pp. 10–13.

43 *Report of the Chapter* . . . 1877, p. 10–11; D. Anderson, *op. cit.*, pp. 10–13; Strangford, *Report on the Bulgarian Peasant Relief Fund*, pp. 18–19; D. Anderson, *op. cit.*, pp. 49–56.

44 *Hospital Training for Ladies*, p. 16.

45 *Bulgarian Peasant Relief Fund*, p. 19. It is very likely that this was the same Miss Barclay referred to in fn. 27.

46 BL Add.MSS 39016 ff. 86–8, Strangford to Layard, 19.10.77; 39017 ff. 367–72, the same, 15.1.78.

47 *Victoria Magazine* XXXI, 1878, pp. 264–5; XXXII, 1879, pp. 389–90. Florence Nightingale's subsequent hostility to Lady Strangford's scheme for training soldiers' wives as military nurses (see next chapter) may have had nothing to do with this encomium.

48 *Report and Record of the Operations of the Stafford House Committee for the Relief of Sick and Wounded Turkish Soldiers* (London 1879), pp. 163, 176.

49 *Bulgarian Peasant Relief Fund*, p. 55.

50 See, however, Mrs E.M. King's 'The Work of an International Peace Society, and Women's Part in it', a paper read to the Congress of Social Science and reprinted in the *Victoria Magazine* XX, 1872–3, pp. 25–32, for an example of pacifist sentiment among women in this period. No information on Mrs King or her associates is available to the author.

51 T. Longmore, 'On the Geneva Convention of 1864, in relation to . . . the late Franco-German War', *Journal of the Royal United Services Institute* XVI, 1873, p. 216.

52 Strangford, *Report on the Bulgarian Peasant Relief Fund*, p. 23.

53 MR, Longmore Papers L 110/3, Cuttings on Franco-Prussian War, p. 25.

54 Daniels, *op. cit., passim*; H. Burton, *Barbara Bodichon* (London 1949), *passim; Victoria Magazine* XXII, 1873, pp. 32–5; XVII, 1871, p. 381.

CHAPTER 6 'COMFORT AFTER COMFORT'

1 *Report of a Committee appointed by the Secretary of State for war to inquire into the Organisation of the Army Hospital Corps*, PP 1883 XVI, p. 511, question 12,816.

2 *Broad Arrow* 29, 1882, p. 787.

3 *Report of the Stafford House South African Aid Committee* (London 1880), pp. 1–2.

4 BL Add.MSS 45805 f.220, Angela Burdett-Coutts to Florence Nightingale, 11.6.79.

5 WO 33/33 f.78, Proceedings of the Mobilization Committee, 5.6.79.

6 MR, Longmore Papers 51/27, Muir to Longmore, 18.6.79.

7 *Report of the Stafford House South African Aid Committee*, pp. 2–3; E.D., *Recollections of a Nurse* (London 1889), pp. 37–8.

8 *Report of the Stafford House South African Aid Committee*, p. 3.

9 WO 32/7793 ff.5–7, Report on the medical services of the Zulu War, 9.1.80.

10 Order of St John, *Report of the Chapter* . . . 1881, p. 6; Viscountess Strangford, *Hospital Training for Ladies* (London 1874); pp. 6–10.

11 Strangford, *The Soldier's Wife*, p. 5; Sister Mary Aloysius Doyle, *Memories of the Crimea* (London 1897), p. 50 fn; *Medical Times and Gazette* 20.11.80, p. 596; *Report of the Chapter* . . . 1881, p. 6. On Sinclair's scheme, see also Chapter 4.

12 *Report of the Chapter* . . . 1881, p.6.

13 BL Add.MSS 45806 f.59, Muir to Adjutant-General, 2.8.80.

14 BL Add.MSS 45827 f. 6, Florence Nightingale notes, 11.8.81.

15 SJAA, Cuttings Collection, *City Press*, 22.6.83; BL Add.MSS 45776 ff. 23–23b, Hawthorn to Nightingale, 25.8.81.

16 BL Add. MSS 45776, *loc.cit.*.

17 BL Add.MSS 45776 ff. 26–8, Nightingale to Hawthorn, 8.11.81.

18 *Report of the operations of the British National Society for Aid to sick and wounded in War*, 18.1.86, pp. 8–9. Many National Society probationers seem to have trained for only one year at Netley.

19 BL Add.MSS 45776 f. 64b, Nightingale to Hawthorn, 22.6.82; Mrs Fellowes had just finished a year's training at St Thomas's when she went to Netley; see GLRO Nightingale Training School records C4/3. Wantage Papers on Egypt, Deeble to Lady Loyd-Lindsay, 21.6.85; 45776 f. 5, Nightingale to Hawthorn, 14.2.81.

20 BL Add.MSS 45775 f. 60, Deeble to Nightingale, July/August 1870; ff. 78–2, the same, 13.2.81.

21 BL Add.MSS 45776 f. 28, Nightingale to Hawthorn, 8.11.81; 45807 ff. 47–8, Nightingale to Loyd-Lindsay, 27.2.83.

22 BL Add.MSS 45806 f. 18, General Gordon to Florence Nightingale, 22.4.80.

23 BL Add.MSS 45776 f. 1, Nightingale to Hawthorn, 4.6.80; f. 6, the same, 14.2.81.

24 BL Add.MSS 45776 ff. 8–10, Hawthorn to Nightingale, 23.3.81; ff. 14–16, Nightingale to Hawthorn, 11.5.81.

25 BL Add.MSS 45776 ff. 39–41, Nightingale to Hawthorn, 23.2.82; ff. 51–2, the same, 18.5.82.

26 *Proceedings of a Court of Inquiry appointed to inquire into Complaints against the Men of the Army Hospital Corps employed in the War in South Africa* (War Office, June 1882), pp. 1, 4, 8–13.

27 *Ibid.*, pp. 9–10.

28 *Report . . . Army Hospital Corps*, PP 1883 XVI, pp. iv, xiv–xv, xix; BL Add.MSS 45776 ff. 100–1. Nightingale to Hawthorn, 2.11.82.

29 BL Add.MSS 45776 ff. 78–9; Nightingale to Hawthorn, 3.8.82; *Report on the operations of the British National Society . . .* 1886, p. 9; BL Add.MSS 45776 ff. 117, 121, Nightingale to Hawthorn, 24.2.85; Wantage Papers on Egypt, Nightingale to Lady Loyd-Lindsay, 12.3.85; E.T. Cook, *The Life of Florence Nightingale* (London 1913), vol. II, p. 347.

30 There is no complete list extant of all the female nurses sent to the Middle East between 1883 and 1886. A War Office list in the Wantage Papers includes neither the Princess of Wales's nurses, nor the nurses sent out as 'cooking sisters'.

31 MR, Longmore Papers 51/41, Muir to Longmore, 21.3.79; Cantlie, *op. cit.*, vol. II, p. 278.

32 BL Add.MSS 45806 ff. 127–9 Fellowes to Nightingale, 23.3.81 and 27.3.81.

33 BL Add.MSS 45776 ff. 91–2, Nightingale to Hawthorn, 17.8.82.

34 Wantage Papers on Army Medical Services, Nightingale to Loyd-Lindsay, 30.7.82; BL Add.MSS 45776 f. 79, Nightingale to Hawthorn, 3.8.82; 45807 f. 12, Nightingale to Solly, 25.8.82.

35 BL Add.MSS 45772 f. 17, Nightingale to Director-General Crawford, 25.11.82; Wantage Papers on Egypt, Nightingale to Lady Loyd-Lindsay, 12.3.85; the same, 16.6.85.

36 BL Add.MSS 45775 ff. 166b, 167b, Airy to Nightingale, 17.11.84; f. 146b, the same, 31.3.84; f. 123, the same, 8.1.83; f. 130b, the same, 15.5.83; 45776 f. 98b, Nightingale to Hawthorn, 2.11.82.

37 BL Add.MSS 45775 ff. 144–6, Airy to Nightingale, 31.3.84.

38 BL Add.MSS 45775 f. 127, Airy to Nightingale, 19.2.83; f. 130, the same, 15.5.83; ff. 139–139b, the same, 19.8.83; WO 163/4, Reports by Heads of Departments on Army Hospital Services, p. 27.

39 Anonymous, 'The Army and the Democracy', *Fortnightly Review*, March 1886, p. 344.

40 WO 33/41 piece 941, Reports by Heads of Departments, etc., . . . 1883, f 633; *Regulations for the Medical Department of H.M. Army* (War Office 1885), sections 238, 241; Wantage Papers on Egypt, Deeble to Lady Loyd-Lindsay, 21.6.85.

41 H. Brackenbury, 'Philanthropy in War', *Blackwood's Edinburgh Magazine*, CXXI, February 1877, pp. 159–60, 169–71.

42 *Report of the Chapter . . .* 1877, p. 5; J. Furley, 'The Proper Sphere of Voluntary Societies for the Relief of Sick and Wounded Soldiers in

War', paper read to the Order of St John, June 1877, p. 14; OSJ, Cuttings Collection, *Morning Post*, 10.9.77; *Kentish Independent*, 22.9.77; *Aid to the Injured*, Proceedings of a Public Meeting convened by the Order of St John of Jerusalem, 6.2.78, pp. 13–14.

43 *Aid to the Injured*, pp. 16–17, 21; OSJ, Cuttings Collection, *Standard*, 24.11.77; *Daily Telegraph*, and *The Times*, 12.1.78. A measure of agreement on a division of labour was gradually reached between the Volunteer Sick Bearers' Association and the SJAA. See *Maidstone and Kentish Journal*, 18.3.78; untitled press clipping, 4.5.78, on the distribution of SJAA certificates to members of the 2nd Middlesex A.V.

44 *Report of the Chapter* . . . 1878, p. 8; Order of St John, Ambulance Department, Report of the Central Committee 1878, p. 19.

45 Order of St John, Ambulance Department, Report of the Central Executive Committee, 24.6.79, pp. 8–11; Supplementary Report of the Central Committee, 4.2.79, p. 21.

46 Ambulance Department, Report of Central Executive Committee, 24.6.79, p. 51; the same, supplementary report, 4.2.79, p. 18.

47 *Aid to the Injured*, p. 12.

48 E. King and H. Luke, *The Knights of St John in the British Realm* (London 1967), p. 189; St John's Ambulance Association, *Report*, 1885–6, pp. 19–20.

49 St John's Ambulance Association, *Report*, 1883, pp. 13–14.

50 N. Corbet Fletcher, *The St John's Ambulance Association* (London 1931), pp. 36–40; *First Aid* August 1897, pp. 210–11; September 1897, p. 220; October 1897, p. 223.

CHAPTER 7 HEROINES FOR THE EMPIRE

1 *Report of the Committee on the Organisation of the Army Hospital Corps, Hospital Management and Nursing in the Field, and the Sea Transport of Sick and Wounded*, PP XVI, 1883, p. 226, question 4808. Langton was the Commandant at the base of operations at Ismailia; RA R53 f. 64, Ponsonby to Childers 12.9.82; *London Gazette*, 27.4.83, pp. 2239–40.

2 RA E25 f. 98, Muir to Ponsonby, May 1880.

3 The Order conferred a pension of £50 per annum 'for a limited period', and an embroidered badge on the left arm. The first three awards were made to nurses at the Westminster Hospital; Elizabeth Wheldon of the Army Nursing Service also received one. J. Langdon-

Davies, *The Westminster Hospital* (London 1952), p. 139, fn; *Englishwoman's Review*, 15.10.80, pp. 472–3. I have not come across records of other conferrals. The award never attained the cachet of the RRC.

4 Order of St John, *Report of the Chapter*, 1877, p. 3; St John's Ambulance Association, *Report*, 1882, p. 5; *Englishwoman's Review*, 14.10.82, pp. 476–7; C. Kinloch Cooke, *A Memoir of H.R.H. Princess Mary Adelaide, Duchess of Teck* (London 1900), vol. II, p. 369.

5 For an interesting discussion of 'official nationalism', see B. Anderson, *Imagined Communities* (London 1983), pp. 81–2.

6 *Nursing Record*, 11.8.94, p. 94.

7 *Victoria Magazine*, January 1872, p. 273; *Englishwoman's Review*, 15.11.84, pp. 533–4; *Nursing Record*, 25.5.01. p. 414.

8 E.C. Laurence, *A Nurse's Life in War and Peace* (London 1912), pp. 1, 14, 285; J. Kamm, *Hope Deferred* (London 1965), p. 216. Rosamund Rolleston wrote amusingly of her journey out to South Africa 'the Sisters, in despair for want of proper exercise, are now being drilled every morning at eight o'clock by a colour-sergeant of the Gordon Highlanders. We go through extension motion, 1st, 2nd and 3rd practice – right and left hand – salutes, etc., with great gravity. It reminds one of being at school again.' *League News*, May 1900, pp. 6–7.

9 *The Queen*, 7.11.91, pp. 734–5; *Englishwoman's Review*, 15.7.91, p. 199; *Catherine Grace Loch, R.R.C., a Memoir*, compiled by Surgeon-Major-General A.F. Bradshaw (London 1905), p. 23; *Woman's Herald*, p. 538; *Nursing Record*, 11.6.91, p. 309.

10 In the 1870s and 1880s, some Girls' Public Day School Trust schools gave an hour a week to cookery and hygiene; some preferred needlework as a non-academic subject. J. Kamm, *op. cit.*, p. 217. At the end of the century, the introduction of cookery and laundry into the elementary school curriculum was said to be 'recent': see A. Zimmern, *The Renaissance of Girls' Education* (London 1898), p. 178.

11 *Nursing Record*, 17.5.88, p. 78; 26.2.98, pp. 170–1; 5.3.98, p. 203.

12 Florence Nightingale, 'Una and the Lion', *Good Words*, June 1868, pp. 362–6; F.B. Smith gives a damning account of Nightingale's concoction of the Jones legend in *Florence Nightingale, Reputation and Power* (London and Canberra 1982), pp. 173–7. On Dorothy Pattison, see J.G. Manton, *Sister Dora* (London 1971).

13 Rev. W.F. Hobson, *Catharine Leslie Hobson, Lady-Nurse, Crimean*

War, and Her Life (London 1888), p. 160; A.P. Stanley, *Memoirs of Edward and Catherine Stanley* (London 1880), p. 344. Mary Stanley had died in November 1879 at the age of 66.

14 V. Hicks Beach, *The Colonial Nursing Association* (London 1914). The Up-Country Nursing Association was founded to meet the needs of British civilians, and some military officers. Nursing candidates had to be Protestant, and 'of earnest religious principle'; *Hospital 'Nursing Mirror'*, 12.2.98, p. 171.

15 *Hospital 'Nursing Mirror'*, 8.4.99, p. 23.

16 *Ibid.*, 14.1.99, p. 155; 12.6.97, p. 97; *Nursing Record*, 11.2.99., p. 123.

17 *Nursing Record*, 5.4.88, p. 2; 21.6.88, p. 137; *The Battle of the Nurses: A full Verbatim Report from official sources of the actual proceedings before the Privy Council, on the application of the Royal British Nurses' Association for a Charter of Incorporation* (London 1893), pp. 6–7.

18 *Nursing Record*, 5.4.88, p. 2; 24.3.94, p. 189; 7.7.00, p. 11.

19 *Ibid.*, 26.5.00, p. 417.

20 Surgeon-Major G.J.H. Evatt, M.D., Army Medical Staff, *A Proposal to form a Corps of Volunteer Female Nurses for service in the Army Hospitals in the Field, with Suggestions as to the Incorporation of the Nursing Profession* (Royal Military Academy, Woolwich, 1885), pp. 1–3; *Nursing Record*, 31.3.94, p. 215.

21 G.J.H. Evatt, *Army Medical Organisation* (London 1883), pp. 6, 73–4; *Hospital Gazette and Students' Journal*, 30.1.86, pp. 52–3. Evatt was a temperance activist, and an unsuccessful Liberal candidate for Parliament. He also founded the Medical Officers of Schools Association, and was President of the Poor Law Medical Officers' Association. He retired from the army in 1903, was active in the RAMC Territorial Force, was recalled to the colours in 1915, and died in 1921.

22 N. Cantlie, *A History of the Army Medical Department* (Edinburgh and London 1974), vol. II, pp. 360–3.

23 B. Bond, *The Victorian Army and the Staff College 1854–1914* (London 1972), pp. 153, 174; Sir T. Longmore, 'The New Military Weapons and Explosives', *British Medical Journal*, 5.3.92, pp. 521–2. See also next chapter.

24 *Nursing Record*, 24.3.94, pp. 188–9; 31.3.94, pp. 204–5.

25 *First Aid*, December 1894, p. 37. Other women who took part in WVMSC meetings were Miss Priestly, Miss Petty, Mrs Grace Goodall, and Miss Mears, Secretary of the Upholsterers' Trade Society. The second meeting was held at the 'Ideal Club', Tottenham

Court Road. See untitled press cuttings, MR, Longmore Papers, L110/4, pp. 114–15.

26 *Nursing Record*, 24.3.94, pp. 118–19; Longmore Papers, *loc. cit.*

27 *Nursing Record*, 7.4.94, p. 218.

28 Longmore Papers, *loc. cit*; *Punch*, 28.4.94, p. 194; *Nursing Record*, 12.5.94, p. 306. Mrs Bedford Fenwick was famous for her sartorial elegance.

29 *Nursing Record*, 24.3.94, pp. 188–9.

30 Longmore Papers, *loc. cit*; *Nursing Record*, 31.3.94, pp. 204–5, quoting Ethel Stokes's letter to the *Standard*.

31 Longmore Papers, *loc.cit.*

32 *Nursing Record*, 31.3.94, p. 205.

33 *Ibid.*, 24.3.94, p. 189, citing the *Standard* of 14.3.94.

34 N. Corbet Fletcher, *The St John's Ambulance Association* (London 1931), pp. 26, 30–1; *First Aid*, 15.2.95, p. 50.

35 *Nursing Record*, 12.5.94, p. 306; *The Queen*, 12.5.94, p. 753. Janet Helen King (1858–1911) was fired by girlhood reading about Florence Nightingale to enter the Tottenham Training Hospital, then run by a religious sisterhood, in 1876. A year later she nursed with the Russian Army during the Russo-Turkish War. She was decorated with the Imperial Russian Red Cross. *Nursing Times*, 29.8.08, p. 676.

36 *The Queen*, 12.5.94, p. 753.

37 *Standard*, 17.3.94, excerpted in Longmore Papers, *loc. cit*; It is interesting to compare the rather sad fortunes of the WVMSC with those of the well-heeled and well-connected FANY between 1909 and 1914; see Chapters 9 and 10.

38 *Nursing Record*, 27.4.95, p. 283; Longmore Papers, *loc. cit*; *First Aid*, November 1897, p. 236.

39 *Nursing Record*, 31.3.94, p. 215; *Nurses' Journal*, March 1894, pp. 28–30; *Nurses' Journal*, March 1894, p. 28.

40 BL Add.MSS 45750 f. 93, Princess Christian to Florence Nightingale, 30.4.94; 45750 ff. 98–100, Florence Nightingale to Princess Christian, 9.5.94; *Nursing Record*, 21.7.94, pp. 44–5.

41 *Nursing Record*, 12.5.94, pp. 305–6.

42 *Ibid.*, 21.7.94, p. 52.

43 *Nursing Record*, 27.4.95, p. 277; *Nurses' Journal*, August 1896, p. 76.

44 *Nurses' Journal*, *loc. cit.*

45 *Nursing News*, March 1897, p. 226; *The Times*, 19.5.97, p. 10.

46 WO 32/7146, Report on the Sixth International Conference of Red

Cross Societies held in Vienna, from 18 to 24 September 1897, by Surgeon-Major W.G. MacPherson, and covering minute by Director-General, Army Medical Services, pp. 4–5.

47 *Ibid.*, covering minute by Surgeon-General Taylor, 10.6.98.

48 WO 32/7147; 7148.

49 *Hospital 'Nursing Mirror'*, 11.12.97, p. 98; 26.2.98, p. 196; 30.4.98, p. 43.

50 D. Bagot, *Shadows of the War* (London 1900), pp. xv, 114. Theodosia Bagot helped to found the Portland Hospital and accompanied it to South Africa. She received the RRC and the South African War Service Medal and became a Lady of Grace of the Order of St John. In 1912 she organised a surgical unit for Serbia in the Balkan War; during the First World War she took hospitals to France and the Belgian Army. In 1927 she was a Vice-President of the Church Army. *WWW*, vol. III.

51 Wantage Papers for 1898, n.d., letter of Miss Phipps.

52 *Report by the Central British Red Cross Committee on Voluntary Organisations in aid of sick and wounded during the South African War* (London, HMSO 1902), pp. 4, 25.

53 *Nursing Record*, 22.10.98, p. 335; 29.10.98, p. 353; 22.10.98, p. 335; 19.11.98, p. 423.

54 *Ibid.*, 21.4.00, pp. 310–11.

55 *Illustrated Naval and Military Magazine*, May 1885, p. 333; June 1885, p. 393.

56 *Englishwoman's Review*, 14.7.83, pp. 328–9.

57 *Hospital 'Nursing Section'*, 22.11.02, p. 110.

58 *Report of the Royal Commission appointed to consider and report on the Care and Treatment of the Sick and Wounded during the South African Campaign*, PP 1901 XXIX, p. 16. See discussion in next chapter of the difficulty of getting an exact figure for female military nurses in South Africa.

59 *Nursing Record*, 4.11.99, p. 369–70; Wantage Papers on South Africa, Princess of Wales to Lady Wantage, 4.12.99; Lady Wantage to Princess of Wales, 7.12.99; *Report by the Central British Red Cross Committee*, p. 25.

60 St John's Ambulance Brigade, *Report of the Commissioner on the Mobilisation of the Brigade for Service in South Africa, 1899–1900* (London 1900), p. 5.

61 *Nursing Record*, 13.10.00, p. 295.

62 Wantage Papers on South Africa, Furley to Wantage, 29.10.00; Central British Red Cross Committee to Chairman, Central Good

Hope Committee, 9.5.00; *The Times*, 15.5.00, p. 4.

63 Lady Jessica Sykes, *Side Lights on the War in South Africa* (London 1900), pp. 29, 131–2, 152. Christina Anne Jessica Sykes was the daughter of George Augustus Cavendish-Bentinck, MP. Her son Mark drew up the Sykes-Picot agreement on Anglo-French spheres of interest in the Near East, during the First World War.

64 Wantage Papers on South Africa, Furley to Wantage, 16.4.00; *The Times*, 16.4.00, p. 4; WO 105/25, I.N. 51, Roberts to GOC Lines of Communication, Cape Town, 27.4.00; *Nursing Record*, 28.4.00, p. 337.

65 The *Nursing Record* reproduced some irresistible lyrics on 12.5.00:

Oh Woman in our hours of ease
Uncertain, coy and hard to please;
When pain and anguish wring the brow,
More terrible than flies art thou. (*The Londoner*)

There was a young belle from North Berwick,
Whose conduct was slightly hysteric,
    She followed the guns
    And distributed buns
To the men who were down with enteric. (*The Sunday Sun*)

66 *Nursing Record*, 16.2.01, p. 127; 10.11.00, p. 379; WO 105/25, I.N. 51, Circular letter of Mrs Chamberlain, Cape Town, 23.4.00.

67 *Nursing Record*, 14.7.00, p. 35; E.C. Laurence, *op. cit.*, pp. 282, 250. By this time, one of her brothers was Judge-President of Griqualand West.

68 W.S. Inder, *On Active Service in South Africa with the St John's Ambulance Brigade* (Kendal 1903), p. 63. The Army Nursing Reserve sisters were on the whole more quick to criticise the orderlies than were the sisters of the regular service.

69 Hospital 'Nursing Mirror', 13.4.01, p. 15. Some nurses had received service medals for their work in campaigns in Egypt, India, and on board hospital ship in West Africa, before this date: information from the General Secretary of the Orders and Medals Research Society.

70 *Nursing Record*, 16.10.97, pp. 302–3; 16.4.98, p. 318; 4.5.01, p. 358. This new editorial note may have owed something to Ethel Bedford Fenwick's recent acquaintanceship with Laura Ormiston Chant, with whom she had co-operated on the Grecian Nursing Committee in 1897. Mrs Chant was a non-denominational preacher, lecturer and writer. Before her marriage to a surgeon, she had been a schoolteacher, a nurse in the London Hospital, and the assistant

manager of a private lunatic asylum. After her marriage, she became well known as an advocate of women's suffrage, temperance, 'purity and Liberal politics'. She was connected with the Women's Peace Association. Before 1897 she had taken relief to Armenian refugees in Bulgaria. *WWW* vol. II (1947), pp. 188–9; *Englishwoman's Review*, 15.4.89, p. 186.

71 *Nursing Record*, 27.5.99, pp. 410–11; 21.10.99, p. 324.

72 E. Haldane, *The British Nurse in Peace and War* (London 1923), p. 3.

73 T. Longmore, 'On the Geneva Convention of 1864 in relation to . . . the late Franco-German War', *Journal of the Royal United Services Institute*, XVI, 1873, p. 216.

74 E. Hobhouse, *The Brunt of the War and Where it Fell* (London 1902), pp. 180–1, 214, 231, 290–1.

75 *Hospital 'Nursing Mirror'*, 18.8.00, p. 269; 20.1.00, p. 213; 11.8.00, p. 257; *League News*, November 1900, p. 29.

76 *Nursing Record*, 31.8.01, p. 172; *Hospital 'Nursing Section'*, 12.10.01, p. 29; *Hospital 'Nursing Mirror'*, 26.5.00, p. 103; 7.7.00, p. 187.

77 WO 108/338, List of Casualties in the South African Field Force, 1.10.99–20.3.00.

78 D. Bagot, *op. cit.*, p. 155.

79 See the Boer War memorial plaque, still in place in St Helen's Town Hall, Lancs.

80 This was at Great Clacton, Essex. See A. Summers, 'Images of the Nineteenth-Century Nurse', *History Today*, December 1984.

81 E.g. 'This rapidly growing army of women came to look upon themselves as soldiers enlisted in a Holy War,' Elizabeth Robins, *Votes for Women*, 4.2.10, p. 291; 'Life in its essence and in its height means conflict. And only the warrior wears the crown,' E. Pethick Lawrence, *ibid.*, 25.3.10. See also Chapter 10.

CHAPTER 8 DISASTERS AND REFORM

1 These figures do not convey the full extent of the medical disaster. A further 9,000 men remained in hospital at the termination of hostilities, and 75,000 sick and wounded were shipped home from South Africa between 1899 and 1902; the fate of these men does not appear to have been registered in the official statistics of the war: *Report of the Royal Commission on the South African War*, PP 1904 XL, p. 43; *ibid.*, PP 1904 XLII, p. 99. Two useful recent works on the Anglo-Boer War are T. Pakenham, *The Boer War* (London 1982) and P. Warwick, ed., *The South African War* (London 1980).

2 *Report of the Royal Commission on the Care and Treatment of the Sick and Wounded during the South African Campaign*, PP 1901 XXIX, p. 5; Pakenham *op. cit.*, pp. 354, 382.

3 *Royal Commission . . . South African War*, p. 245; *Royal Commission . . . Sick and Wounded*, pp. 16, 35. The non-commissioned officers and men of the Medical Staff Corps were united with the medical officers in the new Royal Army Medical Corps in 1898.

4 Surgeon-General W.D. Wilson, *Report on the Medical Arrangements in the South African War* (London, HMSO 1904), pp. 177–8.

5 WO 105/26, I.N. 50, Burdett-Coutts to Col. Cowan, 23.5.1900; *Royal Commission . . . Sick and Wounded*, p. 75.

6 M.J. Parish, *A History of Immunization* (Edinburgh and London 1965), p. 65; L. Colebrook, *Almroth Wright* (London 1954), p. 37.

7 *Royal Commission . . . South African War*, p. 106; Lt Col.R.J. Simpson, *The Medical History of the War in South Africa* (London 1911), pp. 4, 40–2, 44, 54; WO 105/27, piece no. 1321: Dr Turner's report on the health of stations in the Eastern District, 19.11.1900. See also WO 33/195, Recommendations of the Committee directed to consider Sir Thomas Gallway's 'Medical Report on the Campaign in Natal, 1899–1900', p. 5.

8 Pakenham, *op. cit.*, p. 382; *Royal Commission . . . Sick and Wounded*, p. 230, q. 3129, Sir William MacCormac.

9 Pakenham, *op. cit.*, pp. 382–3.

10 *Royal Commission . . . Sick and Wounded*, p. 320.

11 *Nursing Record*, 12.5.00, p. 376; 17.2.1900, p. 132; *Hospital 'Nursing Mirror'*, 6.10.1900, p. 17; 23.6.1900, pp. 159, 167; E.C. Laurence, *A Nurse's Life in War and Peace* (London 1912), p. 147;
Royal Commission . . . South African War, p. 156.

12 W.S. Inder, *On Active Service with the St John's Ambulance Brigade in the South African War* (Kendal 1903), p. 37; *Royal Commission . . . Sick and Wounded*, p. 268, q. 4441 Nursing Sister Richardson, A.N.R., F.E. Fremantle, *Impressions of a Doctor in Khaki* (London 1901), pp. 162, 406; *Royal Commission . . . South African War*, p. 219, qs. 15,569–15,578, General Buller.

13 *Royal Commission . . . Sick and Wounded*, pp. 13, 75. For a discussion of this question in the context of twentieth-century warfare, see C. Enloe, *Does Khaki Become You?* (London, 1983), pp. 125, 153–9.

14 *Hospital 'Nursing Mirror'*, 21.7.1900, p. 213; 9.6.1900, p. 133; *Nursing Record*, 20.1.1900, p. 47; *Hospital 'Nursing Mirror'*, 12.1.01, p. 197.

15 *Royal Commission . . . Sick and Wounded*, p. 209; F. Treves, *The Tale of a Field Hospital* (London 1900), pp. 36–7; *Nursing Record*, 21.7.00, p. 56.

16 *Hospital 'Nursing Mirror'*, 14.4.1900, p. 31; 5.5.1900, p. 71; 23.6.1900, p. 167.

17 *Royal Commission . . . Sick and Wounded*, p. 139, q. 81, Lt-Col. Johnston. *Nursing Record*, 16.6.1900, p. 475; 3.2.1900, p. 93; Treves, *op. cit.*, pp. 36–7.

18 *The Queen*, 12.5.94, p. 753; *Nursing Record*, 21.7.1900, p. 56.

19 *Royal Commission . . . Sick and Wounded*, p. 567, q. 13,970, Col. Gallway; *Nursing Record*, 18.8.1900, pp. 134–5.

20 *Royal Commission . . . South African War*, p. 108, qs. 11998, 12146, Frederick Treves. E.g. *British Medical Journal*, 21.4.1900, p. 972, article by Sir William Thomson, Surgeon-in-Chief, Irish Hospital, Naauwpoort Camp; *Lancet*, 27.6.01, p. 1227, 'Our Suggestions for the Reorganisation of the Army Medical Service'.

21 *Nursing Record* 26.1.01, pp. 66–7, 2.2.01, p. 87; E. McCaul 'Some Suggestions for Army Reform', *Nineteenth Century*, April 1901, pp. 580–7.

22 E.D. Irvine, 'News from the Front: Looking after Tommy', *Medical News* 2.2.1968, p. 7.

23 Quoted in *Nursing Record*, 28.4.1900, p. 337.

24 M. Mostyn Bird, *The Errand of Mercy* (London 1913), pp. 327–8.

25 WO 33/195, Recommendations . . . , p. 2; W. Burdett-Coutts, *The Sick and Wounded in South Africa* (London 1901), p. 216.

26 CAB 17/12, Keogh to Roberts, 17.1.05. One might perhaps wonder if Keogh had been influenced by the 1899 edition of von der Goltz's *Das Volk in Waffen*: 'Suitable plans for convalescents who are to rejoin their units at the earliest opportunity, must also be provided. Good supervision of the sick and those temporarily absent from the ranks in the rear of the army will certainly prevent large numbers being withdrawn from the front without sufficient reason'. (English translation of this edition, *The Nation in Arms*, London 1906, pp. 459–60.)

27 *Royal Commission . . . South African War*, p. 218, q. 15562; WO 105/25, I.N. 51, Report of Col. Hooper 9.7.1900; Simpson *op. cit.*, p. 228.

28 Haldane MSS, 6020 f. 207, Keogh to Elizabeth Haldane, 11.7.08.

29 Jean de Bloch, 'The Transvaal War: its lessons in regard to militarism and Army Reorganisation', *Journal of the Royal United Services Institute*, December 1901, pp. 1316–1339; W.L.C. von der Goltz, *The Nation*

in Arms (London 1906) [translation of 1899 German edition], pp. 145, 159, 469.

30 See G. Searle, *The Quest for National Efficiency* (Oxford 1971); A. Summers, 'Militarism in Britain before the Great War', *History Workshop Journal* 2, Autumn 1976; Anna Davin, 'Imperialism and Motherhood', *ibid.*, 5, Spring 1978.

31 M.G. Fawcett, introduction to H. Morten, *Questions for Women* (London 1899), pp. 9–10. Similar arguments were advanced by May Hill Watt, 'Wanted, Ladies at the War Office', *Womanhood* III, no. 18, May 1900, p. 402; and in a letter from 'A.N.R.', *Nursing Record*, 13.4.01, pp. 303–4.

32 This was the 'Committee of Ladies appointed by the Secretary of State for War' as part of the Concentration Camps Commission. Its other members were Lucy A.E. Deane, Katherine B. Brereton, Alice Knox, Ella Campbell Scarlett, MD, and Jane E. Waterston, MD; its report was published in PP 1902 LXVII.

33 *Nursing Record*, 5.11.01, p. 265.

34 The Committee's members were Frederick Treves of the London Hospital, George Makins of St Thomas's, Sir William Thomson, the King's Surgeon in Ireland, Alfred Downing Fripp of Guy's, Howard Tooth of Bart's, Professor Ogston of Aberdeen University, E. Cooper Perry of Guy's, all of whom had served with military hospitals in South Africa: Surgeon-General Hooper represented the Indian Medical Service, Lt-Col. Keogh and Major H.E.R. James the RAMC; combatant officers were represented by Sir Gerald Morton and Sir James Willcocks, and the War Office by Sir Edward Ward and the Secretary of State.

35 WO 33/208, Discussion of the War Office Committee on Reorganisation of the Army Medical and Army Nursing Services, July 1901, pp. 138–9.

36 *Ibid.*, pp. 137–9. See also Haldane MSS 6020 f. 33, Nora Roberts to Elizabeth Haldane, 14.3.07 '. . . my husband who does not pretend to know anything about nursing. . . .'

37 WO 33/208, Discussion, p. 151.

38 *Ibid.*, pp. 143–4, 153.

39 WO 32/9339, Papers on QAIMNS 1901–2, Memorandum from Queen Alexandra, n.d; *Nursing Times*, 8.7.05, p. 171.

40 WO 32/9338, Papers on QAIMNS, statement of Queen Alexandra's objections to proposals, 26.7.01; WO 32/9339, the Queen's criticisms, n.d.; note by Brodrick, 18.10.01; telegrams from Ogston, Tooth, Willcocks, Thomson and Hooper, November 1901.

41 See following chapter.

42 *Hospital 'Nursing Section'*, 16.4.04. p. 33.

43 *British Journal of Nursing*, 13.12.02, p. 496.

44 *The Hospital 'Nursing Section'*, 5.10.01, p. 51; 25.10.02, pp. 59, 60; 8.11.02, p. 83.

45 Regulations, QAIMNS, October 1902, Nos. 147, 148, 170, 172a–c.

46 Standing Orders for the RAMC and QAIMNS, War Office, November 1903, no. 295; Army Order 114 or 1904.

47 WO 32/9338, Papers on QAIMNS, Queen Alexandra's objections, 26.7.01.

48 WO 163/10, War Office Council, Subjects and Decisions, pp. 363–7, Advisory Board for the Army Medical Services, Third Report on Expansion for War, 10.3.04.

49 WO 33/208, Discussion, p. 123; WO 163/10, War Office Council, p. 368, Report on Comparative Cost of Male and Female Nurses for General and Stationary Hospitals 11.4.05.

50 WO 30/133, A Report upon the Condition of the Chief Military Hospitals in Great Britain, 1902, p. 68.

51 *Report of the Committee appointed by the Secretary of State to consider the reorganisation of the Army Medical Services*, PP 1902 X, pp. 139–40; WO 32/7175, Report of the Army Hospitals Committee on Centralisation of Accommodation, 1903–4; Regulations, QAIMNS, October 1902, Nos. 144, 162c–k, 163–166b; WO 32/9337, Papers on QAIMNS, 1901; *Nursing Record*, 5.10.01, p. 266.

52 WO 163/10, War Office Council . . . Third Report on Expansion for War, 10.3.04, p. 365; *Nursing Times*, 5.8.05, p. 257; *Broad Arrow* LXXVI, 16.6.06, p. 666; WO 25/3956, Nominal and Seniority Roll, QAIMNS.

53 WO 33/208, Discussion, p. 133; Regulations, QAIMNS, October 1902, Appointment and Qualification of Candidates, 3.

54 WO 25/3956, Nominal and Seniority Roll, QAIMNS.

55 WO 25/3995, Nominal and Seniority Roll, Army Nursing Service, ff. 53–6; *WWW* vol. IV.

56 *British Journal of Nursing*, 31.3.06, p. 251.

57 WO 25/3956, Nominal and Seniority Roll, QAIMNS.

58 Standing Orders for the RAMC and QAIMNS, War Office, November 1903, Nos. 300–5; Standing Orders . . . 1907, Appendix 2, pp. 64–6.

59 Regulations, QAIMNS, 1904, no. 149; *Nursing Times*, 10.3.06, p. 205.

60 *Broad Arrow*, 16.6.06, p. 667, 23.6.06, p. 697.

61 *Report of the Committee appointed by the Secretary of State to consider the reorganisation of Army Medical Services*, PP 1902 X, p. 133.

62 WO 163/10, War Office Council . . . Third Report on Expansion for War, 10.3.04, p. 365–6.

63 Haldane MSS, 6020 f. 208, Keogh to Elizabeth Haldane, 11.7.08.

CHAPTER 9 THE BIRTH OF THE VAD

1 Haldane MSS, 6020 f. 25, N. Roberts to E. Haldane 7.3.07.

2 Sydney Holland, 'The Civilian Hospitals and the Army Nursing Reserve', *Hospital 'Nursing Section'*, 10.1.03 pp. 210–11; Haldane MSS, 6019 f. 43, Sydney Holland to E. Haldane, 10.3.06.

3 On Haldane's reforms, see A.J.A. Morris, 'Haldane's Army Reforms 1906–8: the Deception of the Radicals', *History*, 56, 1971, pp. 17–34; E.M. Spiers, *The Army and Society 1815–1914* (London 1980), ch. 10; M. Howard, *Lord Haldane and the Territorial Army* (Haldane Memorial Lecture, London 1966).

4 Haldane MSS, 6020 f. 117, Keogh to E. Haldane 29.10.07; 6011 ff. 53–4, War Office to E. Haldane 16.3.08; *Nursing Times*, 8.6.08, p. 297; *Nursing Mirror* 23.1.09, p. 263; 20.3.09, p. 382.

5 *WWW*, vol. 3 p. 575; Haldane MSS, 6048 f. 214, E. Haldane to her mother, 1.3.06; *Nursing Times*, 31.3.06, p. 262.

6 RA Add. A.21/233 f. 83, Queen Alexandra to Sydney Holland, 13.3.06; Haldane MSS, 6011 ff. 28–9, R.B. Haldane to E. Haldane, 15.3.06.

7 Haldane MSS, 6019 f. 80, Nora Roberts to E. Haldane, 19.6.06.

8 *Ibid.*, 5097 ff. 49–50, N. Roberts to R.B. Haldane, 10.4.06; 6019 f. 79, N. Roberts to E. Haldane, 19.6.06; 6019 f. 83, S. Holland to E. Haldane, 27.6.06.

9 Keogh was Director-General of Army Medical Services from January 1905 to March 1910. He founded the School of Army Sanitation. In October 1914 he was recalled to the post of Director-General.

10 Haldane MSS, 6020, letters of Keogh to E. Haldane ff. 23–4, 7.3.07; ff. 60–3, 19.6.07; ff. 67–8, 1.7.07; f. 88, 12.7.07; ff. 101–6, 24.9.07, ff. 117–23, 29.10.07.

11 *Ibid.*, 6052 f. 139, E. Haldane to her mother, 26.6.12.

12 *Ibid.*, 6020 f. 32, N. Roberts to E. Haldane, 14.3.07; *History of the Great War, Medical Services General History*, vol. I. (London 1921), ed. Major-General Sir W.G. MacPherson, p. 35. The roll numbered 469 in 1913. In that year members were classified under three heads:

those approved by the Nursing Board as suitable for employment, those considered suitable to supplement the first class if emergency arose, and those no longer deemed employable. Although in September 1914 there were still 337 names on the roll, the Army Nursing Reserve's committee ceased to meet after January 1913.

13 Haldane MSS, 6011 f. 58, R.B. Haldane to E. Haldane, 14.4.08.

14 *British Journal of Nursing*, 23.10.09, p. 333; 20.11.09, p. 420; *Nursing Times* 4.11.11. p. 981; 25.11.11, pp. 1055–6.

15 *Nursing Times*, 7.12.07, p. 1087; *Nursing Mirror*, 31.10.08, pp. 71–2; 28.11.08, p. 133; Haldane MSS 6020 f. 117, Keogh to E. Haldane, 29.10.07; 6021 f. 32, Keogh to E. Haldane, 17.2.09.

16 Haldane MSS, 6020 f. 117, Keogh to E. Haldane 29.10.07; *British Journal of Nursing*, 30.1.09, p. 81.

17 *Nursing Mirror*, 27.2.09, p. 329; 19.2.10, p. 338; MacPherson, *op. cit.*, p. 36.

18 *Nursing Mirror*, 20.3.09, p. 382.

19 *British Journal of Nursing*, 21.8.09, p. 152.

20 *Nursing Mirror*, 26.6.09, p. 199; 11.7.09, p. 232; 17.7.09, p. 243; 19.2.10, p. 338.

21 *Ibid.* 20.5.11; p. 119, Haldane MSS, 6022 ff. 100–105, N. Roberts to E. Haldane, 20.10.10; RA Add.A. 21/233 f. 120, Queen Alexandra to Sydney Holland, 2.3.11.

22 M. Howard, *The Continental Commitment* (London 1972), pp. 21–2, 41–6; *Hansard's Parliamentary Debates*, 25.2.07, column 1301.

23 Haldane MSS, 6020 ff. 23–4, Keogh to E. Haldane 7.3.07; *Nursing Times*, 22.3.13, p. 297.

24 MacPherson was Senior MO, North China Command, 1904–5; he was attached to the Directorate of Military Operations at the War Office, 1906–10; he was Director of Medical Services, 1st Army, Deputy Director-General, GHQ, and Director of Medical Services, Macedonia, during the First World War.

25 Lt-Col. W.G. MacPherson, 'The Medical Organisation of the Japanese Army', *Journal of the Royal Army Medical Corps* VI, March 1906, pp. 220 and note, 237–9.

26 *Ibid.*, pp. 468–72.

27 A.K. Loyd, ed., *The British Red Cross Society: The County Branches* (London 1917), vol. I, introduction, pp. xxi–xxiii; B. Oliver, *The British Red Cross in Action* (London 1966), p. 191.

28 *The Times*, 18.7.05, p. 8, col.1.

29 Minutes of the Executive of the British Red Cross Society, 11.7.06,

f. 57; 24.7.06, f. 62; 7.11.05, f. 15; WO 32/7152, Red Cross pamphlet, n.d.

30 Haldane MSS, 6020 f. 117, Keogh to E. Haldane, 29.10.07; 6011 f. 38, R.B. Haldane to E. Haldane, 9.11.07; Loyd, *op. cit.*, p. xxx; War Office Circular Memorandum no. 31, 4.5.08, in Red Cross Executive Minutes, 3.3.08, ff. 149–52.

31 *Scheme for the Organisation of Voluntary Aid in England and Wales* (London, HMSO 1909), pp. 4–6, 8.

32 *Ibid.*, p. 4; SJAA Papers, Keogh to Sir Richard Temple, 5.5.08.

33 N. Corbet Fletcher, *The St John Ambulance Association* (London 1931), pp. 43–4; *First Aid*, July 1905, p. 1.

34 *First Aid*, September 1903, p. 56; October 1903, p. 78; April 1904, p. 155; December 1906, p. 88; Corbet Fletcher, *op. cit.*, p. 43; *First Aid*, April 1907, p. 160.

35 *Nursing Times*, 28.7.06, p. 615; Haldane MSS, 6019 f. 131, Sidney Browne to E. Haldane, 11.8.06; *Nursing Mirror*, 6.4.07 p. 1.

36 *First Aid*, May 1907, p. 161; April 1908, p. 157; September 1908, p. 45; MacPherson, *Medical Services*, p. 30.

37 Order of St John of Jerusalem, *Report of the Chapter General* for 1908, pp. xix–xx; Haldane MSS, 6021 f. 38, Sir H. Perrott to E. Haldane, 20.2.09; 6050 f. 59, E. Haldane to her mother, 25.2.09; 6050 f. 93, the same, 19.3.09.

38 Haldane MSS, 6050 f. 97, E. Haldane to her mother, 20.3.09.

39 *First Aid*, August 1908, p. 19; I. Ward, *F.A.N.Y. Invicta* (London 1955), pp. 21–4; *First Aid*, August 1908, p. 19; *British Journal of Nursing*, 3.7.09, p. 13; *Nursing Mirror*, 17.9.10, p. 373; H. Popham, *F.A.N.Y. The Story of the Women's Transport Service 1907–14* (London 1984), chs. 1 and 2.

40 *British Journal of Nursing*, 13.3.09, p. 209; *First Aid*, March 1909, p. 129.

41 Haldane MSS 6021 ff. 82–5, illegible signature (Lady Maule?) to E. Haldane, 19.4.09.

42 *Ibid.*, 6021 ff. 43–6, Keogh to E. Haldane, 12.3.09; ff. 53–8, Keogh to E. Haldane, 22.3.09; ff. 86–8, the same, 20.4.09.

43 S. Hynes, *The Edwardian Turn of Mind* (Princeton and London 1968), pp. 45–6; Major-General Sir F. Maurice, *Haldane 1856–1915* (London 1937), pp. 235–6; Esher MSS, 2/12, Journal, 3.2.09.

44 *Nursing Mirror*, 20.3.09, p. 381.

45 *B.R.C.S. Devonshire Branch: Devonshire Voluntary Aid Organisation, A Handbook for Workers*, by J.S.C. Davis, County Director (Exeter 1910), p. 8; SJAA papers, Darvil Smith to Temple, 12.11.10; *First*

Aid, August 1912, p. 37; July 1913, p. 19; *Red Cross*, January 1914, p. 4; March 1914, pp. 68, 73.

46 Sources for figures: Red Cross Executive Minutes; SJAA papers; War Office circulars preserved by both agencies; *First Aid*.

47 *Army List* for 1912; E. Haldane, *The British Nurse in Peace and War* (London 1923), p. 187.

48 Red Cross Executive Minutes, 3.8.10, ff. 28–9; *Gloucester Branch of the B.R.C.S: Notes on Raising Voluntary Aid Detachments* (Gloucester 1910) by Capt. Colchester-Wemyss, p. 7.

49 SJAA *Report* for 1910, pp. 14–15, 45–6; Loyd, *op. cit.*, pp. xlvii, lxi; SJAA papers, A.M.D. 3, 29.2.12, statistics on VADs.

50 SJAA papers, Minutes of War Office Advisory Committee on Voluntary Aid, 12.7.10; Red Cross Executive Minutes, 6.6.11, ff. 87–91; 4.7.11, ff. 95–6; 3.10.11, ff. 103–4.

51 *Scheme for the Organisation . . .* , p. 3; SJAA papers, War Office circular 10.1.10; Minutes of Advisory Committee on Voluntary Aid, 12.7.10.

52 *First Aid*, August 1912, p. 34.

53 *Ibid.*, June 1912, p. 205; P.C. Gabbett, *Manual for Women VADs* (Bristol and London 1912), p. 26.

54 *Nursing Times*, 21.1.11, p. 46; SJAB, *Report of the Chief Commissioner*, 1911, p. 290; SJAA *Territorial Branch Report*, 1911, p. 42; 1912, p. 38; 1913, p. 66.

55 *First Aid*, August 1912, p. 34; Imperial War Museum Sound Records, 514.08 p. 3, Daisy Colnett Spickett.

56 Davis, *Devonshire Branch*, p. 10; *British Journal of Nursing*, 9.10.9, p. 294. James Cantlie was Surgeon at Charing Cross Hospital from 1887, a Knight of Grace of the Order of St John of Jerusalem, Surgeon Commandant of the Volunteer Medical Staff Corps 1885–8, Hon. Col. of the 1st London Division, Territorial RAMC, Commandant No. 1 VAD London, 1909–22, and member of the BRCS Council.

57 Red Cross Executive Minutes, 4.10.10, f. 48; *First Aid*, August 1912, p. 34; SJAA *Report* for 1910, pp. 14–15, 46; *First Aid*, May 1912, p. 187; August 1912, p. 34; British Red Cross Society Oxfordshire, *Report*, 12.6.14, p. 2.

58 Haldane MSS 6022 f. 75, Ward to Territorial Force Secretaries (WO Circular) 17.6.10; *First Aid*, March 1914, p. 171; Imperial War Museum, BRCS 8/4, J.R. Taylor, Commandant Kent 44, 'Red Cross Camp Journal', pp. 7–8; *Red Cross*, April 1914, pp. 125–6; Red Cross Executive Minutes, 16.12.12, ff. 192–3.

59 SJAB, *Report of the Central Executive Council* for 1912, pp. 25–6; *Red Cross*, March 1914, p. 72; *British Journal of Nursing*, 9.10.09, p. 294.

60 *First Aid*, August 1911, p. 24; *Red Cross*, February 1914, pp. 55–6; *First Aid*, June 1913, p. 234; April 1914, p. 192.

61 SJAB, *Report of a Conference of Nursing Officers*, 16.4.13, p. 26.

62 Davis, *Devonshire Branch*, p. 8.

63 BRCS Oxfordshire, *Report* for 1910, pp. 6, 13; Report for 1911, pp. 2–3; Advisory Sub-Committee Minutes, 14.1.14, p. 4, in Red Cross Executive Minutes 19.1.14. ff. 5–6.

64 *First Aid*, November 1913, p. 98; Gabbett, *op. cit.*, pp. 30–2. J. Cantlie, *British Red Cross Society: Training Manual No. 3* (London 1911), pp. 15–16, 35.

65 *First Aid*, August 1912, p. 34; *ibid.*, November 1913, p. 98; *Red Cross*, January 1914, p. 13; Red Cross Executive Minutes 16.12.12, f. 193; *First Aid*, June 1913, p. 235; October 1913, pp. 71–2.

66 Davis, *Devonshire Branch*, p. 1; SJAA papers, AMD3, Lt-Col. E. Eckersley to Secretary BRCS, 2.3.11.

67 Haldane MSS, 6024 ff. 159–66, Memorandum, probably by Lady Tullibardine, 28.7.14; *Nursing Mirror*, 29.7.11, p. 285; *Nursing Times*, 23.12.11, p. 1173.

68 Haldane MSS, 6023 f. 9, Lady Tullibardine to E. Haldane, 8.2.11; Loyd, *op. cit.*, p. xliii; *First Aid*, July 1913, p. 14; Red Cross Executive Minutes, 15.6.10, f 9; 3.8.10, f. 20.

69 SJAA papers, Perrott to Temple, 12.1.10; Temple memorandum, 22.3.10; SJAA *Report* for 1910, pp. 14–15, 45–6; Loyd, *op. cit.*, pp. xlvii, lxi; *First Aid*, June 1914, p. 236.

70 SJAA *Territorial Branch Report* 1912, p. 38; Esher MSS 6/3, Princess Christian to Esher, 18.12.12; *First Aid*, March 1913, p. 173.

71 *First Aid*, January 1913, p. 132; February 1913, p. 151; Oliver, *op. cit.*, p. 238.

72 *First Aid*, May 1911, p. 172; *British Journal of Nursing*, 8.3.13, p. 196; 15.3.13, p. 216; SJAA *Territorial Branch Report* 1910, p. 48; *First Aid*, May 1912, p. 188; Katharine Furse, *Hearts and Pomegranates* (London 1940), pp. 291–2; Advisory Sub-Committee Minutes, 1.4.14, with Red Cross Executive Minutes 6.4.14, f. 21.

73 *First Aid*, November 1913, p. 93.

74 *First Aid*, May 1912, p. 187; July 1912, p. 13; December 1913, p. 117; *Red Cross*, May 1914, p. 163; *Nursing Times*, 14.3.14, p. 338.

75 *First Aid*, August 1912, p. 33; November 1913, p. 94; *Nursing*

Times, 23.12.11, p. 1173; 28.2.14, p. 273; 18.7.14, p. 916.

76 Haldane MSS 6024 ff. 159–66, Memorandum, probably Lady Tullibardine, 28.7.14; Davis, *Devonshire Branch*, p. 12; Mary L. Longstaff, *Nine Years for the Red Cross* (privately printed 1922), pp. 13, 25 (at Red Cross Archive, Barnett Hill, Surrey); May Cannan, 'Recollections of a British Red Cross VAD No. 12, Oxford University, 26.3.11–24.4.19', p. 10 typescript, October 1971 (Red Cross Archive; and Imperial War Museum P. 360).

77 Haldane MSS, 6024 ff. 159–60, Memorandum, probably Lady Tullibardine, 28.7.14; Red Cross Executive Minutes 5.4.10, f. 3; Longstaff, *op. cit.*, pp. 14–15.

78 Esher MSS 19/3, 9.2.12, Sandwith to Esher; *First Aid*, May 1912, p. 187; Longstaff, *op. cit.*, p. 11; *First Aid*, November 1913, pp. 94–6; November 1912, p. 94; August 1913, p. 34.

79 *First Aid*, November 1912, p. 94.

80 On 15.1.18 the Chairman of the Red Cross Executive wrote to Bodley's Librarian, Oxford University, to say that Loyd's *British Red Cross Society: the County Branches*, vol. 1, had been 'issued without authority'; Loyd's introduction was highly controversial and might prejudice the joint war work of the Red Cross and St John. Bodley's Librarian promised to keep the book out of circulation 'till well after the war': see letters attached to the copy in the Radcliffe Science Library, Oxford University. No further volumes of the work were published. Neither the Red Cross nor the SJAA archives are able to throw any further light on this incident.

81 Esher MSS 19/3, Duchess of Montrose to Esher, 24.4.12; Lt-Col. A.C. Yate, 'The War Office Voluntary Aid Scheme, 1909', *National Defence*, August 1910, p. 385.

82 *First Aid*, March 1912, p. 146; April 1912, pp. 167–8; Esher MSS 19/3, Treves to Esher, 21.4.12; Esher to Queen Alexandra, 18.4.12, 20.4.12; Duchess of Montrose to Esher, 24.4.12.

83 Haldane MSS, 6023 f. 131, S. Browne to E. Haldane, 14.6.12.

84 *First Aid*, January 1913, p. 134.

85 Red Cross Executive Minutes, 15.7.08, f. 118; SJAA papers, AMD3, Ward to Secretaries Territorial Force Associations, 31.12.10; Red Cross Executive Minutes 21.10.12, f. 185, reproducing WO Circular Memorandum 410, 2.7.12.

86 SJAA papers, Ward to Esher, 13.1.13.

87 *First Aid*, December 1912, pp. 110–11; January 1913, pp. 133–4; November 1912, p. 95.

88 *First Aid*, December 1913, pp. 111–12; March 1914, pp. 174–5.

89 MacPherson, *op. cit.*, pp. 32–3; Loyd, *op. cit.*, p. lx; J. Magill, *The Red Cross, the Idea and its Development* (London 1926), p. 50.

90 MacPherson, *Medical Services*, p. 101.

91 E. Haldane, *op. cit.*, pp. 187, 266; Oliver, *op. cit.*, p. 239.

92 *Reports by the Joint War Finance Committee of the British Red Cross Society and the Order of St John of Jerusalem in England on Voluntary Aid rendered to the Sick and Wounded at home and abroad and to British Prisoners of War 1914–1919* (London, HMSO 1921), p. 194; Oliver, *op. cit.*, p. 240.

93 Oliver, *op. cit.*, p. 239.

94 Olive Dent, *A VAD in France* (London 1917), p. 15.

CHAPTER 10 EMANCIPATION OR MILITARISATION?

1 For an account of the diverse pressures on the British political system in this period, see: G. Dangerfield, *The Strange Death of Liberal England* (London 1935); K.D. Browne, ed., *Essays in Anti-Labour History* (London 1974) P. Kennedy and A.J. Nicholls, eds., *Nationalist and Racialist Movements in Britain and Germany before 1914* (London 1981).

2 On the National Service League, see A. Summers, 'Militarism in Britain before the Great War', *History Workshop Journal*, 2, 1976, pp. 104–23.

3 For a history of the anti-suffrage movement, see B. Harrison, *Separate Spheres* (London 1978).

4 *Votes for Women*, 12.1.12, p. 238; 19.1.12, p. 255.

5 *British Journal of Nursing*, 21.8.09, p. 151.

6 Haldane MSS, 6045 f. 199, Elizabeth Haldane, draft speech.

7 *Nursing Mirror*, 30.5.08, pp. 138–9; 20.3.09, p. 381; 22.7.11, p. 267.

8 *Votes for Women*, 12.1.12, p. 238.

9 *First Aid*, July 1898, p. 9; February 1899, p. 59; May 1899, p. 87; April 1907, p. 160.

10 *Anti-Suffrage Review*, June 1910, p. 1; January 1911, p. 1; December 1908, p. 1. Several members of the Oxford University branch of the Red Cross were also members of their local NLOWS branch: see the latter's Report for 1910–11, and May Wedderburn Cannan, *Grey Ghosts and Voices* (Kineton 1976).

11 *Nursing Times*, 10.2.06, p. 109; Harrison, *op. cit.*, pp. 75, 104, 120.

12 *Anti-Suffrage Review*, December 1912, p. 294; January 1914, p. 272.

13 Haldane MSS 6023 ff. 105–6, V. Markham to Elizabeth Haldane, 6.3.12.

14 Lady Frances Balfour, *Dr Elsie Inglis* (London 1920), pp. 32–3. Dr Inglis formed and led the Scottish Women's Hospital Unit which served in Serbia and Russia in the First World War.

15 Haldane MSS, 6050 f. 131, E. Haldane to her mother, 1.4.09; *British Journal of Nursing*, 21.8.09, pp. 151–3.

16 The term 'pro-Boer' could be used well after the war as a general accusation of anti-patriotism. See A. Summers, 'The Character of Edwardian Nationalism: Three Popular Leagues', in Kennedy and Nicholls, *op. cit.*, p. 79.

17 Haldane MSS, 6045 f. 211, E. Haldane, draft speech.

18 I. Ward, *F.A.N.Y. Invicta* (London 1955), pp. 26, 34–5.

19 *Ibid.*, pp. 30, 37.

20 *National Defence*, March 1909, p. 501.

21 *Englishwoman's Review*, 15.10.09. p. 271; *Aerial Observer*, 1.10.10, pp. 2–3.

22 *Nation in Arms*, January 1911, p. 26.

23 *The Church Nursing and Ambulance Brigade for Women and Girls*, pamphlet, n.d., c. 1912, in SJAA papers.

24 Anthony Wood (D. Chapman), 'With Phil and Jim and Friends', *Oxford Mail*, 2.2.76; 'How militant Christians became military cadets', *Oxford Mail*, 10.3.76.

25 *The Church Nursing and Ambulance Brigade*; SJAA papers, Perrott to Temple, 15.7.09.

26 J. Springhall, *Youth, Empire and Society* (London 1977), p. 131; p. 133, fn. 10.

27 R. Kerr, *The Story of the Girl Guides* (London 1932), pp. 29–31.

28 *Ibid.*, pp. 39, 50, 48.

29 *Ibid.*, p. 73.

30 *Ibid.*, pp. 93–4, 96.

31 *Ibid.*, pp. 77–8.

32 Red Cross Executive Minutes, 4.10.10, f. 48; SJAA papers, Agenda for the Advisory Committee on Voluntary Aid, 29.2.12.

33 *Red Cross*, May 1914, p. 160; Red Cross Executive Minutes, 4.10.10, f. 48; 6.12.10, f. 53; 3.10.11, ff. 102–3; *Red Cross*, February 1914, p. 57.

34 Imperial War Museum Women's Collection, P 360, May Cannan, 'Recollections of a British Red Cross VAD No. 12, Oxford University, 26.3.11–24.4.19', p. 22.

35 *The Red Cross in Gloucestershire during the War* (Gloucester 1919), p. 16; Balfour, *op. cit.*, pp. 32–3.

36 Cannan, *Grey Ghosts and Voices*, p. 68.

37 IWM Department of Printed Books, typescript, Grace McDougal (née Ashley-Smith), 'Five Years with the Allies', p. 10.

38 *Nursing Times*, 25.7.14, p. 944; K. Furse, *Hearts and Pomegranates* (London 1940), pp. 287, 293, 296.

39 Ward, *op. cit.*, pp. 35–6; P. Beauchamp, *Fanny Went to War* (London 1940), p. 7.

40 E.S. Pankhurst, *The Suffragette Movement* (London 1931), pp. 265–6.

41 *Votes for Women*, 4.2.10, p. 291; 25.3.10, p. 409; 21.10.10, p. 41; 28.3.13, p. 361.

42 *The Vote*, 11.11.09, p. 32; 5.8.11, p. 188; 26.10.12, p. 456; 6.6.13, p. 93.

43 *Votes for Women*, 9.6.11, p. 595; *The Common Cause*, 30.5.13, pp. 115–16.

44 *The Vote*, 25.5.12, p. 92; *Votes for Women*, 8.11.12, p. 83; 30.5.13, p. 506.

45 Mrs St Clair Stobart, *War and Women* (London 1913), p. 195; *Nursing Times*, 1.3.13, p. 228.

46 Stobart, *op. cit.*, p. 83.

47 *Ibid.*, pp. xiii–xiv, 233.

48 *Red Cross*, March 1914, p. 73.

49 Furse, *op. cit.*, p. 298. On Katharine Furse's war and post-war career, see *DNB*. She was for ten years Director of the World Association of Girl Guides and Girl Scouts.

50 Lady Angela Forbes, *Memories and Base Details* (London 1921), p. 153.

51 G. McDougal, 'Five Years with the Allies', pp. 17–18.

52 Furse, *op. cit.*, p. 357.

53 See M. Pugh, 'Politicians and the Woman's Vote 1914–18', *History* 59, 1974, pp. 358–74.

54 Beauchamp, *op. cit.*, p. 5.

55 *Votes for Women*, 12.3.09, p. 425.

56 See Cannan, *Grey Ghosts and Voices*; Vera Brittain, *Testament of Youth* (London 1933).

57 Grace McDougall, *The Golden Bowl* (London 1926), pp. 51–2.

58 Cannan, *Grey Ghosts and Voices*, p. 175.

59 G. Braybon, *Women Workers in the First World War* (London 1981), pp. 179–84.

60 R. White, 'Some Political Influences surrounding the Nurses' Registration Act 1919 in the United Kingdom', *Journal of Advanced Nursing* I, May 1976, pp. 211–12, 215.

61 B. Abel-Smith, *A History of the Nursing Profession* (London 1960), pp. 82, 112–14.

62 IWM Sound Records, 514.08, Daisy Colnett Spickett, pp. 2–3.

APPENDIX: THE NURSING OF OFFICERS

1 *Report of the Select Committee on the Army before Sebastopol*, PP 1854–5 IX, Part III, p. 184, q.19969.

2 WO 163/6 p. 167, Army Council Memorandum, 24.11.02; WO 163/4B p. 25, Proceedings of the War Office Council, 8.1.96; *Illustrated London News* 12.11.59, p. 476.

3 MR, LP 51/28, Muir to Longmore 20.6.78.

4 W. Morrison, 'Glimpses of Life from Within from 1860 to 1895', *Journal of the Royal Army Medical Corps* 121, 1, 1975, pp. 46–7.

5 *The Victoria Hospital, Cairo*. Report of the Egyptian Relief Fund, by Viscountess Strangford and Dr Herbert Sieveking (London 1883), pp. 6, 9–10.

6 Wantage Papers on Egypt, C. Munro to Loyd-Lindsay and Mrs Munro to Loyd-Lindsay, 19.4.85.

7 WO 33/41 piece 941, ff. 632–3, Reports by Heads of Departments, etc., on the Recommendations of the Committee on Army Hospital Services 1883.

8 RA 017 f. 48, Loyd Lindsay to Lady Southampton 11.10.82.

9 WO 163/6 p. 167, Army Council Memorandum, 24.11.02; p. 170, Appendix A, Memorandum, 24.11.02; p. 170, Appendix A, Memorandum of Inspector-General of Fortifications 17.11.02.

10 See above, Chapter 4.

11 *The Navy and Army Illustrated*, 3, 1896–7, pp. 208–9.

A NOTE ON SOURCES

1 Surgeon-General W. Munro, *Records of Service and Campaigning in Many Lands* (London 1887), vol. II, p. 408, fn.

2 For example, the bibliography to J.W. Warburton's unpublished PhD thesis, 'A Medical History of the British Expeditionary Force in the East 1854–56', Keele University 1982, lists several collections of military MOs' papers in the author's private possession

3 MR Docs 1901, Major Rundle's Collection on Netley, Col. J. Hyatt to L. Colebrook 26 May 1950.

4 M. Baly's *Florence Nightingale and the Nursing Legacy* (London 1986), is an important contribution to the demystification of the nineteenth century history of the Nightingale Training School; the Royal College of Nursing's History of Nursing Group, with its printed *Bulletin*, is encouraging research into all periods of British nursing history.

BIBLIOGRAPHY

1 ARCHIVES

London, Public Record Office

CAB 17	Correspondence and Miscellaneous Papers.
CAB 18	Miscellaneous Volumes.
WO 1	In-letters.
WO 6	Out-letters, Secretary of State.
WO 25	Registers, various.
WO 30	Miscellanea.
WO 32	Registered Papers, General Series.
WO 33	Reports and Miscellaneous Papers.
WO 43	Selected Correspondence.
WO 105	Roberts Papers.
WO 108	South African War Papers.
WO 123	Army Circulars, Memoranda and Orders.
WO 139	Index to Correspondence.
WO 145/1	Royal Red Cross, register of awards 1883–1928.
WO 163	Proceedings of War Office Council and Army Council.

London, India Office Library

L/MIL/7/11316 Correspondence on the formation of the Indian Army Nursing Service.

London, Royal Army Medical Corps Library, Muniment Room

(These documents have recently been removed to the Royal Army Medical Corps Museum, Aldershot):

Longmore Papers.

801/9   Letters of Florence Nightingale to Col. Clark Kennedy, facsimiles.

801/1   Medical Staff Corps Defaulters' Book, 1864–74.

Aldershot, Queen Alexandra's Royal Army Nursing Corps Museum

Dame Maud Piper McCarthy, ms on military nursing, n.d., presumably inter-war.

London, Imperial War Museum

Women's Collection P. 360 May Cannan, 'Recollections of a British Red Cross VAD No. 12, Oxford University, 26.3.11 – 24.4.19.'

Department of Printed Books, Typescript, Grace McDougal (née Ashley-Smith), 'Five Years with the Allies'.

BRCS 8/4.
Sound Recordings 514.08.

London, British Library Additional Manuscripts

Layard Papers.
Nightingale Papers.

London, Greater London Record Office

Nightingale Collection.
Nightingale Training School records.

Cambridge, Churchill College

Esher Papers.

Edinburgh, National Library of Scotland

Haldane Papers.

Lockinge, Wantage

(Collection recently transferred to British Red Cross Society Archive, Barnett Hill, Surrey)

Wantage Papers.

Barnet Hill, Surrey, British Red Cross Society Archive

Minutes of the Executive, 1906–14.

London, Museum of the Order of St John of Jerusalem:

St John's Ambulance Association, Correspondence 1908–14.

Windsor, the Royal Archive

RA E25
RA F1
RA 017
RA R53
RA Add. A.21/233

2 OFFICAL ARMY PUBLICATIONS

(Place of publication London unless otherwise stated.)

General Regulations and Orders for the Army, 1811.

The Queen's Regulations and Orders for the Army, 1859.

Regulations for the Duties of Inspectors-General and Deputy-Inspectors-General of Hospitals, 1859.

The Queen's Regulations and Orders for the Army, 1868.

Regulations for the Army Hospital Corps, 1875.

Proceedings of a Court of Inquiry appointed to inquire into Complaints against the Men of the Army Hospital Corps employed in the War in South Africa, 1882.

Regulations for the Medical Department of Her Majesty's Army, 1885.

Regulations for the Army Nursing Service, 1888.

Manual for the Medical Staff Corps, 1889.

Regulations for the Army Medical Services, 1894.

Manual for the Medical Staff Corps, 1894.

Regulations, Queen Alexandra's Imperial Military Nursing Service, 1902.

Standing Orders for the Royal Army Medical Corps and Queen Alexandra's Imperial Military Nursing Service, 1903.

Regulations, Queen Alexandra's Imperial Military Nursing Service, 1904.

Standing Orders for the Royal Army Medical Corps and Queen Alexandra's Imperial Military Nursing Service, 1907.

Regulations for Admission to Queen Alexandra's Imperial Military Nursing Service, 1910.

Report of the Army Medical Department, 1861–72.

J.M. Bannatyne, *Royal Warrants, Circulars, General Orders and Memoranda* (Glasgow 1864).

Army List 1861–1914.

Surgeon-General W.D. Wilson, *Report on the Medical Arrangements in the South African War* (1904).

Scheme for the Organisation of Voluntary Aid in England and Wales, 1909.

Scheme for the Organisation of Voluntary Aid in England and Wales, 1910.

Lt-Col. R.J.S. Simpson, *The Medical History of the War in South Africa* (1911).

W. Johnston and H.A. Howell, *Roll of Commissioned Officers in the Medical Service of the British Army, 1727–1898* (Aberdeen 1917).

History of the Great War: Medical Services General History, vol. 1., ed. Major-General W.G. MacPherson (1921).

3 PARLIAMENTARY PAPERS

Report of the Select Committee on the Army before Sebastopol, 1854–5 IX, parts 1–III.

Report upon the State of the Hospitals of the British Army in the Crimea and Scutari, 1854–5 XXXIII.

Report of the Proceedings of the Sanitary Commissioners dispatched to the Seat of War in the East 1855–6, 1857 IX.

Medical and Surgical History of the British Army which served in Turkey and the Crimea, 1857–8 XXXVIII.

Report of the Commissioners appointed to enquire into the Regulations affecting the Sanitary Condition of the Army, the Organisation of Military Hospitals, and the Treatment of the Sick and Wounded, 1857–8 XVIII.

Report on the Site of the Royal Victoria Hospital, near Netley Abbey, 1857–8 XIX.

Report to the Secretary of State for War descriptive of the Herbert Hospital at Woolwich, by Douglas Galton, Assistant Under-Secretary of State for War, 1865 XXVI.

Report of a Committee appointed by the Secretary of State for War to inquire into the Organisation of the Army Hospital Corps, Hospital Management and Nursing in the Field, and the Sea Transport of Sick and Wounded, 1883 XVI.

Report of the Royal Commission appointed to consider and report upon the Care and Treatment of the Sick and Wounded during the South African Campaign, 1901 XXIX.

Report of the Committee appointed by the Secretary of State to consider the reorganisation of the Army Medical Services, 1902 X.

Report of the Committee appointed by the Secretary of State to consider the reorganisation of the Army and Indian Nursing Service, 1902 X.

Report of the Royal Commission on the War in South Africa, 1904 XLI.

4 OTHER OFFICIAL PUBLICATIONS

An Act to consolidate and amend the Statute Law of England and Ireland relating to Offences against the Person, 24 and 25 Vict. c. 100.

Hansard's Parliamentary Debates.

5 REPORTS, ETC., OF SOCIETIES

St John's House, Queen Square, Westminster, London:

Rules of the Training Institution for Nurses for Hospitals, Families and the Poor, 1855.

Order of St John of Jerusalem in England, St John's Gate, Clerkenwell, London:

The Statutes of the Sovereign and Illustrious Order of St John of Jerusalem, Anglia, 1864.

First Annual Report of the Order of St John of Jerusalem in Anglia, 1868.

Memoir of the Bailiwick of Brandenburg of the Order of St John of Jerusalem, 1868.

Nurses for the Sick Poor, Report of the Committee of the Order of St John of Jerusalem in England, 1873.

Aid to the Injured, Proceedings of a Public Meeting convened by the Order of St John of Jerusalem, 6 February 1878.

The Order of St John of Jerusalem, A Brief Notice of its Foundation and Constitution and of its objects in England, 1878.

First Aid to the Injured, St John's Ambulance Association Syllabus of Instruction, 1879.

Annual Report of the Secretary General, 1869, 1870.

Report of the Chapter presented to the Chapter-General of the Order of St John of Jerusalem in England, 1870–81; 1908.

Ambulance Department, Reports of the Central Executive Committee, 1879.

St John's Ambulance Association, Reports 1880–6; 1910.

St John's Ambulance Association, Territorial Branch, Reports 1911–13.

St John's Ambulance Brigade, *Report of the Commissioner on the Mobilisation of the Brigade for Service in South Africa, 1899–1900*, 1900.

St John's Ambulance Brigade, *Report of the Chief Commissioner*, 1911.

St John's Ambulance Brigade, *Report of the Central Executive Council for 1912*.

St John's Ambulance Brigade, *Report of a Conference of Nursing Officers*, 16 April 1913.

St John's Ambulance Association, press cuttings collection.

National Society for Aid to the Sick and Wounded in War/British Red Cross Society:

Questions on the Operations of the British National Society for Aid to the Sick and Wounded in War, 1871.

Report of the British National Society for Aid to the Sick and Wounded in War, 18th January 1886.

Report by the Central British Red Cross Committee on Voluntary Organisations in aid of sick and wounded during the South African War, 1902.

Reports by the Joint War Finance Committee of the British Red Cross Society and the Order of St John of Jerusalem in England on Voluntary Aid rendered to the Sick and Wounded at home and abroad and to British Prisoners of War 1914–19, 1921.

British Red Cross Society Devonshire Branch, *Devonshire Voluntary Aid Organisation*, A Handbook for Workers, by J.S.C. Davis (Exeter 1910).

British Red Cross Society Gloucester Branch, *Notes on Raising Voluntary Aid Detachments*, by Capt. Colchester Wemyss (Gloucester 1910).

The Red Cross in Gloucestershire during the War (Gloucester 1919).

Viscountess Strangford, *Report on the Bulgarian Peasant Relief Fund* (London 1877).

Viscountess Strangford and Dr Herbert Sieveking, *The Victoria Hospital, Cairo*, Report of the Egyptian Relief Fund (London 1883).

Stafford House, London:

Report and Record of the Operations of the Stafford House Committee for the Relief of Sick and Wounded Turkish Soldiers, 1879.

Report of the Stafford House South African Aid Committee, 1880.

Royal British Nurses' Association:

The British Nurses' Association: What the British Nurses' Association is, and what it seeks to do for Nurses (London 1888).

The Battle of the Nurses: A full Verbatim Report from official sources of the actual proceedings before the Privy Council, on the application of the Royal British Nurses' Association for a Charter of Incorporation (London 1893).

The Church Nursing and Ambulance Brigade for Women and Girls:

Report, n.d., London, *c.* 1912.

355

6 PERIODICALS AND NEWSPAPERS

Anti-Suffrage Review.
British Journal of Nursing.
British Medical Journal.
Bulletin Internationale de la Croix-Rouge.
Common Cause.
Englishwoman's Review.
First Aid.
Guardian.
Hospital Gazette and Students' Journal.
Hospital 'Nursing Mirror' (contd as *Hospital 'Nursing Section'*).
Illustrated London News.
Illustrated Naval and Military Magazine.
Lancet.
League News.
London Gazette.
Medical Times and Gazette.
Nation in Arms.
National Defence.
Navy and Army Illustrated.
Nurses' Journal.
Nursing Mirror.
Nursing News.
Nursing Notes.
Nursing Record.
Nursing Times.
Punch.
The Queen.
Red Cross.
The Times.
Victoria Magazine.
Volunteer Rifleman's Magazine.
The Vote.
Votes for Women.
Woman's Herald.

7 UNPUBLISHED THESES

M.E. Baly, 'The Influence of the Nightingale Fund from 1855 to 1914 on the Development of Nursing', PhD, London University 1984.

W.C. Dowling, 'The Ladies' Sanitary Association and the Origins of the Health Visiting Service', MA London University 1963.

D.F. Mackay, 'The Influence of the Italian Risorgimento on British Public Opinion, 1859–61', D. Phil, Oxford University 1959.

J.E. Prince, 'Florence Nightingale's Reform of Nursing 1860–1887', PhD, London School of Economics 1982.

M. Trustram, 'Marriage and the Victorian Army at Home; the Regulation of Soldiers' relationships with women, and the Treatment of Soldiers' Wives', D Phil Bristol University 1981.

J.W. Warburton 'A Medical History of the British Expeditionary Force in the East 1854–56', PhD, Keele University 1982.

8 BOOKS AND PAMPHLETS PUBLISHED BEFORE 1920

D. Bagot, *Shadows of the War* (London 1900).

V. Hicks Beach, *The Colonial Nursing Association* (London 1914).

M. Mostyn Bird, *The Errand of Mercy* (London 1913).

Surgeon-Major-General A.F. Bradshaw, *Catherine Grace Loch R.R.C., A Memoir* (London 1905).

C. Bryce, *England and France before Sebastopol* (London 1857).

W. Burdett-Coutts, *The Sick and Wounded in South Africa* (London 1901).

E.T. Cook, *The Life of Florence Nightingale* (London 1913) 2 vols.

C. Kinloch Cooke *A Memoir of H.R.H. Princess Mary Adelaide, Duchess of Teck* (London 1900) 2 vols.

Mrs Craven, *The Life of Lady Georgiana Fullerton* (London 1888).

E.D., *Recollections of a Nurse* (London 1889).

O. Dent, *A VAD in France* (London 1917).

G. Douglas and G. Dalhousie Ramsay, eds., *The Panmure Papers* (London 1908) 2 vols.

Sister M.A. Doyle, *Memories of the Crimea* (London 1897).

J.H. Dunant, *Un Souvenir de Solferino* (Geneva 1862).

Surgeon-Major G.J.H. Evatt, *Army Medical Organisation* (London 1883). *Notes on the Interior Economy of Army Hospitals in India* (Lahore 1877). *A Proposal to form a corps of Volunteer Female Nurses for service in the Army Hospitals in the Field, with Suggestions as to the Incorporation of the Nursing Profession* (Woolwich 1885).

R. Few, *A History of St John's House* (London 1884).

F.E. Fremantle, *Impressions of a Doctor in Khaki* (London 1901).

J. Furley, *In Peace and War* (London 1905).

P.C. Gabbett, *Manual for Women's VADs* (Bristol and London 1912).

W.L.C. von der Goltz, *The Nation in Arms* (London 1906).

M. Goodman, *Experiences of an English Sister of Mercy* (London 1862).

Rev. C.J. Hardy, *The Five Talents of Women* (London 1888).

T.H. Hayhurst, *A History and Some Records of the Volunteer Movement* (Bury and Manchester 1887).

E. Hobhouse, *The Brunt of the War and Where it Fell* (London 1902).

J.A. Hobson, *The Psychology of Jingoism* (London 1901).

Rev. W.F. Hobson, *Catharine Leslie Hobson, Lady-Nurse, Crimean War, and her Life* (London 1888).

G.J. Holyoake, *Bygones Worth Remembering* (London 1905) 2 vols.

W.S. Inder, *On Active Service with the St John's Ambulance Brigade in the South African War, 1899–1902* (Kendal 1903).

W. Lamont, *Volunteer Memories* (Greenock 1911).

E.C. Laurence, *A Nurse's Life in War and Peace* (London 1912).

A.K. Loyd, ed., *The British Red Cross Society: the County Branches* (London 1917).

R. Loyd-Lindsay, *On Aid to the Sick and Wounded in War* (privately printed, London 1871).

W. Maccormac, *Notes and Recollections of an Ambulance Surgeon* (London 1871).

G.H.B. Macleod, *Notes on the Surgery of the War in the Crimea* (London 1858).

W.G. MacPherson, *The Role of the Red Cross Societies in Peace and War* (London 1907).

C. Marsh, *Memorials of Captain Hedley Vicars, 97th Regiment* (London 1856).

S.M. Mitra, *The Life and Letters of Sir John Hall* (London 1911).

H. Morten, *Questions for Women* (London 1899).

Mrs Motherly, *The Servant's Behaviour Book* (London 1859).

G. Moynier and P.L. Appia, *Help for the Sick and Wounded* (London 1870).

Surgeon-General Munro, *Records of Service and Campaigning in Many Lands* (London 1887) 2 vols.

J.N. Murphy, *Terra Incognita* (London 1873).

M. Nicol, *Ismeer, or Smyrna, and its British Hospital in 1855, by a Lady* (London 1856).

Florence Nightingale, *Subsidiary Notes as to the Introduction of Female Nursing into Military Hospitals in Peace and in War* (London 1858).

Memoirs of Margaret Fuller Ossoli (London 1852) 3 vols.

E. Pearson and L. McLaughlin, *Our Adventures during the War of 1870–1* (London 1871) 2 vols. *Service in Servia under the Red Cross* (London 1877).

E.A. Pratt, *Pioneer Women in Victoria's Reign* (London 1897).

E.H. Sieveking, *The Training Institutions for Nurses, and the Workhouses* (London 1849).

J.F. South, *Facts Relating to Hospital Nurses* (London 1857).

Mrs St Clair Stobart, *War and Women* (London 1913).

Viscountess Strangford *Hospital Training for Ladies* (London 1874).

—— *The Soldier's Wife as his Nurse* (London 1880).

Lord Stanmore, *Sidney Herbert, a Memoir* (London 1905) 2 vols.

A.P. Stanley, *Memoirs of Edward and Catherine Stanley* (London 1880).

M. Stanley, *Hospitals and Sisterhoods* (London 1854).

Lady Jessica Sykes, *Side Lights on the War in South Africa* (London 1900).

Frances Margaret Taylor, *Eastern Hospitals and English Nurses by a Lady Volunteer* (London 1856) 2 vols.

Frances Margaret Taylor, *Eastern Hospitals and English Nurses*, 3rd edition (London 1857).

F. Treves, *The Tale of a Field Hospital* (London 1900).

S. Trimmer, *The Economy of Charity* (London 1801) vol. II.

Lord Wantage V.C., K.C.B., A Memoir by his Wife (London 1907).

J. Williams, ed. *the Autobiography of Elizabeth Davis, a Balaklava Nurse* (London 1857) 2 vols.

A. Zimmern, *The Renaissance of Girls' Education* (London 1898).

9 ARTICLES PUBLISHED BEFORE 1920

Anon., 'The Report from the Select Committee on the Army before Sebastopol and the Report on the State of the Hospitals of the British Army in the Crimea and Scutari', *British and Foreign Medico-Chirurgical Review* XVI, 1855, pp. 285–304.

Anon., 'The Employments of Women', *Gentleman's Magazine*, 1855, pp. 488–91.

Anon., 'Maids and Mistresses', *Temple Bar* XI, 1864, pp. 43–51.

Anon., 'Military Reform', *Fraser's Magazine* 74, 1866, pp. 681–97.

Anon., 'The National Rifle Association', *Macmillan's Magazine* XVI, 1867, pp. 177–88.

J. de Bloch, 'The Transvaal War: its lessons in regard to militarism and Army Reorganisation', *Journal of the Royal United Services Institute* XLV, 1901, pp. 1316–44, 1413–51.

H. Brackenbury, 'Philanthropy in War', *Blackwood's Edinburgh Magazine* CXXI, pp. 152–74.

Rev. J.S. Brewer, 'Workhouse Visiting', in Rev. F.D. Maurice, ed., *Lectures to Ladies on Practical Subjects* (Cambridge 1855), pp. 262–83.

Major C. Burgess, 'Recollections of the Red Cross', *Illustrated Naval and Military Magazine*, I, 1884, pp. 412–20.

E.E. Cuthell, 'Nursing in Indian Military Hospitals', *Army and Navy Magazine* XIII, 1886–7, pp. 134–9.

F.C.P., 'The Decoration of the Royal Red Cross', *Illustrated Naval and Military Magazine* I, 1884, pp. 63–6.

Sydney Holland, 'The Civilian Hospitals and the Army Nursing Reserve', *The Hospital 'Nursing Section'*, 10.1.1903, pp. 210–11.

E.M. King, 'The Work of an International Peace Society, and Women's Part in it', *Victoria Magazine* XX, 1872–3, pp. 25–33.

'A Lady', 'Servants *vs.* Mistresses', *Churchman's Family Magazine* VIII, 1866, pp. 543–55.

F. Lees, 'In a Fever Hospital before Metz', *Good Words* 1873, pp. 322–8.

T. Longmore, 'The New Military Weapons and Explosives', *British Medical Journal*, 5.3.1892, pp. 521–2.

—— 'On the Geneva Convention of 1864', *Journal of the Royal United Services Institute* X, 1866, pp. 162–82.

—— 'On the Geneva Convention of 1864, in relation to . . . the late Franco-German War', *Journal of the Royal United Services Institute* XVI, 1873, pp. 206–21.

Lt-Col. W.G. MacPherson, 'The Medical Organisation of the Japanese Army', *Journal of the Royal Army Medical Corps* VI, 1906, pp. 219–50, 467–78.

E. McCaul, 'Some Suggestions for Army Reform', *Nineteenth Century* April 1901, pp. 58–87.

Jessie White Mario, 'Experiences of Ambulances', *Fraser's Magazine* XV, 1877, pp. 768–85.

—— 'Garibaldi in France', *Fraser's Magazine* XVI, 1877, pp. 452–77, 602–18, 720–35.

H. Martineau, 'Nurses Wanted', *Cornhill Magazine* 1865, XI, pp. 409–25.

H. Morten, 'Her Majesty's Nursing Sisters', *Illustrated Naval and Military Magazine* May 1890, pp. 72–8.

F. Nightingale, 'Una and the Lion', *Good Words*, 1.6.1868, pp. 360–6.

E. Pearson and L. McLaughlin, 'Under the Red Cross', *St James's Magazine* n.s. IX, 1872, pp. 120–30.

S. Tytler, 'Girls who won Success', *Atalanta* August 1888, pp. 639–45.

M. Hill Watt, 'Wanted, Ladies at the War Office', *Womanhood* 3, May 1900, pp. 402–5.

Lt-Col. A.C. Yate, 'The War Office Voluntary Aid Scheme, 1909', *National Defence* August 1910, pp. 380–6.

10 BOOKS AND PAMPHLETS PUBLISHED AFTER 1920

B. Abel-Smith, *The Hospitals, 1800–1948* (London 1964).

—— *A History of the Nursing Profession* (London 1960).

Z. Alexander and A. Dewjee, eds., *Wonderful Adventures of Mrs Seacole in Many Lands* (London 1984).

B. Anderson, *Imagined Communities* (London 1983).

D. Anderson, *The Balkan Volunteers* (London 1968).

P.F. Anson, *The Call of the Cloister* (London 1964).

S. Ardener, ed., *Women and Space* (London 1981).

Lady Frances Balfour, *Dr Elsie Inglis* (London 1920).

M.E. Baly, *Florence Nightingale and the Nursing Legacy* (London 1986).

P. Beauchamp, *Fanny Went to War* (London 1940).

E. Bolster, *The Sisters of Mercy in the Crimean War* (Cork 1964).

B. Bond, *War and Society in Europe, 1870–1970* (London 1984).

—— *The Victorian Army and the Staff College 1854–1914* (London 1972).

G. Braybon, *Women Workers in the First World War* (London 1981).

V. Brittain, *Testament of Youth* (London 1933).

W. Brockbank, *The History of Nursing at the M.R.I., 1752–1929* (Manchester 1970).

K.D. Brown, ed., *Essays in Anti-Labour History* (London 1974).

S. Burman, ed., *Fit Work for Women* (London 1979).

H. Burton, *Barbara Bodichon* (London 1949).

May Wedderburn Cannan, *Grey Ghosts and Voices* (Kineton 1976).

N. Cantlie, *A History of the Army Medical Department* (Edinburgh and London 1974) 2 vols.

G. Kitson Clark, *Churchmen and the Condition of England 1832–1885* (London 1973).

L. Colebrook, *Almroth Wright* (London 1954).

H. Cunningham, *The Volunteer Force* (London 1975).

G. Dangerfield, *The Strange Death of Liberal England* (London 1935).

E.A. Daniels, *Jessie White Mario, Risorgimento Revolutionary* (Ohio 1972).

P. Deane and W.A. Cole, *British Economic Growth 1688–1959* (Cambridge 1962).

F.C. Devas, *Mother Magdalen Taylor* (London 1927).

A. Digby, *Pauper Palaces* (London 1978).

J. Donnison, *Midwives and Medical Men* (New York 1977).

R.E. and T.N. Dupuy, *The Encyclopaedia of Military History* (London 1980).

B. Ehrenreich and D. English, *Witches, Midwives and Nurses* (London 1974).

C. Enloe, *Does Khaki Become You?* (London 1983).

N. Corbet Fletcher, *The St John's Ambulance Association* (London 1931).

S. Fletcher, *Feminists and Bureaucrats* (Cambridge 1980).

Lady Angela Forbes, *Memories and Base Details* (London 1921).

J.W. Fortescue, *A History of the British Army* (London 1930).

K. Furse, *Hearts and Pomegranates* (London 1940).

F. Garnett, *Florence Nightingale's Nuns* (New York and London 1961).

E. Haldane, *The British Nurse in Peace and War* (London 1923).

B. Harrison, *Separate Spheres* (London 1978).

A. Hayter, *Mrs Browning* (London 1962).

D. Hewlett, *Elizabeth Barrett Browning* (London 1953).

M. Hill, *The Religious Order* (London 1973).

E. Hobsbawm and T. Ranger, eds., *The Invention of Tradition* (Cambridge 1984).

R.G. Hodgkinson, *The Origins of the National Health Service* (London 1967).

L. Holcombe, *Victorian Ladies at Work* (Newton Abbot 1973).

M.E. Howard, *The Continental Commitment* (London 1972).

—— *The Franco-Prussian War* (London 1960).

—— *Lord Haldane and the Territorial Army* (London 1966).

S. Hynes, *The Edwardian Turn of Mind* (Princeton and London 1968).

K. Jones, *A History of the Mental Health Services* (London 1972).

J. Kamm, *Hope Deferred* (London 1965).

P. Kennedy and A.J. Nicholls eds., *Nationalist and Racialist Movements in Britain and Germany before 1914* (London 1981).

R. Kerr, *The Story of the Girl Guides* (London 1932).

E. King and H. Luke, *The Knights of St John in the British Realm* (London 1967).

J. Langdon-Davies, *The Westminster Hospital 1719–1948* (London 1952).

W.L. Langer, *The Diplomacy of Imperialism 1890–1902* (New York 1951).

C. Lloyd and J.L.S. Coulter, *Medicine and the Navy 1200–1900* (Edinburgh and London 1963) vol. IV.

M.L. Longstaff, *Nine Years for the Red Cross* (privately printed 1922).

J. Luvaas, *The Education of an Army* (Chicago 1964).

G. McDougal, *The Golden Bowl* (London 1926).

C. Maggs, *The Origins of General Nursing* (London 1983).

J. Magill, *The Red Cross, the idea and its development* (London 1926).

J.G. Manton, *Sister Dora* (London 1971).

Major-General Sir F. Maurice, *Haldane 1856–1915* (London 1937).

E.W. Morris, *The London Hospital* (London 1926).

B. Oliver, *The British Red Cross in Action* (London 1966).

E.S. Pankhurst, *The Suffragette Movement* (London 1931).

M.J. Parish, *A History of Immunization* (Edinburgh and London 1965).

M. Pelling, *Cholera, Fever and English Medicine 1825–65* (Oxford 1978).

M.J. Peterson, *The Medical Profession in mid-Victorian London* (Berkeley 1978).

H. Popham, *F.A.N.Y., the Story of the Women's Transport Service 1907–1984* (London 1984).

F.K. Prochaska, *Women and Philanthropy in 19th Century England* (Oxford 1980).

R.G. Richardson, ed., *Nurse Sarah Anne* (London 1977).

J. Rose, *Elizabeth Fry* (London 1980).

A. Rosen, *Rise Up, Women!* (London 1974).

C. Rover, *Women's Suffrage and Party Politics in Britain* (London 1967).

G. Searle, *The Quest for National Efficiency* (1971).

A.R. Skelley, *The Victorian Army at Home* (London and Montreal 1977).

F.B. Smith, *Florence Nightingale, Reputation and Power* (London and Canberra 1982).

W.G. Spencer, *Westminster Hospital* (London 1924).

E.M. Spiers, *The Army and Society 1815–1914* (London and New York 1980).

J. Cantlie Stewart, *The Quality of Mercy, The Lives of Sir James and Lady Cantlie* (London 1983).

J. Springhall, *Youth, Empire and Society* (London 1977).

F. Steegmuller, ed., *The Letters of Gustave Flaubert 1857–1880* (London 1982).

H.F.A. Strachan, *Wellington's Legacy: the Reform of the British Army 1830–1854 (Manchester 1984).*

R. Strachey, *The Cause* (London 1928).

R. Strong, *Reminiscences* (Edinburgh, privately printed 1935).

M. Trustram, *Women of the Regiment* (Cambridge 1984).

Sir H. Verney, ed., *Florence Nightingale at Harley Street* (London 1970).

M. Vicinus, *Independent Women* (London 1985).

I. Ward, *F.A.N.Y. Invicta* (London 1955).

W.R. Ward, *Religion and Society in England 1790–1850* (London 1972).

P. Warwick, ed., *The South African War* (London 1980).

F. Widdowson, *Going up into the Next Class* (London 1983).

Cecil Woodham-Smith, *Florence Nightingale* (London 1950).

J. Woodward, *To do the sick no harm* (London 1974).

11 ARTICLES PUBLISHED AFTER 1920

G. Anderson, 'An Oversight in Nursing History', *Journal of the History of Medicine*, 3, Summer 1948, pp. 417–26.

O. Anderson, 'The Growth of Christian Militarism in mid-Victorian Britain', *English Historical Review* 86, 1971, pp. 46–72.

M. Baly, 'The Nightingale Nurses 1860–1970', *Bulletin of the History of Nursing Group at the Royal College of Nursing* 8, Autumn 1985, pp. 8–25.

E.H. Benton, 'British Surgery in the South African War: the work of Major Frederick Porter', *Medical History* 21, 1977, pp. 275–90.

B. Bond, 'Recruiting the Victorian Army 1870–1892', *Victorian Studies* 5, 1962, pp. 331–8.

—— 'Mechanized warfare and the growth of pacifism' in A. Briggs, ed., *The Nineteenth Century, The Contradictions of Progress* (London 1970), pp. 185–214.

M.H. Darrow, 'French Noblewomen and the New Domesticity, 1750–1850', *Feminist Studies* V, 1979, pp. 43–63.

L. Davidoff, 'Class and Gender in Victorian England: the Diaries of A.J. Munby and Hannah Cullwick', *Feminist Studies* V, 1979, pp. 89–125.

—— 'Mastered for Life: Servant and Wife in Victorian and Edwardian England', *Journal of Social History* 7, 1974, pp. 406–28.

A. Davin, 'Imperialism and Motherhood', *History Workshop* 5, Spring 1978, pp. 9–66.

J.A. Davis, 'Garibaldi; and England', *History Today* 32, December 1982.

J. Dobson, 'The Army Nursing Service in the 18th Century', *Annals of the Royal College of Surgeons* XIV, 1954, pp. 417–19.

J. Fleetwood, 'An Irish Field Ambulance in the Franco-Prussian War', *Irish Sword*, 6, 1963–4, pp. 137–47.

M.W. Flinn, 'Medical Services under the new Poor Law', in D. Fraser, ed., *The New Poor Law in the Nineteenth Century* (London 1976), pp. 45–66.

E. Gamarnikow, 'The Sexual Division of Labour', in A. Kuhn and A.M. Wolpe, eds., *Feminism and Materialism* (London 1978), pp. 96–123.

J.R. Gillis, 'Servants, Sexual Relations, and the Risks of Illegitimacy in London, 1801–1900', *Feminist Studies* V, 1 1979, pp. 147–63.

Col. J.L. Gordon, 'The Department of Army Health', *Journal of the Royal Army Medical Corps* 107, 1961, pp. 23–32.

B.C. Hacker, 'Women and Military Institutions in Early Modern Europe: a Reconnaissance', *Signs*, VI, 1981, pp. 643–71.

C. Hall, 'The Early Formation of Victorian Domestic Ideology', in S. Burman, ed., *Fit Work for Women* (London 1979), pp. 15–32.

S.F. Holloway, 'The All Saints' Sisterhood at University College Hospital, 1862–99', *Medical History* 3, 1959, pp. 146–56.

E.D. Irvine, 'News from the Front: Looking after Tommy', *Medical News* 2.2.1968, pp. 9–10.

N.D. Lankford, 'The Victorian Medical Profession and Military Practice:

Army Doctors and National Origins', *Bulletin of the History of Medicine* 54, 1980, pp. 511–28.

A.J.A. Morris, 'Haldane's Army Reforms 1906–8: the Deception of the Radicals', *History* 56, 1971, pp. 17–34.

R.J. Morris, 'Religion and Medicine: the cholera pamphlets of Oxford, 1832, 1849, 1854', *Medical History* 19, 1975, pp. 256–70.

William Morrison, 'Glimpses of Life from Within from 1860–1895', *Journal of the Royal Army Medical Corps* 120, 1974, pp. 4–18, 116–29, 176–89; 121, 1975, pp. 38–52, 87–100, 149–62, 204–19.

E.M. Palmegiano 'Women and British Periodicals 1832–67: a Bibliography', *Victorian Periodicals Newsletter* March 1976, pp. 3–36.

S.A. Plotkin, 'The Crisis at Guy's Hospital', *Guy's Hospital Gazette* 75, 1961, pp. 45–50.

M. Pugh, 'Politicians and the Woman's Vote 1914–18', *History* 59, 1974, pp. 358–74.

B. Rose, 'The Volunteers of 1859', *Journal of the Society for Army Historical Research* 37–8, 1959–60, pp. 97–110.

R. Roxburgh, 'Miss Nightingale and Miss Clough: letters from the Crimea', *Victorian Studies* 13, 1969, pp. 71–89.

J. Shepherd, 'The Civil Hospitals in the Crimea', *Proceedings of the Royal Society of Medicine* 59, 1966, pp. 199–204.

A. Summers, 'The Character of Edwardian Nationalism: Three Popular Leagues', in P. Kennedy and A.J. Nicholls, eds., *Nationalist and Racialist Movements in Britain and Germany before 1914* (London 1981), pp. 68–87.

—— 'A Home from Home – Women's Philanthropic Work in the Nineteenth Century' in S. Burman, ed., *Fit Work for Women* (London 1979), pp. 33–63.

—— 'Images of the Nineteenth-Century Nurse', *History Today*, December 1984.

—— 'Militarism in Britain before the Great War', *History Workshop Journal* 2, 1976.

V.A.J. Swain, 'The Franco-Prussian War of 1870–1; Voluntary Aid for the Wounded and Sick', *British Medical Journal* 3, 1970, pp. 511–14.

E.G. Thomas, 'The Old Poor Law and Medicine', *Medical History* 24, 1980 pp. 1–199.

R. White, 'Some Political Influences surrounding the Nurses' Registration Act 1919 in the United Kingdom', *Journal of Advanced Nursing* 1, May 1976, pp. 209–17.

A. Wood (D. Chapman), 'With Phil and Jim and Friends', *Oxford Mail*, 2.2.1976, p. 4.

—— 'How militant Christians became military cadets', *Oxford Mail*, 10.3.1976, p. 8.

INDEX